Beside the
Stone Wall

in
Fredericksburg
Virginia

To
Cousin Morgan,
The South never surrendered
her honor. Harriet Bey Mesic

Harriet Bey Mesic

FIRESIDE FICTION
2005

FIRESIDE FICTION
AN IMPRINT OF HERITAGE BOOKS, INC.

Books, CDs, and more—Worldwide

For our listing of thousands of titles see our website
at
www.HeritageBooks.com

Published 2005 by
HERITAGE BOOKS, INC.
Publishing Division
65 East Main Street
Westminster, Maryland 21157-5026

International Standard Book Number: 0-7884-3152-8

This book is dedicated to the memory of Lewis Wrenn.

TABLE OF CONTENTS

LIST OF PHOTGRAPHS

INTRODUCTION

It has been said that of all the towns impacted by the Civil War, none suffered more than Fredericksburg, Virginia, which changed hands ten times during the course of the war, was the scene of two major battles, and was pillaged and sacked like no other place. The once prosperous town was left desolate, and the once wealthy residents were reduced to poverty.

Of all those who lived in Fredericksburg, none suffered more than the people of very modest means who lived on the edge of town along the Sunken Road and on Wellford's Field. Their homes were located right on the battleground of two major battles, and were left bullet riddled and heavily damaged by rifle and artillery fire. These people did not own summer homes in the country, nor have wealthy relatives where they could find refuge. When $170,000 was sent to Fredericksburg to help the townsfolk recover, the money was not shared with these people.

Of all those who lived along the Sunken Road and on Wellford's Field, none suffered more than Lewis Wrenn, who was twice taken as a hostage by Federal troops, through no fault or action of his own, and sent first to the infamous Old Capital Prison in Washington D.C. and next to Fort Delaware Prison, the Andersonville of the North.

Utilizing history books, diaries, court records, and family traditions, I sought to make the story of Lewis Wrenn as historically accurate as possible. Where historical evidence was lacking concerning Lewis, I assumed that he shared the same fate as the other citizens of Fredericksburg. Thus, Lewis' story is also the story of all the brave people of Fredericksburg.

The conversations are not original to the speakers, but are taken from diaries of various other people and documents of sundry sources, and reflect the attitudes of Virginians at that time.

The 1860 Fredericksburg, Virginia Census and the 1860 Fredericksburg Tax Record of people who lived along the Swift Run Gap Turnpike, the Sunken Road, and Wellford's Field were used to identify the people in the neighborhood.

I found Lewis Wrenn to be an enigma. He owned a tavern, his wife owned slaves, and he was somewhat of a schemer and a scoundrel in his early years. Yet, in his later life, he became a very religious man and an active leader in the Baptist church. His obituary said that he was "full of faith and filled with the Holy Spirit." I concluded that at some point in his life he had an epiphany experience that changed him.

The identity of his second wife, Eliza Pilcher Wrenn, has eluded me. It was not until the records of a lawsuit were discovered in the basement of the Fredericksburg Courthouse Annex that I learned that she was Eliza Carter before she became Eliza Pilcher, prior to becoming Eliza Wrenn. I could not find a record of her marriage to a Pilcher and do not know if it was a legal marriage, a common-law marriage, or if Pilcher was her maiden name or an assumed name. I could find no record of her after Lewis Wrenn's death and do not know where or when she died.

Although I could not locate a business license for an ordinary, or tavern, after 1847, I was able to establish that Lewis Wrenn was operating a tavern in his home after that time from the inventory of his furniture, when the court ordered that his house and all his possessions be sold at auction in 1852. He had two dozen chairs in his house, a strong indication that the tavern was in his home. Also on January 27, 1870 he signed a complaint to have Elsey Paine evicted from the house. Apparently, she was a non-paying guest in the inn.

I have not attempted to make this book politically correct. Instead, I strove for historical accuracy, ignoring the propaganda and myths that are prevalent today. Open your mind to this period of history from the Southern point of view; leave your preconceptions at the door and read on.

Harriet Bey Mesic

ACKNOWLEDGEMENTS

My special thanks go to Bessie Humphreys Gray, Sandra Bey Jaconetta, Jillyne Keene, and especially my husband, Harry Randolph Mesic, for helping me with the research, and to Eric J. Mink at the Fredericksburg and Spotsylvania National Military Park, Barry L. McGee at the Fredericksburg Court House, and Tony Kent at the Central Rappahannock Heritage Center for the assistance they gave me in Fredericksburg.

CHAPTER 1
WILLIAMSVILLE TAVERN

The back door of the tavern swung open and a slender, distinguished looking man with gray hair and a neatly trimmed beard stepped out of the darkness, squinting his eyes in the late afternoon sunlight. He had been quite a dashing fellow in his youth, and now, in spite of his advancing years, women still thought him to be quite handsome.

He yawned, stretched, and then took a milk pail from the hook by the back door. With a slight swagger in his step, he walked toward the cowshed, where he could hear Bossy lowing for him to milk her. He was unconcerned by her distress. That was the beauty of owning a tavern—he could nap in the afternoon. It was not like when he owned a farm,[1] and had to do chores from sunup to sundown.

Lewis Wrenn was born into a working class family—a common laborer with royal blood in his veins, forced to live by his wits and brawn on the fringe of society, among wealthy and aristocratic neighbors.

He knew there had been times when he made unwise decisions, and times when his actions were a little too rash, but he had no regrets. He had always done what he thought was best at the time and stoically suffered the consequences for his actions. At sixty-two years of age[2] most of his life was behind him now. The year was 1862, and he expected that life would not hold many more surprises for him.

Because of his rough and tumble life-style, most men would never guess that there was a bit of a poet and a romantic in him. Women knew it instinctively. That was part of the attraction they felt towards him.

On a spring day like this, all he had to do was close his eyes, and he was a child again—back on the family farm in Spotsylvania County.[3] He could clearly picture the farm in all the different seasons. He had always thought it looked magical, when it was covered with snow in winter, especially when a fresh, white blanket on the ground sparkled like finely ground sugar in the sunlight, and the ice on the tree branches gleamed like the clearest crystal.

Elizabeth, the wife of his youth, used to say that winter is more enjoyable from inside the house, looking out the window. He agreed

1

with her, but there was something about spring that was best enjoyed out-of-doors. He had to taste the air, smell the sweet, damp earth, hear the birds singing, and hold the moist loam in his hands to enjoy the mystery of spring.

He paused and inhaled deeply of the warm balmy air and felt the enchantment he always experienced every spring. He could almost believe that God in heaven really cared about him on a day like this.

He wondered if springtime in the rest of the world were as magnificent as it is in Virginia. Somehow, he thought that it could not be. Virginia was God's own special place on earth. There was something mysterious about the way the cold and gray of winter with its bitter, icy winds blowing off the Rappahannock River gave way to a few, warm, sunny days, and suddenly spring came—all at once. The trees were no longer barren, but shimmering with emerald green leaflets. Tender blades of grass were bravely pushing their way up through the cold, moist earth, and the sweet, balmy air was filled with the songs of birds. In the woods the wildflowers, dogwoods and redbud trees burst into bloom, and the clear, blue sky seemed so far, far away.

Lewis was sort of a Jack-of-all-trades. In his day he had been a farmer, repaired tin ware,[4] worked with almost any metal you could name,[5] installed tin roofs,[6] and did coopering work.[7] He was one of those men who were willing to do almost anything to make a dollar. He had owned a retail store where he sold grates, stoves, refrigerators, shower baths, pumps, etc.,[8] a grocery store,[9] a tavern,[10] and a house of private entertainment.[11] When he did not have the money to buy the required licenses, he operated his businesses without them,[12] but he had always worked.

He had "robbed Peter to pay Paul" to stay solvent, borrowing from the next creditor to pay the previous one, until it all caught up with him in 1852 and he was convicted of fraud. He had borrowed money from one of his sons to build the tavern addition on his house, and had given him a lien against his property to secure the loan—and they called that fraud. He truthfully swore in court that he had been poor all his life, but he had always worked, and been thrifty. He fully intended to pay all his debts, and that he never intended to defraud anyone.[13]

Yet, the people in the Fredericksburg Methodist Church turned against him, and kicked him out of their church.[14] That really stung him. They did it before he even came up for trial, and that was used against him in court, making him look guilty. Who knows what the outcome would have been if they had rallied around him? He had not set foot in a church since that day.

It was not his fault that the economy had been uncharacteristically bad for most of the nineteenth century in Fredericksburg, while the rest of Virginia had prospered.[15] It seemed that all his life, all he ever had was a "hard-row-to-hoe"—especially after he opened Wrenn's Store. It should have been a big financial success, if you could believe the books that John English had shown him before he bought the business. It is funny that no one ever thought that John English did anything wrong. The Methodist Church[16] stood by him, but castigated Lewis, even though Lewis paid Mr. English every cent he owed him. He mortgaged everything he owned, including his wife's slave to make those payments.[17]

After he was disgraced in court, and the Methodist Church turned its back on him, he still did a little tin work and handyman work, but he gave up his big ambition of owning a store. He planted a vegetable garden behind his tavern—one big enough to provide most of the food that he and his second wife, Eliza, needed, but small enough that it did not require too much work. He had a horse, a couple of hogs, a cow,[18] and some chickens[19] too, and they had fresh eggs to eat every day.

His tavern was located beyond the tree-lined streets and stately houses of the prosperous people of Fredericksburg. It was beyond the clapboard cabins of the poor whites, and even poorer free blacks of Liberty Town, Thornton Town, and Sandy Bottom. It was beyond the Mill Race Canal, which cut across the landscape west of town, and beyond George Rowe's impressive, two story, brick mansion with its double white porticos. It was beyond the open meadow known as Wellford's Field, where the land sloped gently upward. It was located where the Swift Run Gap Turnpike abruptly ended at the Sunken Road, when you reached a string of hills known as Marye's Heights. On top of the heights, the huge, white pillared brick mansion called Brompton[20] stood on the crest looking majestically towards the city.

Lewis did not live at Brompton. He lived at the foot of Marye's Heights beside a stone wall on the northeast corner of the Turnpike and the Sunken Road.[21] His house was a modest, clapboard building with two front doors, one that opened into the parlor and the other into

3

the tavern. Nearby were other small, clapboard homes and shops, where people of very modest means lived sandwiched between the mansions of George Rowe and Brompton.

Although signs of spring were everywhere, the air suddenly turned chilly again during the late afternoon of Saturday, April 12, 1862. The wind became blustery, and low hanging, ominously dark clouds skittered across the gray sky. Lewis finished his chores quickly and returned inside where a crackling fire had been lit in the large fireplace sending a warm glow across the wide plank floors of the tavern, but it did little to dissipate the cold.

The oil lamps were lit early, because it was swiftly becoming dark. Even with the light reflecting off the mirror on the wall, the room was dimly lit and would soon be filled with the haze of smoke from pipes burning very fine, Virginia tobacco.

Lewis and Eliza ate together in the tavern, while Eliza's mahogany-colored slave, Phillis, ate alone in the kitchen. Afterwards Phillis silently cleared the dishes from the table, while Eliza and Lewis unlocked and entered the cage, where the tap was located and the ardent spirits were kept. They expected customers to start drifting in very shortly.

Most of the men who frequented Williamsville Tavern were conservatives, who believed in the Jeffersonian principles of government. They believed in the rights of the states to determine their own destiny, and opposed the election of Abraham Lincoln. Even so, when he won the election, they had not wanted Virginia to secede from the Union—until Lincoln ordered troops to be sent to South Carolina.

They were appalled at the idea of being part of anything that was illegal according to the Constitution of the United States, such as using force to bring the South Carolinians back into the Union. Instead, they chose to suffer rather than to be an accomplice in that outrage against constitutional liberty.[22] At that point, most of those in Fredericksburg became ardent Rebels. They favored Virginia joining the Confederacy[23] and proudly sent their able-bodied young men off to stop the Union invasion of their homeland and to defend the state they loved. They believed it was their sacred duty. They were willing to fight for their home and country, and to defend the principle of a free government along the lines of the thoughts of Thomas Jefferson and the framers of the Declaration of Independence and the

Constitution. They believed that the right to govern arises from and is coexistent with the consent of the governed.[24]

This had not been an easy decision for Virginians. After all, a Virginian held the pen that had written the Declaration of Independence. The sons of Virginia had been foremost in the fight for Independence. It was Virginians who had been chiefly instrumental in giving the nation its Constitution.

Most had believed that the Northern troops would be stopped in one major battle, but in the aftermath of Battle of Manassas, that did not happen. Although the Confederacy won the battle, the Federals troops kept returning to Virginia soil.

Now cannons were being rolled into place on Stafford Heights, on the other side of the Rappahannock River, and were being pointed down at Fredericksburg. To make matters worse the 30th Virginia (which was comprised of local men, including Lewis' youngest son, John Kobler Wrenn,) had very recently been sent to Goldsboro, North Carolina.[25] That left the town defended only by a small garrison of Confederate soldiers and the home guard—mostly boys who were too young and men who were too old to enlist.

As customers began drifting into the tavern, Lewis took up his post on a high stool and unlocked the wicket. He was dressed in a white shirt with the sleeves rolled up, a tie, and wool vest, as befitted the owner of a tavern. He had his pencil ready behind his ear, and his ledger book in front of him. His job was to keep a running tally of the beverages sold.

Lewis looked up observing Eliza's actions. She was a plump, buxom woman, ten years younger than he was. She had coarse, reddish hair, which was beginning to turn gray. An unruly strand of it had slipped out of her bun, and was hanging in her face. She tried to tuck it back in place, but it stubbornly kept slipping out again. She wore a drab colored, calico dress with long sleeves, covered by a heavy white apron. Her plain face was lined from years of hard work. She had been a good wife to him, and a caring stepmother for his children. He had married Eliza shortly after his first wife died in childbirth.[26] He had been forty-two then.

The baby, John, had been a 'change of life' baby, a complete surprise, thirteen years younger than the next sibling.[27] Lewis and Elizabeth had adjusted to the idea of having another child to raise, but

5

neither of them had suspected that his birth would cost Elizabeth her life, and bring Lewis the greatest sorrow he had ever known.

In the beginning, the older children had been resentful of the baby, because of their mother's death, but he had been such a good, sweet-natured child, that he was soon the 'darling' of the whole family and the apple of Lewis' eye. As is often the case where there is a stepparent, the children were less than happy with Lewis' marriage to Eliza. He understood that they were still grieving for their mother. Why, he grieved for her, himself. The truth was that he really did not have too much of a choice about marrying Eliza. He either had to find a new wife for himself, or let relatives raise his baby—and he certainly did not intend to give up his youngest son. John was the only one of his children who never had a problem with his stepmother. She was the only mother he had ever known. He adored her, and she loved him dearly.[28]

Women were not lining up, volunteering for the job of being his wife, and raising Elizabeth's infant, especially considering that Lewis was not financially well off. All that he had to offer a woman was his handsome, good looks, and charming personality.

When he needed a wife, Eliza had fallen for his charm. Her wealthy, but older, first husband had married her when she was a child of eleven.[29] When he died, she had inherited a portion of his estate, but the lion's share of his money had gone to his children from his first marriage.

When Elizabeth died, Eliza was not only available and willing, but she had her own money. He had never regretted marrying her, and they were well suited for each other.

She was proud to be his wife, and spent her days trying to please him, tending to his every need. She kept house, cooked the tavern meals, and fixed the drinks in the tavern, with only Phillis to help her. Her workday began shortly after dawn and ended when the last patron left the tavern at night.

Eliza was the one who first suggested that she and Lewis use her dowry money to open a tavern. If nothing else catastrophic happened, they should be completely out of debt in a few more years.

All of Lewis' children were grown now, and John was in Goldsboro, North Carolina with the 30th Virginia Infantry Regiment of the Confederate Army. The other boys had moved far away from Fredericksburg—Lewis W. to Lynchburg, Robin[30] to Alexandria,

George[31] to Botetourt, and Marshall[32] to Kelly's Ford, but he understood that, too. Lewis W. and George had settled in southwestern Virginia, and Robin and Marshall wanted to get away from the disgrace and family embarrassment after the fraud case. Besides, the economy had been so bad in Fredericksburg, that they did not have much of a future here—and they all had families to support. He seldom was able to see any of them, nor his grandchildren, and that grieved him. He hoped that John would settle down close to him when the war was over.

Lewis' attention returned to the tavern, where Monroe Stevens had sprawled wearily into a chair, and tilted it back on two legs. He was a lean, muscular man, in his late thirties, with dark, unruly hair, and the ruddy, leathery complexion of a man who spent most of his waking hours outdoors. He had rough, calloused hands, and his leather jacket and trousers were the soiled and worn, work clothes of a drayman.[33] He was a hard working, frugal, young man saving every penny he could in the hopes of being able to buy some farmland. He lived next door, to the east of Lewis on the Turnpike.[34]

Lewis looked on Monroe as almost being a member of his family. "You're early tonight, son," he remarked.

"I didn't have much work today," he admitted glumly, as he took a pipe from his pocket and toyed with it. "You know, Mr. Wrenn," he confessed, "I don't mind transporting furniture and other goods, but carrying children in little wooden boxes to the cemetery really gets me down."

"Thank God, this scarlet fever epidemic seems to be burning itself out." Eliza remarked. "How many of our children do you think have died from it?"

"Maybe twenty-five, but a lot more of our soldiers have died from it. There are over a hundred new graves in the City Cemetery, and four times that many in Potters Field.[35] I just hope today was the last coffin I will have to carry. Anyway, my regular work will pick up soon."

The door had opened while he was talking, causing a chilly draft to rush through the tavern. The fire flared up, throwing off a shower of sparks. Shadows danced wildly across the wall—a sequence that repeated itself every time the door was opened.

Richard Bozel appeared in the doorway. He was a tall, stoop-shouldered man with watery, blue eyes, dark blond hair, and a neatly trimmed beard, who lived across the street from the tavern.[36]

Eliza gave Lewis an uneasy look, and he told her quietly. "Don't worry. I'll limit him to two drinks, and I'll send him about his business if he becomes belligerent or begins to act drunk."

Mr. Bozel gave the two of them a sheepish look, then walked over to the table where Mr. Stevens was sitting, and said "Come over to my shop. I will give you plenty of work to do. I do declare, those boys in the infantry can wear out their shoes faster than we can make them."

"I'd rather shoot myself than sit around in your dark, stuffy shop all day making smelly shoes," Mr. Stevens scoffed.

"I think you're wrong about that. Everybody needs shoes, and I don't have to make them outside in the rain and snow," Mr. Bozel countered as he eased himself into a chair at the table with Mr. Stevens. He sat facing the door and with his back to Lewis and Eliza. "Besides, they don't smell unless you put your big, smelly feet into them."

"But I like working out-of-doors in the fresh air," Mr. Stevens protested as he lit his pipe.

"If you like fresh air so much, why are you dirtying up the air in here with that awful pipe?"

Lewis knew those two would be bickering with each other all evening, and enjoying every moment of it.

In spite of the terrible thing Mr. Bozel had done, Lewis reminded himself that business is business. One man's dollar helps to pay the mortgage as well as another's. To his knowledge, Mr. Stevens did not know their dreadful secret so he adopted the roll of a friendly tavern keeper and asked, "Mr. Bozel, have you heard from your son in Goldsboro?"

"After being in such a hurry to enlist, William[37] is homesick. He says that it rains all the time, and he hates North Carolina. He says they drill in the rain and mud all day long, and he is wet, tired, and hungry all the time. He thinks the camp will be full of snakes and mosquitoes as soon as it gets warm."[38]

"I don't understand that. John is having the time of his life there. He says that after roll call and services on Sunday, he goes into town to eat at some captain's house. I suspect that the captain has a pretty daughter, and that's why John likes Goldsboro so much."[39]

Meanwhile, Eliza drew two mugs of ale for the men from the tap and handed them through the wicket to Phillis, who carried them to the table in a slow, deliberate way. She made no comment nor did her facial expression change. She had a way of doing no more, nor no less, than what was expected of her, then just quietly blending into the background. People forgot she was there, unless they wanted something. Lewis had come to believe that she was simpleminded. Eliza, who was a bundle of nervous energy, thought Phillis was lazy. Phillis was not concerned with what either one of them thought about her. She just tried to make her life of servitude as easy as possible.

By now, James Jennings had come in and was calling for ale. He lived about half way between the millrace canal and Sunken Road on the south side of Mercer Square a few blocks to the south.[40] He was the cousin of Lewis' first wife, Elizabeth, but there was a strained relationship between Lewis and James. He had given an unfavorable deposition against Lewis' son, Robin, in the fraud case.[41] Nevertheless, business was business. If James wanted to spend money in his tavern, Lewis would take it.

Suddenly the door was thrown open violently, hitting the wall with a bang, as a small, mean-looking man with dirty gray hair stomped into the room. He looked around scowling, then selected a chair in a dark, shadowy corner, where he could watch the other people and drink undisturbed. It was John Bryce, the neighborhood drunk and wife-beater,[42] who lived behind the tavern over on the Plank Road near Poplar Spring.[43] It was obvious that he had already had a few drinks before he arrived. It was just as well that he chose to sit alone. No one would want to share a table with him. When Lewis asked Mr. Bryce how he was doing, he just shrugged and grunted in reply, then demanded a pint of ale. The other men ignored him.

"This is a house of private entertainment," Lewis reminded him. "I can serve, or not serve, whom I please. You can stay here only as long as you behave yourself."

"House of private entertainment!" Mr. Stevens exclaimed. "I thought this was a tavern, and a house of private entertainment was what Mrs. Stephens has down the street!"

"A house of private entertainment is not a brothel!" Lewis declared. "The differences between it and a tavern are that, although I have to have a business license, I don't have to be certified by the court, I don't have to provide stableage and fodder for horses, and I can serve, or not serve, whom I please. The accommodations and food are generally better in a house of private entertainment."

A tall, handsome man with wavy, dark hair and an olive complexion came into the tavern while Lewis was talking. Mr. Allan Stratton did not look the role in his work clothes, but he was the owner of a very successful business. He owned a large wheelwright shop[44] located southeast of the tavern.[45] He was a very likeable person, and at one time, he had been a highly respected figure in the neighborhood. Because of his currently unpopular political beliefs,[46] his popularity was waning. He joined Mr. Stevens and Mr. Bozel at their table and challenged Mr. Bozel to a game of checkers.

Phillis brought them the game pieces. The squares of the game board were painted on the table. As they were setting the pieces in place, Mr. Stratton said, "Fredericksburg is sure going through one, big, building boom! I'll guarantee you I did the work of two men today."

While they were talking, Mr. John Marye, the master of the aforementioned Brompton estate, and his good friend, the rotund Rev. George Rowe, entered the tavern with a great show of dignity and reserve. They sat at their usual table in the prime spot near the fireplace. It was an unwritten rule among the patrons, that this table was reserved for them.

Mr. Marye was a distinguished looking lawyer in his early sixties, impeccably dressed in a black suit, white shirt, black silk tie, and supple leather shoes.

Rev. Rowe had a round, kindly face, but he was quite a bit overweight. He weighed over three hundred pounds,[47] so Lewis had built an extra sturdy chair for him, with an extra wide seat. Even so, when he sat down, his fat bottom hung over the sides of the chair.

Unlike Mr. Marye, Rev. Rowe had not been born into wealth and privilege. Although he lacked educational advantages, he had a good head for business and investments. He made his fortune in Fredericksburg, and then ten years ago, he retired from business and became an ordained minister in the Baptist Church. In 1857, he became the minister of the African Baptist Church, which had seven hundred members.[48] He was a good-natured person, whom people liked and trusted immediately.

While the others satisfied themselves with the cheaper choice of ale, Mr. Marye ordered a whiskey. Rev. Rowe, who was a teetotaler, asked for a piece of 'Mrs. Wrenn's delicious pie' and a cup of coffee.

About that time, Mr. Bryce started cursing at Phillis and demanding another ale.

"All right, out!' Lewis ordered, emerging from the cage. "Go home and sleep it off."

Mr. Bryce started to protest, but as Lewis started menacingly towards him, he reluctantly got up and fished in his pocket for the money to pay his tab.

"I don't have to drink here, you know," he declared. "I can always take my business to Mrs. Stephens.[49]"

"You do that," Lewis answered, "but I'm not going to have that kind of language in here!"

As he left, Mr. Marye called out in a deep, sonorous voice, "Wrenn! Do you know why I patronize your little tavern?" Then without waiting for a reply, he answered his own question, "It's because this is a nice, homey, neighborhood place. There's no coarse language or brawling going on in here."

Mr. Jennings chuckled and turned to Mr. Marye, winking. "That's because Lewis won't tolerate it! He earned his reputation in the good old days, when his tavern was in Liberty Town. He used to haul the riffraff outdoors by the scruff of their necks, and show them his fists—and I don't think he ever lost a fight!"

"Don't let my white hair fool you," Lewis answered gruffly. "I can still haul the riffraff outdoors by the scruffs of their necks—and use my fists, too, if I have to. I can be like a bull dog when I want to be."

"I believe you," Mr. Marye assured him, nodding his head. "I believe you."

"I have no respect for a man who mistreats his family," Lewis said in disgust. "His wife told me that he locks up the food and won't give them enough to eat. When little Billy[50] sneaked a piece of bread, he took the boy and squeezed him until he was spitting blood."[51]

"We can hear the screams at Brompton,"[52] Mr. Marye added, shaking his head in disapproval.

"There should be a law against such behavior!" Mr. Bozel exclaimed before he realized what he had said. His face turned a deep shade of red, and he looked down at the table hoping no one had noticed. Eliza nodded her head slightly and stared defiantly at him.

"Well, the reason I patronize your place, Mr. Wrenn, is that Mrs. Wrenn makes the best apple pie in Fredericksburg," Mr. Rowe interjected, smacking his lips.

Just then, two more neighbors came into the tavern.

Mr. David Sisson was a mild-mannered, slender man with wire-rimmed glasses perched on the end of his nose. He and his wife had a small, neighborhood, grocery store, located on a triangle of land at the intersection of the Turnpike, Fair Street, and Hanover Avenue, one block east of the tavern.[53] Folks said he ran the store, and his wife ran him.

Henry Ebert, who had emigrated from Prussia, also owned a small grocery store. It was located a couple of blocks south on the corner of the Sunken Road and Mercer Street.[54]

Mr. Sisson told the group that their neighbor, Elizabeth Bayne, had been notified that her son, Otho, had been captured by the enemy.[55] The men commiserated with the news, then fell silent as their thoughts turned to their own sons and other relatives. After a while, they were once again cheerfully bantering with each other. Then a lively discussion began about the state of affairs in the Confederate nation.

Soon Mr. Marye was presiding over the discussion like a self-appointed judge.

"I can tell you that I have studied constitutional law extensively, and I know beyond a shadow of doubt that secession is absolutely, positively legal under the Constitution of the United States of America," Mr. Marye explained to the group, as he lit a cigar and tilted his chair back on two legs. "That's why Lincoln did not want to test the legality of secession in the courts."

The other men listened intently, but Mr. Stratton scowled darkly into his mug.

"Had the case been heard in court, as Jefferson Davis wanted, the Confederacy would most certainly have won," Mr. Marye assured them, "and we wouldn't be engaged in this awful war now."

"Sending Federal soldiers down here and waging war against the South is also absolutely illegal, not to mention imperialistic," Mr. Marye added, shaking his head knowingly.

"Also totally immoral," Rev. Rowe reminded them.

"Since Lincoln could not win in the courts, war was the only way he could think of to preserve the Union," Mr. Marye stated. "Lincoln said in his inaugural address that he would not be bound by the decisions of the Supreme Court in making vital decisions—that 'there is a law higher than the Constitution.' He was speaking of the Yankee conscience,[56] of course. It goes back to the Puritans, who also obeyed a 'higher law' and hated anyone who did not think or believe the way they did."

"That 'higher law' garbage is their justification to use political power to do anything they wish,"[57] Lewis said.

"While Lincoln was publicly professing to seek peace, he was secretly provoking war," Mr. Marye continued. "Now they are saying South Carolina started the war by firing on Fort Sumter. That is nonsense! Before that happened, Lincoln had already started the war. It started when Lincoln's Secretary of State, Mr. Seward,[58] gave Southern representatives the most positive assurances that Fort Sumter would be speedily evacuated, while Lincoln secretly made plans to strengthen and hold it. The war started with Lincoln's deception."

"It's true," Rev. Rowe added, "that the one who starts an assault is not necessarily the one who strikes the first blow—or fires the first shot. It's really the one who provokes the assault who starts it."[59]

"Lincoln deliberately provoked the firing on Fort Sumter[60] to incite the North to invade the South with fire and sword," Mr. Marye explained. "He forced the South and tricked the North into war. The South did not want war, and did everything they could to avoid war.[61] Even if the firing on Fort Sumter had been unprovoked, instead of provoked, Lincoln still would not have been justified to use an unlawful method of redressing the situation."[62]

"I am amazed that Lincoln was able to deceive so many men into taking up arms against what is obviously the cause of truth, justice, and freedom," Lewis declared.

"There is no question that making war on us was an immoral, unrighteous thing for the North to do," Rev. Rowe added.

"The Constitution says that the President cannot use the military to put down an insurrection in a state, unless he is called upon by the State Legislature or the Governor of that state to do so.[63] Do any of you remember South Carolina, or Virginia for that matter, calling upon Lincoln to send troops into her state to put down an insurrection?" Mr. Marye asked.

The men reacted by shaking their heads back and forth.

"That means when Lincoln called for 75,000 men to invade the Southern States to put down what he called an insurrection, he was violating the law which he had just taken an oath to uphold!"[64] Rev. Rowe exclaimed.

"That's right," Lewis added. "Only Congress has the power to declare war, not the president."

"They think they are justified by the fact that the South fired on the flag," Mr. Marye went on. "In 1807 when a British man-of-war fired on an American ship, killed and wounded several of the crew, abducted four American sailors, and hung one of them, there was no great outcry from New England about avenging the flag that was fired upon. In addition, the flag the British fired on was floating in the Chesapeake Bay, to which they had absolutely no claim. South Carolina did have a legal claim to Fort Sumter. Now, since 1807, do you think that the North has developed a greater love for the flag, or could it be that they have developed a greater hatred for the South?"[65]

"They say they want to preserve the Union," Mr. Stevens interjected in disgust. "They want to preserve the Union by killing half of the people in it—our half."

"Doesn't make sense, does it?" Mr. Bozel asked. He hunched over his mug, as if it were one of the shoes he skillfully made in the cobbler shop, while he contemplated his next checkers move.

"Now the North is saying that if the President doesn't have the power to send troops down here, he 'ought to' have the power.[66] Well, there's a provision in the Constitution for powers that the President 'ought to' have and it is called a Constitutional Amendment," Mr. Marye continued.

Mr. Stratton abruptly stood up, bumping the table, and knocking the checker pieces out of place. "I think I had better leave now, before I say something that will offend my long time friends."

All conversation came to an abrupt halt as he paid his tab, and then quickly strode out of the tavern, noisily closing the door.

"There goes a good Union man," Mr. Stevens declared, pointing towards the door. "Let's hope the Union turns out to be as loyal to him, as he is to them."

"Stratton's not a bad man," Rev. Rowe said in his defense. "In the beginning all of us wanted Virginia to remain in the Union. It's just that we changed our minds, but he didn't."

"All Yankees are just a bunch of hypocrites!" scoffed the Mr. Jennings. "The reason for this war is not to preserve the Union. It's because they hate Southerners."

"If they really wanted to preserve the Union, they would be wooing us back into it. But, no, they're down here trying to kill us. Now just tell me, how can you preserve a union by destroying half of it?" Mr. Stevens asked.

This was a sentiment shared by all present.

"Yeah!"

"You're right about that!"

"They could outvote us in Congress," Mr. Marye added, "because there are so many of them and so few of us. They used their numerical advantage to tax the South to death. Did you ever notice that they had a way of passing laws that only affected the South? Like their tariffs? Mark my words, if we had stayed in the Union—and they ever freed the slaves—it would only be the slaves in the Southern states! It would take a Constitutional amendment to free them in the North. We have made concession after concession, surrendered right after right, submitted to unjust taxation, and consented to compromise after compromise. Each time we have done it the South has been weakened and the North has been strengthened. If we had seceded forty years ago, instead of making all those compromises, there would not have been a war. Our problem is that we loved the Union too much and for too long."[67]

"What they really would like to do is make all of us white Southerners slaves to the North!" Mr. Jennings said heatedly.

"I will never understand their hatred for Southerners," Rev. Rowe added. "In their editorials and cartoons, we are portrayed as evil, mean, and unscrupulous people. I know the people of Fredericksburg. Our morals are as good as theirs are, and we are probably more God-fearing. I know that we treat our immigrants a lot better than they treat theirs. In fact we treat our slaves better than they treat their immigrants!"

"In my travels to New York, I could not help noticing that the poor white immigrants in the North live in far worse conditions than our slaves!"[68] Mr. Marye declared.

"If I had settled in the North, my wife would probably be working in a sweat shop, and I would be collecting rags and bottles," Mr. Ebert said in his thick Prussian accent. "Here I own my own home and a grocery store, and my three little children have a comfortable life."

"We shouldn't lose sight of the fact that no matter how much we dislike and disagree with the way they do things up North, Virginia would never have the arrogance—or the audacity—to send troops up there to force our Southern way of life on them," Mr. Marye said.

"Yeah!"

"Hear! Hear!"

"And we did not start this war. The North committed the first act of war by not relinquishing Fort Sumter to South Carolina as they repeatedly promised. Instead, they tried to bring in more munitions and point loaded cannons at the city of Charleston. The Confederates had to either silence the guns at Fort Sumter, or face the combined fire of the fort and their fleet,"[69] Mr. Marye added. "We did not want war, but every proposal for peace that we made was ignored by Washington. We could not sit back and let them re-supply Fort Sumter so they could bombard Charleston out of existence."

"The Yankees seem to think that every white person in the South lives on a great, big plantation with a hundred slaves," Mr. Sisson timidly contributed.

"They also think we are lazy and have a bunch of slaves to do all of our work for us, while we sit around sipping mint juleps and giving orders. I would like to have them spend one day with me, so I can show them how hard this white man works, without the help of any slaves," Mr. Stevens bristled.

"And we are always portrayed as mistreating our slaves. They must think we're stupid, because a man would have to be just, plain stupid not to take very good care of something as valuable as a slave," Mr. Marye interjected.

"The fact that almost all of the slaves are very loyal and devoted to their masters is evidence that their slave owners are not cruel and barbarous," Rev. Rowe stated. "But that's sort of a moot point. With or without the war, I don't think slavery can last for more than about a dozen more years."

It never occurred to any of the men to ask Phillis for her opinion of slavery. Throughout this conversation, she stood to one side, the expression on her face never changing.

There was a lull in the conversation, as the men nursed their drinks and puffed their pipes and cigars, while the air became heavy with smoke. Then the subject inevitably turned to the progress of the war. As soon as the Federal troops on Stafford Heights were mentioned, there was an undercurrent of anxiety in the room, as the men contemplated what the Federals intended to do next.

"Why on earth are they interested in our little town?" Mr. Ebert asked Mr. Marye.

"Because of our location! We're the front door to Richmond!" Mr. Marye exclaimed.

"Letters from my boys say that the Federal army, and especially that General Pope[70], is committing atrocities against the civilian populations," Lewis informed them. "Abraham Lincoln has done nothing to stop Pope, and seems to approve of his policies against civilians. I dread to think of them coming to Fredericksburg. I hear they have devastated the country on the other side of the river."

"You'll never hear Jeff Davis' name associated with atrocities or war crimes," Mr. Jennings declared with pride and satisfaction. "He is a man of honor. Lincoln, on the other hand, is totally unscrupulous, and untrustworthy."

"I have been able to obtain copies of some of Pope's general orders," Mr. Marye declared. "They give the Federal Army permission to subsist off the countryside without mention of compensation to the farmers. In other words, their army has a license to steal whatever they want from Southerners.

Southern civilians, not the Confederate Army, are to be held responsible for any disruption in their supply or communication lines. Anytime a rail line, wagon road, or telegraph line is sabotaged, all civilians in a five mile radius are to be rounded up to repair the damages.

Any citizen who fires on a soldier is to be punished by having his house burned to the ground, and/or by making him pay for damages. In either case the person is to be shot without the benefit of a trial.

Southerners who refuse to take the oath of allegiance are to be turned out of their homes and sent behind Rebel lines. If they attempt to return to their homes, they are to be shot."[71]

"Isn't it strange," Rev. Rowe added, "that their generals studied at the same military academy—West Point—with our generals. Our generals learned the international laws of warfare and what constitutes a war crime, but their generals apparently did not."

Mr. Sisson nervously solicited Mr. Marye's opinion. "Do you really think they're going to fire on the town?"

"Well, we don't intend to just give them our town, now do we?" Mr. Marye answered incredulously. "Just because there are bridges across the river, that doesn't mean we are going to let them waltz across them without a fight."

"Just let them try to take Fredericksburg. Even the boys in our home guard can make those yellow-bellied, Yankee cowards turn and run," Mr. Jennings boasted.

"Yeah, remember what happened at Manassas?" Mr. Stevens joined in. He paused for effect before adding, "Run, Bull Run!"

Recalling how the Yankees took three days to march from Washington, DC to the Bull Run Creek near the Manassas train junction, but only twelve hours to turn around and run back, the men enthusiastically chanted,

"Run, Bull Run! Run, Bull Run! Run, Bull Run..."

---

[1] Spotsylvania, Virginia Deed Book BB, Page 35–37.

[2] 1850 and 1860 Fredericksburg, Virginia Censuses.

[3] Spotsylvania, Virginia Deed Book T, Page 444, .James Lindsay and Sarah his wife to John Wren, April 4, 1814.

[4] 1850 Fredericksburg, Virginia Census.

[5] *Fredericksburg News*, 2 Jan 1852.

[6] Ibid.

[7] *Weekly Advertiser*, 12 Nov 1853.

[8] *Fredericksburg News*, 2 Jan 1852.

[9] "Assessment of Ordinaries and houses of private entertainment for the year commencing the 1st day of May 1846," Central Rappahannock Heritage Center Archives.

[10] In order to receive his license, Lewis had to promise to "constantly find and provide in his ordinary good and wholesome and cleanly lodging and Diet for travellers (sic) and stableage, fodder and provender, or

pasteurage (sic) & provender, as the season may require for their horses ... and not suffer or permit any unlawful gaming in his house nor on the Sabbath (sic) day suffer any person to tipple and drink more than is necessary..." [Ordinary Bond/Lewis Wren/May 1846.]

An inventory of the household goods in 1853 indicated that there were two dozen chairs in the house, [E.L. Parker & Co. vs. Lewis Wren, Robertson B. Wrenn et al, 1851–August 1852, Fredericksburg Chancery Court Records, in the basement of the Fredericksburg Courthouse Annex.] a strong indication that he had moved his tavern to his home on the turnpike. However, the business may have fallen into the category of a house of private entertainment [see explanation in footnote 13] rather than a tavern.

"Assessment of Ordinaries and houses of private entertainment for the year commencing the 1st day of May 1846," Central Rappahannock Heritage Center Archives

[11] Although a 'house of private entertainment', sounds very much like a brothel, that was not the case. When asked to explain the difference between a "tavern" or "ordinary" and a "house of private entertainment" in antebellum Virginia, this is the answer given by James D. Watkinson, PhD, Archives Division, Library of Virginia:

"The difference seems to have been two-fold. Those who applied for licenses to operate taverns/ordinaries were required to provide 'stableage, fodder, and provender, as the season shall require, for [guests'] horses,' in addition to food and 'cleanly lodging,' a term which obviously had wildly varying interpretations. Those keeping houses of private entertainment were not required to look after the horses, apparently.

Also keepers of ordinaries had to have an entry in the county court records attesting to their character, as well as post bond or security, owners of private houses did not."

"List of Ordinary Keepers & Keepers of Private Entertainment in St. Georges's Parish 1847," Central Rappahannock Heritage Center Archives.

[12] "A list of merchants, grocers, ordinary keepers, and keepers of private entertainment, who have not taken license for the year 1844," Record in the Fredericksburg Courthouse Annex basement.

[13] .In a series of deals to raise money, Lewis Wrenn:

First, signed a Deed of Trust to John Marye on Dec 27, 1847 using the turnpike property as security against a bond for $400 to pay John Marye for the property. [Fredericksburg Deed Book P, Pages 6–7.]

Then, second, to raise money to pay John English for the "stock in trade" purchased from him, he signed another Deed in Trust to John L. Marye on December 10, 1949 using the land and the stock in trade as security against a bond for $533. [Fredericksburg Deed Book P, Pages 380–382.]

Third, he signed another Deed in Trust to John Marye on Nov. 23, 1850 using a female slave named Phillis, two horses, and two buggies as security against a bond for $180.75. [Fredericksburg Deed Book Q, Page 1.]

Fourth, he signed another Deed in Trust to John Marye on June 13, 1851 using the house and lot on the turnpike, his stock in trade, consisting of stoves, grates, etc. as security against a bond for $325. [Deed Book Q, Page 98.]

Fifth, he bought goods on credit, hoping to make a profit off of them before the payments were due, from:

> September 26, 1851, from Samuel H. Grafton, Baltimore, Maryland, $82.65.
>
> December 15, 1851, from Downs & Co., Fredericksburg, Virginia, $98.70.
>
> April 9, 1852, from Hayward, Bartlett Co., Baltimore, Maryland, $411.68.
>
> March 22, 1852, from E.L. Parker & Co., Baltimore, Maryland, $118.02.

In his deposition, James Tanner states, "Mr. Wrenn gave me a list of his debts to send on the amt was about $3400." [E.L. Parker & Co. vs. Lewis Wrenn et al, Fredericksburg Courthouse Annex Basement.]

Sixth, he borrowed $500 from William Williams to pay John Marye. He had hoped to be able to borrow $1,000 so he could also pay E.L. Parker & Co. and other creditors.

Seventh, he signed a Deed in Trust to George F. Chew on October 15, 1851 using his house and lot on the turnpike, all his stock in trade consisting of stoves, grates, etc, books of accounts, etc as security against a bond for $515 to pay William S. Williams. [Fredericksburg Deed Book Q, Page 161.]

Eighth, he signed a Deed in Trust to George F. Chew on November 10, 1851 using the house and lot on the turnpike, all his stock in trade, consisting of stoves, grates, etc. as security against a bond to pay Robertson B. Wrenn two bonds, one for $475, and the other for $450. [Fredericksburg Deed Book Q, Pages 169–170.]

Ninth, he advertised, but was unable to sell, his house and lot, and his household and kitchen furniture. [Fredericksburg News, March 16, 1852.]

The Chancery Court ruled the Deed in Trust to pay Robertson B. Wrenn as fraudulent and void on January 26, 1853. The court ordered the auction of Lewis Wrenn's house and personal property by John Marye,

Commissioner, to pay Lewis' debts. An advertisement for an auction on August 19, 1852 appeared in the Fredericksburg News. John Marye submitted his report of the auction to the court on October 14, 1853. Eliza Wrenn had bought the house and lot in the auction for $551. [Fredericksburg Deed Book Q, Page 491.]

[E.L. Parker & Co. vs. Lewis Wren, Robertson B. Wrenn et al, 1851–August 1852, Fredericksburg Chancery Court Records, in the basement of the Fredericksburg Courthouse Annex.

[14] E.L. Parker & Co. vs. Lewis Wren, Robertson B. Wrenn et al, 1851–August 1852, Fredericksburg Chancery Court Records, Fredericksburg Courthouse Annex Basement

[15] James Hunnicutt, preacher/editor, *Christian Banner* [Fredericksburg], cited in *Fredericksburg News*, April 13, 1860.

[16] John English was a member of the Fredericksburg Methodist Church. [*Methodist Episcopal Church, Fredericksburg Records, 1834–1852*. Virginia State Library.]

[17] Fredericksburg Deed Book Q, Page 1.

[18] 1870 Tax List for Fredericksburg, Virginia.

[19] William Kepler describes going to the last house on Hanover Street (which would be the Wrenn house) during the Battle of Fredericksburg in December 1862 and finding chickens locked in the outhouse. [*History of Three Months' and Three Years' Service, Fourth Regiment Ohio Volunteer Infantry in the War for the Union* by William Kepler, PhD, Cleveland (1886) page 93.]

[20] John L. Marye owned Brompton during the Civil War. The original house on the site dates to the mid-eighteenth century. The State of Virginia purchased and restored Brompton in 1946 as the residence of the President of Mary Washington College.

[21] Fredericksburg Deed Book P, pages 6–7.

[22] This opinion is expressed in *Defending the Southern Confederacy: The Men in Gray* by Robert Catlett Cave, edited by Walbrook D. Swank, Burd Street Press, Shippensburg, Pennsylvania (2001). Page 13.

[23] "Rebellion on the Rappahannock: Secession in Spotsylvania County, Virginia," (M.A. thesis, Louisiana State University by A Wilson Greene, 1977, pages 13–18, cited *in Fredericksburg Civil War Sites: December 1862–April 1865*, by Noel G. Harrison, H.E. Howard, Inc. Publisher, page 15.

[24] Ibid. Page 14.

[25] The 30th Virginia went to Goldsboro, North Carolina on March 23, 1863. [*30th Virginia Infantry* by Robert K. Krick, H.E. Howard, Inc., Publisher (1985) Page 10.]

[26] The Minister's Return and Virginia Marriage Register gives the marriage date of Lewis Wrenn and Eliza Pilcher as September 20, 1842. Elizabeth Mills Wrenn probably died shortly after the birth of her last child, John Kobler Wrenn, who was born July 24, 1841.

[27] There may have been at least one more child, a daughter named Elizabeth. The 1840 Virginia Census shows a female aged 5 to 10 in the household of Lewis Wrenn. (This child may possibly be Hellen Wrenn, daughter of Achilles and Mary Ann (Poartch) Wrenn, who is listed in the household of Lewis Wrenn on the 1850 Fredericksburg, Virginia Census. Apparently, Mary Ann (Poartch Wrenn) died before 1850.)

Included in the George King Papers at the Virginia Historical Society in Richmond, Virginia is a letter from Richard Thurtle, now deceased, who married a descendent of John Kobler Wrenn. He claims that Lewis had a daughter, Elizabeth, born in 1831. He does not give any sources for his information. Supporting his claim, perhaps, is an entry in the Virginia Baptist Historical Society's Records of the Fredericksburg Baptist Church stating that Elizabeth Wrenn died in 1844. If Lewis Wrenn did have a daughter, Elizabeth, who was born in 1831 and died in 1844, she would have been nine years old (aged 5 to 10) on the 1840 census, and 13 years old when she died. This raises the question, however, of why would Lewis Wrenn bury his daughter at the Baptist Church when he was a Methodist.

If Elizabeth Wrenn did not exist, then Phillip Marshall Wrenn would be the next to the youngest child, and 13 years older than John Kobler Wrenn.

[28] Letter dated June 18, 1979, from Paul Gillikin to Marion Elizabeth Wrenn Humphreys concerning family records and his memories of his Grandfather, John Kobler Wrenn. A copy is in the possession of the author.

[29] Caroline County Marriage Record.

[30] Robinson Boswell Wrenn

[31] George Henry Wrenn

[32] Phillip Marshall Wrenn

[33] 1860 Fredericksburg, Virginia Census.

[34] Fredericksburg Deed Book Q, Page 258.

[35] *The Journal of Jane Howison Beale: Fredericksburg, Virginia 1850–1862*, Historic Fredericksburg Foundation, Inc. (1995). Entry for April 28, 1862.

[36] Fredericksburg Deed Book M, page 166.

[37] William M. Bozel

[38] This opinion is expressed in *30th Virginia Infantry* by Robert K. Krick, H.E. Howard, Inc., Lynchburg, Virginia (1985) page 14.

[39] According to family lore and a letter dated June 18, 1979 from Paul Gillikin, grandson of John Kobler Wrenn, to Marion Elizabeth Wrenn Humphreys, in which he describes his memories of John Kobler Wrenn, John Kobler Wrenn walked from Fredericksburg, Virginia to Goldsboro, North Carolina to marry Martha Elizabeth Phillips. She was fifteen years old at the time of their marriage. A copy of the letter is in the possession of the author.

[40] Fredericksburg Deed Book S, Page 115.

[41] E.L. Parker & Co. vs. Lewis Wren, Robertson B. Wrenn et al, 1851– August 1852, Fredericksburg Chancery Court Records, in the basement of the Fredericksburg Courthouse Annex.

[42] Bryce vs. Bryce Divorce Case, November 25, 1871, Fredericksburg Courthouse Annex Basement.

[43] Fredericksburg, VA deed book V, page 181.

[44] *Fredericksburg Civil War Sites: Volume Two, December 1862–April 1865* by Noel G. Harrison, H.E. Howard, Inc., Lynchburg, Virginia (1995). Page 174.

[45] Fredericksburg Deed Book R, Page 473.

[46] *Fredericksburg Civil War Sites: Volume Two, December 1862–April 1865* by Noel G. Harrison, H.E. Howard, Inc., Lynchburg, Virginia (1995). Page 181.

[47] *Minor Sketches of Major Folk* by Dord C. Jett, Old Dominion Press (1928) page 97.

[48] *Fredericksburg Ledger*, 26 Jan 1866, *Fredericksburg News*, 1 Dec 1857, 2x2.

[49] Martha Farrow (Ennis) (Stephens)

[50] William F. Bryce

[51] Bryce vs. Bryce Divorce Case, November 25, 1871, Fredericksburg Courthouse Annex Basement.

[52] Ibid.

[53] Fredericksburg Deed Book R, Page 100.

[54] Fredericksburg Deed Book S, Page 385.

[55] *30th Virginia Infantry* by Robert K. Krick, H.E. Howard, Inc., Publisher (1985) Page 81.

[56] This opinion is expressed in *Defending the Southern Confederacy: The Men in Gray* by Robert Catlett Cave, edited by Walbrook D. Swank, Burd Street Press, Shippensburg, Pennsylvania (2001). Page 11.

[57] Ibid. This opinion is expressed on pages 69, 72.

[58] William H. Seward

[59] This opinion is expressed in *Defending the Southern Confederacy: The Men in Gray* by Robert Catlett Cave, edited by Walbrook D. Swank, Burd Street Press, Shippensburg, Pennsylvania (2001). Page 30.

[60] Ibid. This opinion is expressed on page 28.

[61] Ibid. This opinion is expressed on page 28, 33, 81.

[62] Ibid. This opinion is expressed on page 36.

[63] Ibid. This opinion is expressed on page 33.

[64] Ibid. This opinion is expressed on page 34.

[65] Ibid. This opinion is expressed on page 35.

[66] Ibid. This opinion is expressed on page 35

[67] Ibid. This opinion is expressed on pages 8–9.

[68] This opinion is expressed in *Three Years in Camp and Hospital* by E.W. Locke (Boston 1870) Pages. 52–53.

[69] This opinion is expressed in *Defending the Southern Confederacy: The Men in Gray* by Robert Catlett Cave, edited by Walbrook D. Swank, Burd Street Press, Shippensburg, Pennsylvania (2001), Page 29.

[70] Gen. John Pope

[71] *War of the Rebellion: A compilation of the Official Records of the Union and Confederate Armies*, Series 1, Vol. 12, Part 2. Page 51.

CHAPTER 2

FEDERAL OCCUPATION

The confidence Lewis felt in the tavern with the other men was put to the test a few days later, when the rumble of cannon fire shook the neighborhood and rattled the windows. It was an unsettling feeling to know that your hometown was under attack, your whole life was about to be irrevocably changed, and nothing you did, one way or the other, would have any effect on the course of events.

Lewis thought of John in Goldsboro, and fleetingly wished that the 30th Virginia were back in Fredericksburg. Then it occurred to him that was not what he really wanted. What he really wished was that he were young enough, himself, to go and fight the Yankees. Anything was better than waiting helplessly for others to determine the outcome your life.

Eliza was busy, energetically cleaning the house, as though the danger would go away, if she ignored it.

Phillis was not being much help to her. She was terrified, cringing, and crying out with each boom of artillery fire.

Lewis fed the animals and went about his daily chores, while anxiously waiting for news. When none was forthcoming, he thought about walking down to the river, to see for himself what was happening. He knew that thought was foolishness. It was safer to stay put, and he would know the outcome soon enough.

One afternoon as he looked towards town, he saw billows of smoke darkening the sky. From the location on the horizon, he correctly surmised that the Confederate soldiers were burning the Rappahannock bridges that connected Fredericksburg to Stafford County.[1] Unfortunately, that did not dissuade the Federals. They just brought boats up the river so their troops could cross anytime they chose.[2]

On May 2, 1862, the Federals began firing their cannons on the town again.

Realizing they could not win against the superior numbers of the enemy, the Confederate soldiers withdrew into Spotsylvania County.[3]

Lewis stood outside the tavern with Eliza and watched with a heavy heart, as the Confederates trudged past them, up the dusty Turnpike, across the Sunken Road, then out the Plank Road. He waved his handkerchief to show his support for the army.

Unseen, Phillis stood in the shadows and watched the soldiers from the upstairs window.

Lewis realized very clearly what was at stake in this war—everything he had ever hoped for, and dreamed about, had worked his whole life to achieve—his whole way of life as a Virginian. To him the war was not about preserving a Union that treated half of its members as outcasts. It was not about emancipating the slaves, which was already being accomplished, slowly, but surely, through the Colonization Societies.[4] It was a war for independence, the same thing his grandparents' generation fought for in the Revolution—the right for his state to govern her own affairs. These rights had been granted in the Constitution, but now the North was usurping those rights and denying Southern states equal privileges with those of the North. He knew that the South had to win, at any cost, or the South would be irreparably changed, and his life would never be the same again.

Lewis could not help comparing this dismal spectacle of the troops withdrawing from Fredericksburg with the glorious departure several weeks before of the 30th Virginia. Then, the soldiers had jauntily marched to the train station, while their band played lively tunes. The proud townsfolk had lined the streets cheering and waving handkerchiefs. It had been awe-inspiring!

Well, he was still waving his handkerchief, but there were neither cheers nor music.

Eliza openly wept. "What happens to us, once they're gone?" she sobbed. "Who will protect us?"

Lewis put his arm around her shoulder and tried to comfort her. "We'll find out soon enough what will happen—but whatever it is, we'll survive. Don't worry, I'm here, and I'll take care of you."

When the last soldiers disappeared from sight, leaving a cloud of dust as a silent witness to their passing, he went behind the house and began digging a trench. He lined the trench with straw and put into it a wood chest containing their silver and few valuables. He added another layer of straw, and then covered everything with a piece of canvas. He threw a layer of dirt over the canvas, then, lastly, he covered the trench with a pile of horse manure.

Within hours, the Federal army entered the city of Fredericksburg and placed it under military rule. If they had expected to be greeted as conquering heroes, they were surely disappointed. Instead, they found a hostile, uncooperative population, who considered them to be robbers, plunderers, and murderers.[5]

The harsh treatment of civilians began immediately.[6] The Federal policy toward the people of Fredericksburg was to starve them into submission.[7] The town was sealed. Armed guards were put around the perimeter of the town with orders to arrest anyone coming into or leaving Fredericksburg. All news sources and supplies from the South were cut off.[8] The railroads had been destroyed and the bridges had been burned. Those in Fredericksburg were unable to see or hear from friends or family, even if they lived just a few miles away. Those suspected of conveying letters or papers were arrested, even women.[9] The townsfolk could not even go into the woods to gather firewood for cooking or heating.[10] The soldiers could invade and search anyone's premises on any pretext.[11] Anyone attempting to speak to a Confederate soldier was to be treated as a spy and hung.

The quiet life, which the townspeople had always enjoyed, was disrupted frequently by noisy cheers, firing of guns, and loud strains of military music as the invading forces celebrated any report of a Union triumph. These displays only increased the hatred that the people of Fredericksburg felt for the Union.[12]

The men from the neighborhood continued their habit of coming to Williamsville Tavern to discuss current events.

"How are we supposed to survive without food supplies?" Mr. Jennings demanded.

"We're not," Mr. Bozel answered. "We're supposed to starve to death."

"At least we have our gardens,"[13] Lewis assured them, "and there is food enough in most of our pantries to last for a while. We'll just have to swap the things that we have for things that we need."

"That's well and good for Mr. Sisson and Mr. Ebert, who have groceries to swap, and for you, Mr. Wrenn, with your stash of liquor that is as good as cash—but what does a drayman have to swap? Horse manure?" Mr. Stevens asked.

"You'd better think of something," Mr. Jennings answered, "or start digging a garden."

"And what are we supposed to do for firewood for our cook stoves?" Lewis asked. "Eliza and I have just about used up our supply."

"Why don't you use your fence for firewood?" Mr. Sisson asked.

"Hah!" Lewis hooted. "Then my animals would end up in the stew pot of some Yankee!"

"I had been getting firewood from my relatives' plantations," Mr. Marye replied. "They were having one of their servants bring it to us after dark, using little known trails through the woods.[14] But the last time I asked for some, they said that the Yankees had carried off all the cut wood."[15]

"My relatives don't own plantations and servants to bring me wood," Mr. Bozel declared.

"Well, I have managed to buy firewood," Rev. Rowe said, "but at enormous prices. The last I bought was ten dollars a cord."[16]

"My family can't afford those enormous prices," Mr. Jennings answered.

"Well, I for one don't intend to burn my fence, or my furniture in the cook stove," Lewis declared, "but I think I know where I can get my hands on some wood that is not being used for anything important."

"Don't be tempted to do anything rash. God willing, we'll all devise a way to survive the inconveniences of this occupation," Rev. Rowe warned.

That evening, just before dark, Lewis hitched his horse to the old utility cart and headed for the Fredericksburg Aqueduct Company.[17]

Lewis reasoned that the Aqueduct Company did not need their fence as long as the Federal Troops occupied the town, but he did. He took a sledgehammer and began knocking the boards off the frame, and loading them into his cart. When the cart was full, he headed home.

The next morning the sheriff came to the house with a warrant for Lewis' arrest for stealing the fence.[18] Phillis was sent to fetch Mr. Marye, who accompanied Lewis to the courthouse. The magistrate before whom Lewis appeared was, Mr. Marye's cousin,[19]

Montgomery Slaughter, a portly, balding man, who enjoyed his positions of power as both a magistrate and the mayor of Fredericksburg. He set Lewis' bail at one hundred dollars each for Lewis and Mr. Marye.[20]

On their way home, Lewis remarked to Mr. Marye, "Can you believe that in a time of war, when we are struggling to just survive, that the Fredericksburg Aqueduct Company would have me arrested over a fence? Or that I would have to post one hundred dollars bail for a common, old, board fence?"

"Don't worry," Mr. Marye said, "I can almost guarantee you that this will never come to trial.[21] I will talk to Monty and see what can be done about getting back our bail money. He knows that my wedding to Jane Hamilton[22] will take place at the same time as the July court session, and he is a romantic, sentimental sort. He would not want to interfere with my wedding. Besides, if he can slip away from Fredericksburg, he wants to attend the festivities, himself."

On June 1, the Federals could be observed hastily moving their baggage to the other side of the river, which had become swollen from continual rain. The town was thrown into a panic when a rumor circulated that the Yankees planned to shell the town during the night. Many of the blacks in Fredericksburg fled across the Rappahannock.[23]

Trains no longer came into Fredericksburg, but a train whistle could be heard on the other side of the river. Military supplies and newspapers were being ferried over by boat, as the pontoon bridges the Federal troops built had washed away.[24] Some northern goods were available, but at such inflated prices, that most folks had to do without. Southern currency was discounted forty percent.[25]

When their clothes became faded, Eliza took them apart at the seams and turned them inside out. She mended and repaired clothes that in former days would have been discarded.

In early June newspapers from the north reported that a huge battle had been fought near Richmond.[26]

Judging by the increased surliness of their captors, Lewis reckoned that the South had beaten them good.

At first, Lewis felt nothing but pride, when he contemplated the Confederate victory near Richmond. Then he thought of his sons. As for his older sons, he expected they were too old and had too many children to be tempted into joining the military.

John was with the 30th Virginia and was safe in Goldsboro, North Carolina. Or was he? If the regiment could be put on a train and sent to Goldsboro, it could be put on another one and sent to Richmond. Was John in Goldsboro or Richmond? If in Richmond, was he okay?

In addition, where was his next to the youngest son, Marshall? He had joined the Confederate infantry as a private when he was thirty-two years of age and the father of five children! He had left his farm and family to fight with Stonewall Jackson in the Valley. Lewis was glad to hear that Marshall's company had disbanded last November, and hoped he would not be foolish enough to reenlist. Since that time Marshall's sixth child, Phillip Jackson, had been born. What would his wife, Sarah, do if anything happened to him? She certainly could not farm the land alone. If she sold the farm, she would not get enough money to raise six children, especially when the oldest child was only eleven.

Lewis felt a sense of uneasiness go through him. It suddenly occurred to him that he did not know for sure where any of his children were, or if they were alive or dead.

He had noticed the gaunt, pinched little faces of the young children, especially those in Liberty Town and Sandy Bottom,[27] where many of Fredericksburg's poor people lived. He saw the wide eyes and the swollen bellies that accompany hunger. He did not know if his own grandchildren were safe, or if they had food enough to eat. Moreover, he had no way of finding out.

Later that afternoon, he was in the garden picking insects off the plants and dropping them into a jar of kerosene. He could hear the loud, raucous voices of the soldiers patrolling along the Sunken Road, but they could not see him. He was concealed from view behind his six foot high, board fence. It irritated him that they were cursing and using vile language, telling coarse stories in voices loud enough to be heard in the house by Eliza. They had a total lack of manners and no respect for the women of Fredericksburg.

There was something about the way they swaggered with such haughty looks on their faces that irritated Lewis. They acted as if they had the God-given right to be here in Fredericksburg. They had no shame. In fact, they thought there was nothing wrong with starving the women, children, and elderly of the town.

Lewis had been a fighter all his life and it galled him that he was in such a helpless position now. He was willing to do anything it took for Eliza and him to survive—anything—but he did not know what he could do. All he knew was that living under the occupation of the enemy was intolerable, and he could not stand this feeling of helplessness, this feeling of being trapped.

When the rains subsided, the Yankees rebuilt the pontoon bridges over the Rappahannock. On June 23, another storm caused the river to rise, and during the night, the bridges washed away again. The townsfolk were elated that even their river would not submit to Yankee rule.[28]

Everyone pinned his or her hopes on a rescue by the Confederate Army.[29] As they anxiously waited for the army to appear, days dragged into weeks and weeks into months. The only news they could get was from the Northern papers, and, of course, they were biased.

At the end of July, a report began to circulate that a large number of Confederate soldiers were nearby.

All businesses were ordered to close.[30] Williamsville Tavern was declared off limits, and to emphasize that point, boards were nailed across the doorframe.

The neighborhood men were accustomed to gathering at Williamsville Tavern in the evenings to discuss daily events. The front door being nailed shut did not deter them. They just came to the back door for entrance.

Lewis took the precaution of not selling food or drinks to the neighbors, so he could not be accused of still operating the tavern. It was just a neighborhood gathering of friends.

The neighbors planned to move their meetings to Rev. Rowe's parlor,[31] if the Federals stopped them from meeting in the tavern.

On July 23 when all the neighbors were together, Rev. Rowe stood up and announced to those present, "The minister of the Baptist Church, Dr. William Broaddus, was arrested[32] last night." There was a collective gasp, as everyone tried to comprehend what he was saying. "He has been taken to Washington, and is being held as a hostage in the Old Capitol Prison." There were louder gasps, because everyone knew the reputation of that notorious prison.

Rev. Rowe paused to let the news sink in, then consulted a scrap of paper and continued, "Arrested also were Thomas Barton, Thomas Knox, Beverly Gill, Charles Wellford,. James McGuire, and James

Bradley.[33] They will to be held until the Confederate government agrees to exchange them for two traitors to the Confederacy being held in the Libbey Prison in Richmond.[34]

"You mean they arrested seven innocent people to swap for two traitors? That hardly seems fair," Mr. Sisson remarked.

"That's right," Rev. Rowe answered. "They also have orders to arrest Edwin Carter and Wiley Mason,[35] but they haven't been able to find them."

Lewis was stunned. These men were among the most prominent citizens of Fredericksburg. Mr. Barton was the son of one of the most highly esteemed lawyers in town. Mr. Bradley was the director of the Bank of Virginia.[36]

Not one man in the group had ever committed a crime, or even been accused of anything minor. Their reputations were unimpeachable —and none of them was young. In fact, Mr. Barton was in very ill health.

"I just don't understand how men who have done nothing wrong could be arrested," Mr. Bozel protested.

"When you live in an occupied town, you have no civil rights," Mr. Marye explained. "The conquerors can do anything they please to the conquered. Your only recourse is to appeal to the military commander of our town. In this case, it would do no good. The orders came out of Washington.

In the North, in that 'great Union' that Lincoln is 'preserving,' the people there no longer have any rights, either," Mr. Marye continued as he stood up and faced the group. "In defiance of the Constitution, Lincoln has suspended the right of habeas corpus. The freedom of the press no longer exists. Letters sent through the post office are being censored. There is no freedom of speech—because people are afraid they will be deported, if they express opposition to the government—and judges are prevented from enforcing the law on the behalf of individuals. Now, as the final insult, 'lettres de cachet' are being used—letters bearing an official seal of the United States Government, authorizing the imprisonment, without trial, of the persons named in the letter.[37]

Does all of that sound familiar? There a war, that involved all of Europe, over those same issues. Abraham Lincoln has become an American Napoleon! He has become a dictator and tyrant!"[38]

"God help us!" Rev. Rowe implored.

"What happens if the Confederate government refuses to exchange the traitors?" Lewis asked.

"I guess Rev. Broaddus and the others will just rot in prison," Mr. Marye answered.

"Do you know what they call controlling people by fear?" Mr. Ebert asked. "In Europe we understood it well. It's called a 'Reign of Terror.'"[39]

"I don't see how they can get by with this," Mr. Jennings said. "I don't see what any of us can do to stop them," Mr. Marye answered.

"We can write letters of protest, but it would not be wise to try anything else on your own," Rev. Rowe cautioned.

A sense of dread settled over the community. The rescue everyone hoped for still had not materialized.

---

[1] *The Journal of Jane Howison Beale: Fredericksburg, Virginia 1850–1862,* Historic Fredericksburg Foundation, Inc. (1995). Entry for April 27, 1862.

[2] Ibid.

[3] Ibid. Entry for May 2, 1862.

[4] The American Colonization Society had chapters throughout the South. The goal of the American Colonization Society was to encourage all slave owners to free all of their slaves gradually. It helped freed blacks by feeding them, finding housing for them, and educating them, until they could become self supporting. They taught them a trade, and then the Society raised money for their transportation to Liberia.

[5] *The Journal of Jane Howison Beale: Fredericksburg, Virginia 1850–1862,* Historic Fredericksburg Foundation, Inc. (1995). Entry for May 14, 1862.

[6] In a correspondence dated August 2, 1862 from Commanding General Robert E. Lee, CSA to the General Commanding U. S. Army, Washington, Lee complains about the ill treatment of Southern civilians by Federal troops. He accuses the United States of violating an agreement between the United States and the Confederacy by commencing "a campaign of indiscriminate robbery and murder" by directing "the military commanders of the United States to take the property of our people for the convenience and use of the Army without compensation. A general order issued by Major General Pope on the 23rd of July last ... directs the murder of our peaceful citizens as spies if found quietly tilling their farms in his rear, even outside his lines. And one of his brigadier generals, Steinwehr, has seized innocent and peaceful inhabitants to hold as hostages to the end that they may be murdered in cold blood if any of his soldiers are killed by some unknown persons whom he designated as

'bushwhackers.'" [*The War of the Rebellion: A compilation of the Official Records of the Union and Confederate Armies*, Series II, Volume IV, pages 329–330.]

[7] For those who doubt that the Federal government would have a starvation policy against civilian populations of women, children, and elderly people, refer to:

"Rebellion has assumed that shape now that it can only terminate by the complete subjugation of the South...It is our duty to weaken the enemy, by destroying their means of cultivating their fields, and in every other way possible." Ulysses S. Grant [*War of the Rebellion: A compilation of the Official Records of the Union and Confederate Armies*, Volume XXIV, pt. III, pages 186–187, Government Printing Office (1899).]

"I propose to eat up all the surplus, and perhaps the entire crops in the country, take all serviceable stock, mules, horses...These people are proud arrogant rebels...The hands of all Federal officers should fall justly but heavily upon them, so that they should respect us—not from love, for they never will do that, but from fear of the power of our Government." [*War of the Rebellion: A compilation of the Official Records of the Union and Confederate Armies*, Volume XXXI, pt. III, page 262, Government Printing Office (1899).]

"The Government of the United States has...any and all rights which they choose to enforce in war—to take their lives, their homes, their lands, their everything...war is simply power unrestrained by constitution...To the persistent secessionist, why, death is mercy, and the quicker he or she is disposed of the better..." William T. Sherman, [*War of the Rebellion: A compilation of the Official Records of the Union and Confederate Armies*, Volume XXXII, pt. II, pages 280–81, Government Printing Office (1899)].

"There is a class of people [Southerners] men, women, and children, who must be killed or banished before you can hope for peace and order." William T. Sherman, [*War of the Rebellion: A compilation of the Official Records of the Union and Confederate Armies*, Volume XXXIX, pt. II, page 132, Government Printing Office (1899).]

Secretary of War Stanton in Washington replied to this letter stating: "Your letter of the 21st of June has just reached me and meets my approval." [Ibid, page 157.]

"No squad of men...can live anywhere we have been. The people have neither seed, corn, nor bread, or mills to grind the corn in if they had it, as I burned them wherever found...I have taken from these people the mules with which they would raise a crop the coming year, and burned every surplus grain of corn." [*The Civil War in Louisiana* by John D. Winters, Louisiana State University Press, Baton Rouge, LA (1963) page 414.]

"...guerrilla parties...are becoming very formidable...I know of no way to exterminate them except to burn out the whole country." Phillip Sheridan, [*War of the Rebellion: A compilation of the Official Records of the Union and Confederate Armies*, Volume XLIII, pt. II, page 340, Government Printing Office (1899).]

[8] *The Journal of Jane Howison Beale: Fredericksburg, Virginia 1850–1862*, Historic Fredericksburg Foundation, Inc. (1995). Entries for May 28, 1862 and June 16, 1862.

[9] Ibid. Entry for June 16, 1862.

[10] Ibid. Entry for May 14, 1862.

[11] Ibid..

[12] Ibid. Entry for May 14, 1862.

[13] Ibid. Entry for August 11, 1862. She describes how the people of Fredericksburg are unable to procure food from the countryside and must rely on the few vegetables from their gardens to subsist.

[14] Ibid. Entry for May 3, 1862. She describes a road through the forest used by persons wishing to visit Fredericksburg without using public roads and coming under the observation of the enemy.

[15] Ibid. Entry for August 19, 1862.

[16] Ibid.

[17] Tax records show that the Fredericksburg Aqueduct Company owned property on Wellford's Field. Perhaps this is the location where Lewis stole the fence, since it is very close to where he lived.

[18] "Recognizance of Bail to Answer Bill of Indictment" May 19, 1862, Fredericksburg Courthouse Annex Basement.

[19] John Marye and Montgomery Slaughter were first cousins, once removed. Montgomery Slaughter was the son of John Marye's first cousin, William Slaughter. William Slaughter's father, John Suggett Slaughter, and John Marye's mother, Mildred Slaughter, were brother and sister. They were the children of Col. John H. Slaughter, born 1732. [*Ancestry World Tree*, Ancestry.com.]

[20] Court Records, Fredericksburg Courthouse Annex Basement.

[21] The case was dropped without being prosecuted in 1865. [The Commonwealth vs. Wrenn, 1865, CR-HU-R, 474-15.]

[22] John Marye married Jane Hamilton July 7, 1862 in Cumberland County, Virginia. They were third cousins, once removed. They were both descendants of Robert Slaughter, born 1671. [*Ancestry World Tree*, Ancestory.com.]

[23] *The Journal of Jane Howison Beale: Fredericksburg, Virginia 1850–1862*, Historic Fredericksburg Foundation, Inc. (1995). Entry for June 24, 1862.

[24] Ibid. Entry for June 6, 1862.

[25] Ibid. Entry for June 1, 1862.

[26] Ibid. Entry for May 28, 1862.

[27] Liberty Town and Sandy Bottom were poor neighborhoods located on the western edge of Fredericksburg. Both whites and free blacks lived lived peacefully in the communities without problems between the two races.

[28] *The Journal of Jane Howison Beale: Fredericksburg, Virginia 1850–1862*, Historic Fredericksburg Foundation, Inc. (1995). Entry for July 23, 1862.

[29] Ibid.

[30] Ibid.

[31] *Hospital Life in the Army of the Potomac* by William H. Reed, Boston 1866. Reed mentions the fact that secret meetings took place in the cellar of the Rowe house when the house was occupied as a hospital by Union forces. He said, "We felt that we were living over a powder mine, which at any moment might explode."

[32] *War of the Rebellion: A compilation of the Official Records of the Union and Confederate Armies*, Series 2, IV, pages 366, 375-6, 528, 866.

[33] *War of the Rebellion: A compilation of the Official Records of the Union and Confederate Armies*, Series 2, IV, pages 366, 375–6, 528, 866.

[34] The two "traitors" were:

(1) Major Charles Williams. He was a native of Fredericksburg, and died there several years after the war. He was reputed to be a "wild talker" but a kindhearted man.

(2) Burnham Wardell of Richmond. He was a northern man who had been appointed superintendent of the penitentiary when Virginia was made "Military District No. 1, with headquarters at Richmond.

After the Confederate government agreed to release the above named men, the Federal government changed its requirements and added the following names to the list:

(3) Peter Couse, resident of Spotsylvania. He emigrated from Pennsylvania about fifteen years before his arrest. He was making arrangements to move to back to Pennsylvania at the time of his arrest. He had a reputation for honesty, industry, and good conduct.

(4) Squire Ralston was arrested on charges of seeking to depreciate the Confederate currency while a laborer in the woolen factory of Kelly, Tackett, Ford & Co.

(5) A.M. Pickett of Richmond.

(6) Thomas Morrison, resident of Spotsylvania. The Morrison's moved to Spotsylvania from Delaware five or six years before their arrest. They were reputed to be honest, industrious, and inoffensive men. Charges that they had expressed disloyal sentiments were brought against them by two or three of their neighbors.

(7) Moses Morrison, resident of Spotsylvania.

[*The History of the City of Fredericksburg Virginia* by S.J. Quinn, The Hermitage Press, Inc., Richmond, VA (1908) pp. 76, 79–80. Quinn erroneously identified two of the men as being named Turner instead of Morrison.

War of the Rebellion: A compilation of the Official Records of the Union and Confederate Armies, Series 2, IV, pages 375–6, 528, 861–862, 866.]

[35] *War of the Rebellion: A compilation of the Official Records of the Union and Confederate Armies*, Series 2, IV,. Pages 366, 376.

[36] *Fredericksburg News,* 29 Jan 1861, 2x3.

[37] In this passage, John Marye is expressing sentiments shared by those in Europe and published in *The Quarterly Review in London:*

"Fate has indeed taken a malignant pleasure in flouting the admirers of the United States. It is not merely that their hopes of its universal empire have been disappointed ... the mortification has been much deeper than this. Every theory to which they paid a special homage ... has been successively repudiated by their favourite (sic) statesmen. They were Apostles of Free Trade: America has established a tariff, compared to which our heaviest protection-tariff has been flimsy ... she has become a land of passports, of conscriptions, of press censorship and post-office espionage, of bastilles and lettres de cachet [a letter bearing an official seal, authorizing the imprisonment without a trial of a named person] ... there was little difference between the Government of Mr. Lincoln and the Government of Napoleon III. There was the form of a legislative assembly, where scarcely any dared to oppose for fear of a charge of treason." [*The Quarterly Review*, London 1862, cited in "The Second American Revolution: A British View of the War Between the States" by Charles Adams, *Southern Partisan*, Vol. XIV (First Quarter 1994) page 21.

See also:

Constitutional Problems Under Lincoln by J. G. Randall, (Urbana IL 1951) p. 149.

"Aiding and Abetting: Disloyalty Prosecutions in the Federal Civil Courts of Southern Illinois, 1861–1866," by Kellee Green Blake, *Illinois Historical Journal* 87 (1994) pages 95–108.]

[38] This opinion is expressed in *Abraham Lincoln, Constitutionalism, and Equal Rights in the Civil War Era* by Herman Belz, (New York 1998) pages. 18–43

[39] This term is used in a letter from Sarah Ann French Alsop of Fredericksburg to her children, dated May 31, 1863. [Virginia Historical Society, Richmond, Virginia.]

CHAPTER 3

THE OLD CAPITOL PRISON

Wednesday, August 13, 1862 had been what is known as a 'scorcher,' as the hot sun seared the earth from a cloudless sky. Before the war the windows had been left open all night in the summertime to draw the cool night air through the house. Now, with rowdy soldiers patrolling the streets all night, Lewis was afraid that open windows downstairs would be an open invitation for looting—or worse. At twilight, in spite of the heat, Lewis was closing and locking the shutters in preparation of going to bed.

Except for the occasional barking of a dog, the neighborhood was quiet. Eliza was in the parlor taking advantage of the last light of the day. She was working on a pair of socks for John, her knitting needles making a rhythmic clicking sound.

Suddenly a very loud pounding on the front door disturbed their solitude.

A voice shouted, "Open in the name of the Government of the United States of America!" Lewis looked at Eliza with alarm. His first thought was of the clandestine meetings he and his neighbors had been having. He walked cautiously to the door with Eliza right behind him.

He turned the key in the lock, but before he could open the door, himself, it was flung open. Four men in blue uniforms pushed their way, uninvited, into the house. One of them had a drawn sword.[1] They surrounded Lewis, shouldering Eliza out of the way.

"Are you Lewis Wrenn?" the one with the sword coldly demanded.

"Yes, I am. What can I do for you?" Lewis asked quietly.

"I have a warrant for your arrest by order of the Secretary of War and signed by P.H. Watson, Assistant Secretary of War."[2]

In spite of the arrests of Dr. Broaddus and the others, Lewis had never thought that this could happen to him. Those men were of the elite of Fredericksburg. He was just a plain, ordinary man.

"His arrest!" Eliza shrieked. "Why? What has he done?"

"What am I being charged with? What crime have I committed?" Lewis stammered.

"My orders simply say to arrest you and take you to our headquarters at the Farmers' Bank."[3]

"Should he pack some clothes or take anything with him?" Eliza asked, the terror she felt evident on her face and in her voice.

"He won't need anything except a blanket,"[4] was the curt reply.

Lewis' heart sank. If he did not need to pack a bag, he might not live long enough to require a change of clothing.

The soldier was obviously enjoying their distress. He paused to let them suffer a little more, before telling Eliza, "You can bring a bag of his things to headquarters early tomorrow morning."

Eliza hurried upstairs and returned with an old quilt. Lewis was silently thinking of making a run for it, once they got outside. If he could get out into the countryside, he would make his way to one of Mills' family farms, and hide out. No one would think to look for him with the relatives of his dead wife.

Lewis took the quilt from Eliza, and the men roughly prodded him out the door. He was surprised to see the house surrounded by armed soldiers.[5] There must have been thirty or more of them. "There will be no chance to run," he thought glumly.

With soldiers in front, behind, and on each side, they started walking east in the gathering darkness, down the dusty, tree-lined Turnpike onto Hanover Street. There were no streetlights, and in the gathering darkness, they had nothing to light the way. The houses they passed were dark and shuttered.

Stars began to appear in the sky, but Lewis did not notice them. Gloom had settled over him like the way night was settling over the landscape.

At sixty-two years, his age was catching up with him. The long walk down the rutted road was more difficult than he anticipated, and he had a hard time keeping pace with the soldiers, who were much younger than he was. Lewis was not about to show them any weakness. He did not intend to let these Yankees get the best of him, so he held his head erect, set his jaw, and tramped resolutely towards the dark town.

When they finally reached the Union Headquarters at the Farmers' Bank, they entered by the side door. Their footsteps echoed in the spacious foyer. He was escorted to a room with a high ceiling, large, draped windows, and an unlit fireplace. It was furnished with about a dozen or more unoccupied, utilitarian-looking, wooden chairs.

Col. Henry Kingsbury,[6] the military Governor of Fredericksburg was waiting for him. "You are being held as a hostage," Col. Kingsbury informed Lewis curtly, "for certain Union men now detained in Libbey Prison in Richmond. Early tomorrow morning you will be sent to the Old Capitol Prison in Washington." Then he motioned for Lewis to take a seat.[7]

Lewis felt numb as he selected a chair in the far corner and sat down, but he managed to maintain his composure.

With a feeling of deepening apprehension, Lewis began to comprehend the enormity of the situation. He was a hostage, accused of no crime, being illegally held by a harsh, uncaring, government. He recalled John Marye's words. What did he call it? 'Lettres de cachet'!

A few minutes later, he heard footsteps approaching the door. His eyes were fixed on the doorway, when much to his surprise George Rowe's son, the lawyer George Henry Clay Rowe, stepped into the room. At first, Lewis thought Mr. Rowe was there to give him legal counsel, but how could Eliza have gotten word to him so quickly? Besides, Mr. Marye handled all of their legal work, not Clay Rowe.

Without acknowledging Lewis' presence, Mr. Rowe sat down by the door, rested his elbows on his knees, and looked gloomily at the floor. It was then that Lewis realized that Mr. Rowe was under arrest, also.

Mr. Rowe, who was a young man in his early thirties, was known for his mercurial personality. His moods swung back and forth between hearty cheerfulness and deep, dark broodings. It was easy to see what mood he was in tonight.

Almost immediately, a very nervous William Norton joined them, and sat down next to Mr. Rowe. Mr. Norton was the owner of a housewright shop. Before the occupation, he had been a major supplier to the Confederate Army. When Lewis had built the tavern addition to his home, he had bought all the materials from Mr. Norton. Lewis nodded toward him, and Mr. Norton returned a weak smile.

Lewis was wondering how many more men were going to join them when John Berrey, the owner of a local general store arrived. Mr. Berrey had four sons in the Confederate Army.[8]

Lewis had originally had friendly, pleasant dealings with him. Everything turned sour however, when he agreed to sell the stand he bought from Mr. English to Mr. Berrey. At the last minute, Mr. Berrey reneged on the deal, leaving Lewis in a very precarious position. Promissory notes had come due, and without the money from Mr. Berrey, he could not pay them. Before it was over, the holders of the promissory notes charged him with fraud, sued him in court, and everything he owned was sold at auction. If it had not been for Eliza, he would have lost everything.[9]

He had no doubt that Mr. Berrey had been instrumental in having him kicked out of the Methodist church, too. How else would the church have known about the lawsuit?

The only thing that tempered his hostility towards Mr. Berrey was the fact that two of Mr. Berrey's sons were serving in the Thirtieth Virginia with his son, John.[10]

While he was contemplating these things, Benjamin Temple walked calmly in, looking very dignified and stately.[11] He was a very wealthy farmer, but you would never guess that fact from his down to earth, friendly manner, and modest clothing. One of his sons was a lieutenant in the Thirtieth Virginia.[12] Although he did not know him well, Lewis had always admired and respected Mr. Temple. He had heard that the Mr. Temple refused to let the Yankees get water from his well, or sit in the shade of his porch.[13] Mr. Temple had six sons in the Confederate Army.

Next, Abraham Cox joined the group, looking like he was about to die of fright.[14] It was apparent that Mr. Cox expected to receive ill-treatment at the hands of the enemy, because he was on the verge of hysterics.

He was a tailor, and had been Lewis' Sunday school teacher at the Methodist Church.[15] No doubt, Mr. Cox had voted to kick him out of the church. Lewis wondered where all his self-righteous indignation was tonight? The only sympathy he had for him was because Mr. Cox's son, Morgan, was in the same company of the Thirtieth Virginia as John.[16] He did admire the fact that Abraham Cox had reputedly been one of those who passed himself off as a British citizen to smuggle mail through the enemy lines.[17]

The unhappy group of men silently waited to see what would happen next. After a while, the thump, thump, thump of a walking stick could be heard long before old John Roberts with his long white beard tottered into the room. His son, William, was also in the same company of the Thirtieth Virginia, as John.[18]

Mr. Roberts collapsed exhausted into the nearest empty chair, clutched his heart, and then wiped his brow with an enormous handkerchief. He began describing his many physical ailments, organ by organ, to the colonel. He apparently believed he was so ill, he would die within forty-eight hours, if he were separated from the genteel care he received in his own home.

When he finished, the colonel callously replied, "You needn't worry. You will be under the care of an excellent physician at the prison."[19]

Almost immediately after that Dr. James Cooke, the owner of the largest drug store in town, walked quietly in with his arms crossed[20] and his head hanging down, and dejectedly sat down in a chair near Lewis. The Confederate Army had been his biggest customer before the Yankees arrived in Fredericksburg.[21]

The next to arrive was the blacksmith, Michael Ames, one of the men who testified against Lewis' nephew, Achilles Wrenn, when Achilles was accused of unlawful gambling last year.[22] He staggered into the room, his bushy hair in wild disarray, and his shaggy, unkempt beard stained with snuff. He looked terrified. He did not sit down but stood there fingering his snuffbox, wide-eyed with shock.[23]

Lewis thought that he seemed to have lost his self-righteous indignation along with Mr. Cox, and was keeping silent before his captors.

Mr. Ames' son, Samuel, was a corporal in the Thirtieth Virginia.[24]

Within a few minutes, John Coakley arrived, looking pale and drained, trembling with fear. He looked at the colonel, his eyes wide and terrified, as though begging for compassion, but the colonel just pointed at a chair. Mr. Coakley sank into the chair and sat there shaking.[25] It must have added insult to injury for him to be held prisoner in the bank where he was a director.[26]

After a while, Mr. Coakley gathered the courage to look around him and seemed to calm down once he realized he was not alone.[27]

The last one to arrive was Montgomery Slaughter, the portly mayor of Fredericksburg. It looked like all of Lewis' old adversaries were being arrested tonight. He could have really enjoyed the situation if he were not under arrest himself.

Mr. Slaughter was out of breath, but had a forced smile on his face, as though he was trying very hard to maintain his dignity. It was too late for that. In truth, he looked like he was going to cry. Mr. Slaughter walked up to the colonel and stammered a speech that he obviously had prepared in his mind ahead of time. It was about the illegality of holding civilians as hostages during a time of war. His efforts were wasted, because the colonel was not moved.[28]

Mr. Rowe apparently became worried about something, because he requested that Col. Kingsbury allow him to go to his office to take care of a few things. Much to Lewis' surprise, the colonel agreed to let him go with an escort.[29]

Shortly after Mr. Rowe left, John Scott arrived looking angry and defiant, with a scowl on his face and holding himself ramrod straight. Mr. Scott was a folk hero to the townspeople. Before the occupation, he had produced armaments for the Confederacy. When the Federal army confiscated his foundry, he left them a little surprise—loaded mines in the forges.[30] It was common knowledge among the townsfolk that he had passed himself off as a British citizen in order to smuggle mail through the enemy lines.[31]

In addition to his defiance, Lewis could detect lines of grief on Mr. Scott's face. Two of his children had passed away since the first of the year. His ten-year-old daughter died in January[32] during the scarlet fever epidemic, and his youngest son was killed in fighting near Mechanicsville in June. The boy joined the Confederate Army a few days after his seventeenth birthday and died two months later.[33]

After Mr. Scott joined the group, the prisoners were escorted upstairs to spend the rest of the night.[34] The room where they were taken had no furniture, or carpet. A single candle provided the only light. There was barely enough space for all of them to stretch out.

With much grumbling the men got down on the floor. Most of them put their blankets under them, but Lewis rolled up his quilt and used it as a pillow. He tried without success to fall asleep. Part of him still could not comprehend that he was being sent to prison. The other part dreaded what he knew was going to happen.

He was surrounded by the most unhappy group of men he had ever had the bad luck to be among. Apparently, the other men could not sleep either. After a while, the door opened and Mr. Rowe joined them. He had forgotten to bring a blanket, so he pulled some of Mr. Slaughter's blanket from under him, sat down, and looked at the group of miserable men. Then he made a joke about Mr. Slaughter being their head goose, who was leading his flock in the wrong direction— flying them north instead of south. Perhaps it was because they were so tense, that the joke seemed so funny. Everyone snickered.

"I knew I was in trouble when I saw that tough, old bird, Mr. Wrenn, sitting in the room," Mr. Norton quipped. "I didn't want to share his cage."

"Well, I knew I was in trouble when Mr. Scott walked through the door," Lewis replied. "I realized then that I wasn't going to get off Scot-free."

Before long the men were laughing uproariously and making jokes about each other.[35] Thus, they passed some of the long hours of their first night of captivity, before they fell fitfully asleep.

The next morning Lewis woke un-refreshed and exhausted. He stood up stiffly and stretched. All of his muscles ached. "I'm too old for this," he thought.

Mr. Rowe was sleeping peacefully nearby. He wondered about Mr. Rowe as he looked around at the other men. Mr. Rowe was about thirty-two, while the rest of the men were fifty and older. Could it be that the Yankees made a mistake and arrested the wrong man? Could they have arrested George Henry Clay Rowe, the son, instead of George Rowe, the father? It seemed strange that they had selected all older men with this one exception. "Serves the Yankees right!" Lewis thought. "This will be easier on Clay than it would be on his father."

They were a strange mix of men. William Norton, John Scott, Abraham Cox, and Michael Ames were skilled laborers. John Coakley, Montgomery Slaughter, John Berrey, and Lewis were tradesmen. Benjamin Temple was a farmer. James Cooke and Clay Rowe were professionals. John Roberts was retired.[36]

Half of the men were well to do. That group included Benjamin Temple, Montgomery Slaughter, John Coakley, Clay Rowe, William Norton, and John Scott. James Cooke, John Berrey, Abraham Cox, John Roberts, Michael Ames, and Lewis were middle class.[37]

To make matters worse for Lewis, there were strained feelings between him and Abraham Cox, Michael Ames, Montgomery Slaughter, and John Berrey.

"Wait 'til you see what they brought us to wash with," Mr. Roberts remarked sourly, bringing Lewis' attention back to his surroundings. "One basin, one pitcher of water, and one towel for the twelve of us.[38] This is going to be the death of me."

As Lewis washed his face in the dirty, murky water, the door opened.

"Well, aren't you fellows lucky?" a guard loudly announced as he brought in two hampers of food. "Some of your friends sent you some breakfast."[39]

"We better eat up," Michael Ames said, eagerly rubbing his hands and smacking his lips at the sight of the repast. "This is the last home cooked meal we will have for a while."

Lewis suddenly felt very hungry.

The men sat on the floor, as though they were having a picnic, and shared the food, greedily eating as much as they could.

Afterwards they were escorted downstairs to a room where their family and friends were assembled.[40] Eliza was standing alone, anxiously waiting for Lewis with a carpetbag of clothes and toiletries she had packed for him to take to prison. She looked as though she had not gotten much rest, either. Her eyes had dark rings and were red from crying.

She threw her arms around Lewis' neck and clung to him. "Why would they want a bunch of old men like the lot of you?" she asked, tears running down her cheeks. Lewis could not answer her because he was as puzzled as she was. He did not know why he had been selected.

"You didn't walk here did you?" Lewis asked worriedly.

"No, Monroe drove me. He's waiting outside."

"He's a good boy. Go to him if you need help with anything." Then, pulling Eliza aside, he lowered his voice to a whisper. "You saw where I hid the silver. If you need anything, dig it up and use it a piece at a time to barter with. Be sure that you conceal the stash again the way I did—and do not let anyone see you, not even Phillis. Do you understand what I am telling you? Don't let anyone see."

Eliza shook her head.

"Until last night we have never been separated during twenty years of marriage," she said wistfully.

"You're a strong woman. You have been through hard times and lonely times before. You will do all right until I can come home again," Lewis assured her, trying to conceal how worried he was.

They were required to listen to a pompous speech by Col. Kingsbury that spoiled their short time together. He arrogantly reminded everyone that the men were prisoners and were going to be treated as such.[41] Lewis quickly kissed Eliza good-by, before falling into line behind Mr. Roberts. They left the bank, each man carrying his blanket and luggage. For once Lewis was glad he was not rich, as he easily carried the carpetbag with all his things. He made quite a contrast to Mr. Slaughter and Mr. Coakley, who were laboring along with their large portmanteaus.

The men were marched to the Rappahannock, where they crossed the river on a temporary wire bridge the Union troops had constructed to Chatham,[42] the 800-acre estate in Stafford County of the James Lacy family.[43]

Guards accompanied them with fixed bayonets.[44]

"How foolish this must look," Lewis thought as he watched Mr. Roberts hobbling along in front of him with his cane and personal effects. "A bunch of decrepit old men with gray hair being herded along by energetic young men with bayonets—as though they are afraid we might try to run away, and they wouldn't be able to catch us!" With that mental picture, he smiled in spite of himself. He caught sight of Mr. Rowe and Mr. Scott proudly marching military style, and decided to follow suit. He squared his shoulders, lifted his chin, and defiantly marched the rest of the way to Chatham.

On the other side of the river, they climbed the stone steps leading from terrace to terrace, until they reached the beautifully landscaped lawns of Chatham, sweetly scented by flowering shrubs. Weeds were beginning to choke out the beds of roses and other plants, from the lack of attention given the estate, since General Burnside had established his headquarters here. The house and grounds had been seized by General Irvin McDowell in April 1862, and, while he was there, he had maintained them in the condition in which he found them.[45]

The Lacy's large brick house overlooked the center of Fredericksburg. It was two stories tall with double porticos in the center. Enclosed passages connected the one-story dependencies on each side to the main building.

When the hostages arrived, General Burnside came outside on the porch and stood facing them. He made a grand impression wearing a new-looking uniform, with his neatly trimmed hair and beard. His posture was very erect and he looked every inch of a great general. He asked if any of the men were willing to take the oath of allegiance to the Union. Of course, they all refused.

Then Mr. Slaughter spoke up and said pleasantly, "General I have been a labor-saving machine for you in Fredericksburg. I hope, if you can't get along there, you'll send for me."

General Burnside replied, "The arrests are not by my order, but that of Secretary Stanton."[46]

He quietly dismissed the armed guard, and, much to Lewis' surprise, politely announced that the men were paroled to stroll around the grounds at their pleasure.[47] Lewis had not expected the general to be so courteous, after their treatment by the pompous colonel in Fredericksburg.

Around noon, the men were required to assemble in front of the porch. As they stood there waiting, General Burnside brought out a bottle of very fine whiskey and invited the men to join him in a drink.[48] The bottle was passed from man to man, and when it was Lewis' turn, he took a long, slow drink from it. He figured that he had better fortify himself for what was to come.

Three carryalls were brought up for the men.[49] They clambered into them with their personal effects and sat on their luggage. Armed guards accompanied them, as they jolted along over a rutted wagon trail until they reached the rail station. The men boarded a train and took a short journey to Acquia Creek, where the steamer, Keyport, was waiting at the wharf. As soon as the men were aboard, the steamer started up the Potomac River towards Washington.[50]

No restrictions were put on the men, so Lewis went into the dining room with Mr. Roberts and they ordered a sumptuous dinner. Both men wrapped some biscuits and slices of meat into a handkerchief and tucked them into their carpetbags, just in case they did not get anything else to eat that day. After dining, they strolled around the deck and enjoyed the invigorating sea air and the pleasant scenery.[51]

About twenty miles from Washington the steamer stopped in lower Maryland to pick up a huge mob of people who were returning home from a picnic. Mr. Rowe later said that he counted over a thousand of them getting on board.[52]

The steamer was packed so full of the loud, sweaty revelers, that the rest of the trip was miserable. One red-faced woman tried to jostle her way past Lewis and Mr. Roberts.

"Who are you?" she demanded. "I don't remember seeing you before."

"We are political prisoners' en route to Washington from Fredericksburg," Mr. Roberts answered.

"Confederate sympathizers, huh?" she asked.

When they nodded their heads affirmatively, she indignantly replied, "Well, I hope they hang you[53] both, when you get there."

"Why, thank you, ma'am, for your kind concern," Lewis answered with a courtly nod. "And if you ever visit our fair city, we will extend the same hospitality to you."

Both men laughed off the incident, but Lewis was glad to see the skyline of Washington come into view.

It was twilight when the ship docked and they were escorted by guards to three carriages[54] that were waiting for them. From the wharf they were driven to the Old Capital Prison, on the corner of First and A Street N. E.[55] It was a very old, brick, three storied, ell-shaped building with wooden slats nailed across the tall windows to prevent escapes. Lewis did not think the slats were much of a deterrent to escapees. He could kick them out without too much trouble, but the armed guards patrolling the perimeter of the building put a damper on his thoughts of escape.

The Old Capitol building had seen better days. For several years following the burning of Washington in the War of 1812, this now derelict building had been the Capitol of the United States. John Quincy Adams had been sworn in as president in this building. Later it became the Congressional Boarding House. The great statesman, John C. Calhoun, had lived and died here. For a brief time it had been a boarding school. When existing prisons had been filled to overflowing, the Old Capitol had been turned into a holding prison for those waiting to be shipped to more permanent quarters.[56]

The reluctant men were ushered inside, where neglect was immediately apparent to Lewis in the well worn, creaking floors and stairways, the dirty walls with the peeling paint and holes in the plaster, and most of all in the dank, moldy smell.

He followed the others into a small office where the commandant wrote down each of their names.[57]

"Are any of you prepared to take the oath of Allegiance to the United States?" the commandant asked. "If you do, you will be free to leave immediately."

"Not me," Lewis replied. "I will remain a Confederate until the day I die."

"Me, neither."

"Not me. I'm a loyal Confederate."

"I would die first, before I would betray my country."

"Well, I guess you will all be staying with us for a while," the commandant replied.

After that, the prison keeper, a rotund, fast-talking, profane man,[58] with only a candle to light their way, led them down a wide hallway to a long, dark, musty room with a low ceiling. When the door was opened, the odor that assaulted their nostrils was intolerable. The men slowly shuffled in and dejectedly sat down on their luggage, not yet ready to accept the fact that they would be living in this nasty room and sleeping in these vermin-filled bunks.[59]

As the door slammed shut, and the key made a raspy sound turning in the lock, a depressive spirit settled over all of them. Their faces were lit from below by the candlestick, which was sitting on the floor, giving them even sadder and more haggard countenances.

Lewis had not felt so helpless, or so violated, since Elizabeth died. He had wept then, but now he could not impugn his manhood by revealing such emotions. Since he had not been charged with any crime, and he had been denied the right of a trial or hearing, it was impossible for him to know how long he would be here. There was a possibility that he would be imprisoned for the duration of the war, and who could predict how long that would be? The not knowing was perhaps the hardest aspect of his incarceration to accept.

For a few minutes no one spoke, each man engrossed in his own sorrow, until Mr. Roberts broke the silence.

"No civilized man can live in this dampness and dirt," he complained. "I will most likely be dead by morning."[60]

With a mischievous gleam in his eye, Mr. Rowe tried to put the group into a lighter mood. "I can tell from the distinctive smell of this room that it must have been occupied by soldiers, before we got here. Mr. Roberts had better be careful, because he is sitting too near the bunks, where some of them must have slept. He had better check to see that he hasn't gotten lice."

"Oh, my God! I can feel something crawling on me!" Mr. Roberts cried out in alarm, as he jumped to his feet and started yanking his clothes off. In a few seconds, his garments were lying in a heap on the floor, and he was dancing around in great discomfort, brushing imaginary lice off his completely nude body.[61] Now Mr. Roberts was fifty-five years old, as skinny, and knobby as a rail. A more ludicrous sight, Lewis had never seen.

Mr. Rowe doubled over in laughter, and soon the other men joined him. Mr. Roberts seemed to have forgotten his gout and other illnesses in his zeal for cleanliness.[62]

In his mind, Lewis devised a plan to share a bunk with Mr. Roberts. It should not be hard to do, as the other men had already grown tired of listening to his incessant griping and complaining, and his numerous 'organ recitals.' If Lewis could accomplish this, he would not have to worry about lice in his own bed. Mr. Roberts would be sure to pick both beds scrupulously clean.

While Mr. Roberts was dressing himself in a clean change of clothing, a Negro poked his head in the door to ask if the men wanted supper. Of course, they all did. While they were waiting for the food, Mr. Roberts sat crossed legged on the floor and minutely inspected his discarded clothes, before putting them into his commodious carpetbag.[63]

When the supper arrived, it consisted of a few hunks of foul smelling, half-raw beef, several loaves of stale bread, and a large pot of greasy coffee. The sight and smell of the food made Lewis' stomach retch in disgust. He retrieved the treats he had saved on board the liner, as did most of the other men. Mr. Rowe soon learned, much to his chagrin, that he was the only one who had not thought to save some of his dinner, but the other men generously shared with him.[64]

After eating, they began selecting beds for the night. Lewis quickly claimed one of the lower bunks, and called, "Mr. Roberts! Why don't you share a bunk with me? I'll let you take the top bunk, where the air should be cleaner and better for your lungs." Mr. Roberts gratefully accepted his offer.

The filthy, stained mattresses stank of sweat and urine. Lewis was positive they were crawling with vermin.[65] Mr. Roberts gingerly pulled his mattress off the bed and threw it on the floor. "I'm not sleeping on that until I can inspect it in day light," he complained, spreading his blanket on the top bunk.

Lewis followed his example. After he stripped down to his underwear, he stretched out on top of his quilt, and used his rolled up shirt and trousers for a pillow. As he lay there in the oppressive darkness, his thoughts turned uneasily to Eliza. Their home was in a remote part of town, and she was all by herself, unarmed, with no way to protect herself. Security had never been a worry before the war. They did not even lock the doors at night, and in the summer, the windows were left wide open. All that changed when the Federal Army came. Soldiers patrolled near the house all night, but no one was patrolling them. They often drank and became rowdy before morning. Without a male presence to discourage them, it would be easy for them to break into the house.

Lewis silently said a prayer for her protection. It was the first time he had prayed in years, and the first time in his life, he had been brought to a point where of himself, he could do nothing. He was totally dependent on God to protect him and his loved ones.

The next morning a guard escorted the men to a one-story frame building where about three hundred soldiers were already eating a meal much like the one they had been served the night before.[66]

Mr. Rowe took one look at their breakfast and left the building in disgust. Lewis sat on a bench and stared at the food on the table in front of him. He was not hungry enough, yet, to risk his life and health by eating it.

After a while, Mr. Rowe rushed excitedly back into the room. "I just saw Dr. Broaddus! He invited us to have breakfast with him, and I accepted for all of us."[67]

After eagerly exiting the dining hall, the men had a joyous reunion with the beaming Dr. Broaddus. He was not a handsome man, being heavyset and slope shouldered, with a mild-looking, pale, square face, hanging jowls, thick lips, and dark, bushy eyebrows. He had thinning, dark gray hair, which had receded exposing a broad forehead. Wire-rimmed, half-glasses were perched halfway down his long nose beneath his watery blue eyes, which were partially hidden by his drooping eyelids. Yet, kindness and caring shone out of his face, and the men felt better, just being in his presence.

The kindly gentleman led the way up four sets of rickety stairs. Charles Wellford, Beverly Gill, Thomas Knox, James Bradley, and James McGuire were waiting in a room on the third floor, with a veritable feast of fried ham, cold chicken, fresh bread, and strong Java coffee.[68]

It was strange that Lewis' appetite, which was nonexistent a few minutes before, was now voracious. All of the men dug into the food with great enthusiasm.

Afterwards, they were given permission to go into the exercise yard. The enclosed space was formed on two sides by the walls of the prison, and on the other two by a stockade fence about twelve feet high. The yard was about sixty paces long and forty paces wide.[69] This small space was already filled with about three hundred and fifty prisoners from every station in life—from well-dressed doctors, lawyers, and politicians, to modestly-clad editors, merchants, laborers, and skilled workers, to ragged deserters and vagabonds. The greatest majority, though, were dirty, half-dressed soldiers—Yankee deserters and Confederate prisoners of war[70]—who were using sticks and knives to scrape lice off their bodies.[71]

Lewis was appalled, but he knew that he needed fresh air and exercise to keep up his strength. He did his best to avoid contact with anyone accept the party from Fredericksburg.

At the end of the half hour, the men returned to their room, where Mr. Rowe, much to his disgust, discovered a large louse crawling on his neck. Mr. Roberts' performance on the previous evening could not hold a candle to the speed with which Mr. Rowe jerked off his clothes. Mr. Roberts and Mr. Berrey laughed uproariously. Now it was Mr. Rowe's turn to sit on the floor and inspect his clothes carefully for vermin.[72]

Shortly after Mr. Rowe donned clean clothes, the prison keeper called out in a loud raucous voice, "Occupants of cell number three! Evacuate your damned cell and get the hell out here right now!"

As the men filed towards the door, the boisterous keeper appeared in the doorway with a grin on his face.

"I just ordered those damned men in cells nine and thirteen upstairs to get the hell out of those cells and move their butts downstairs, so that the 'elite from Fredericksburg' can have the cells adjoining Dr. Broaddus and the other 'elite from Fredericksburg.' I thought you might like to all be together!" The twelve men lost no time gathering their blankets and luggage and going upstairs. Their new rooms were very much like, but slightly smaller than, the one occupied by the other Fredericksburg prisoners. On three sides of their cells were bunks attached to the wall. On the other side were a small cupboard and a ventilation grate.[73] Lewis once again shared a bunk with Mr. Roberts.

Lewis, John Roberts, John Berrey, John Coakley, James Cooke, Benjamin Temple, and Michael Ames shared one cell, while Clay Rowe, Montgomery Slaughter, William Norton, Abraham Cox, and John Scott shared a cell with a Mr. Richard Washington.[74]

Mr. Washington had been arrested for assisting the Confederates in the capture of Confederate deserters, and in the destruction of two vessels being used by the deserters to plunder along the Potomac. The Federals considered the destruction of the two vessels to be a very serious crime.[75]

The men spent the rest of the day arranging their belongings and dividing the chores.[76]

When they learned they could buy their own supplies and provisions, the men in the other cell decided to purchase a table and six chairs.[77]

Lewis had brought very little money with him and had no way of getting any more. His son, Robin, lived nearby in Alexandria, but Lewis could not ask him for a loan, considering that the last time he borrowed money from him, Robin had been sued and found guilty of fraud.

Lewis and Eliza had been living without any income since the occupation force had closed the tavern in July.[78] They owed mortgage payments, which John Marye had deferred until he could reopen the inn. He was reluctant to spend what little cash he had on furniture. Most of the men in his cell shared his sentiments.

Mr. Temple, who was very wealthy, magnanimously offered to put the money up for the men, and keep a running tab on anything they purchased while they were in prison. He said they could repay him after the war.

It soon became apparent that they needed more than the furniture, so they purchased cooking utensils, sheets, pillows, and other provisions.[79]

The men wanted Lewis, because of his experience operating an inn, to be their cook and make the coffee. Lewis really did not have any experience in cooking, but he had observed the women close at hand often enough to know what needed to be done.

Mr. Temple, because of his generosity, was appointed the relatively easy task of setting the table. Mr. Roberts and Mr. Cooke, both known for their cleanliness, were to clean up after meals and wash the dishes. Mr. Coakley was to make the beds and sweep the floor. Mr. Berrey was to keep them supplied with ice water. Mr. Ames, who was never known for neatness or attention to personal hygiene, was to empty the slop bucket.

The men were no longer confined to their room, but could move about freely, and visit each other's rooms, as long as they did not leave the third floor. There was not even a guard in their passageway.[80] Generous friends in Washington and Baltimore, who sympathized with their plight, often brought food to them.[81] Vegetables could be purchased in the prison commissary room,[82] and they could have friends shop for meat and other supplies.[83]

That evening they began a practice that they continued until their release.[84] They all gathered in Dr. Broaddus' cell for prayers and Scripture reading.[85]

Lewis went along with the rest, but in the beginning, he felt uncomfortable and stayed toward the back of the room. He was well versed in scripture and could quote it chapter and verse, and was capable of praying in public and giving his testimony, thanks to the training he received at the Salem Baptist Church[86] in his youth—but after his experience in the Fredericksburg Methodist Church, he had lost his zeal for God.

On Sunday mornings, Rev. Broaddus or another prisoner, Rev. Leachman, a Baptist minister from Prince William County, would give a sermon for the men from Fredericksburg and other prisoners who wanted to attend. At the same time, the prison chaplain preached in another area of the Old Capitol. Col. Wood, the superintendent of the prison, would make an announcement of the services by crying out, "All who wish to hear the gospel according to Abraham Lincoln come this way, those who wish to hear it according to Jeff Davis go over there," and he would point to Dr. Broaddus and his congregation.[87]

One Sunday when Rev. Leachman was preaching, he said, "We are in the lions' den. The same God who delivered Daniel can deliver us from this tyrannical keeper," and he nodded toward Col. Wood.

Lewis was afraid that remark would get the men in trouble, but Col. Wood remarked to the preacher, "Old gentleman, I wish, when you preach here next time, you wouldn't be so damned personal."[88]

The men spent much of every evening on their knees,[89] and it was during these prayer sessions that Lewis began to see his 'old adversaries' in a different light.

One day Rev. Broaddus pulled Lewis aside in the hallway and said, "Mr. Wrenn, I know what has gone on in Fredericksburg, and I know the pain in your heart. Don't you know that Jesus did not come to save the rich and famous? He came to heal the brokenhearted and set the captives free. He came to save men like you."

That night during prayers, Lewis heard himself praying aloud, "Father, forgive me for the bitterness I have felt in my heart toward some of my fellow inmates. I want you to root that bitterness out of heart and replace it with your love."

Mr. Cox immediately prayed, "Father, forgive me for any role I may have played in planting a seed of bitterness in Mr. Wrenn's heart. Teach us to love one another."

Mr. Berrey took up the chorus, "Father, forgive me for any role I may have played in planting a seed of bitterness in Mr. Wrenn's heart. Teach us to love one another."

Then each man, one by one, prayed the same prayer. Even those, who had never offended Lewis in any way, prayed for forgiveness.

Rev. Broaddus told the men, "The Bible teaches us that there is a friend who sticketh closer than a brother. I want you to know that I am willing to be that friend to each of you."

"So am I. If any of you ever need help, I am willing to do anything I can for you," Mr. Temple said.

"So am I," Mr. Norton added.

"So am I."

"So am I."

Each of the men pledged their friendship and aid to one another. From that time onward there was a bond of friendship between all the men that lasted for the rest of their lives.

All eighteen men met together daily to discuss plans for obtaining their release. The depressing conclusion of each of these meetings was that they were going to be left indefinitely in the Old Capitol.[90] Mr. Rowe was appointed to draft a paper that they would all sign and send to the Secretary of War making a plea for their release.[91]

In a cell across from the three cells occupied by the 'elite of Fredericksburg,' was a young man named John Hunter. He had been arrested when he tried to cross the Potomac River to join the Confederate Army.[92] He was about the same age as Mr. Rowe, and they became fast friends. One day when the two of them were walking up and down the hall, Mr. Rowe called for everyone to come out in the hall. Lewis crowded into the hall with the others. "Tell them what you just told me, John," Mr. Rowe said.

"Do you see these holes in the floor?" Mr. Hunter said, pointing to several small holes along the passageway. Lewis and the others looked at the holes and nodded. "Now look at the ceiling." Lewis was surprised to discover a hole in the ceiling directly over each hole in the floor.

"Do you know what made those holes?" Mr. Rowe asked incredulously.

"They are bullet holes," Mr. Hunter explained, "from guns being fired inside the building."

Lewis was aghast. If someone had been standing in the wrong place, he would have been killed by a bullet coming through the floor.

"Why, in God's name, would they be firing guns inside the building?" Mr. Scott asked.

"They'll shoot a prisoner for any trifling reason," Mr. Hunter answered, "like putting your hands outside the bars in the windows, or giving a smart-alecky answer to a guard. There was a case of a Mr. Steuart from Baltimore, who had been arrested as a Southern sympathizer. He paid a guard fifty dollars to help him escape. The guard took his money, called him out of his cell about midnight, and told him everything was ready. He pointed out which way for Mr. Steuart to go. Mr. Steuart went to the part of the fence that had been designated, climbed to the top, and the guard—the one who accepted the bribe—shot him through his heart."[93]

Mr. Hunter's stories added a new dimension of worry, to Lewis' misery. Now he realized he could be killed at any moment by an unexpected bullet being fired through the floor. "Perhaps I should have taken a top bunk," he thought. One day shortly after they arrived at the prison, while descending the stairs to go to the exercise yard, the men were startled to discover an elegantly dressed and very pretty, young woman confined on the second floor of the prison. Mr. Rowe nodded his head toward her and called, "Good morning!"

"No communication with this prisoner is permitted!" the guard in the hallway barked, pointing his rifle with its fixed bayonet at Mr. Rowe. "Keep moving!" The men hastily continued on their way.

"That's the famous Confederate spy, Belle Boyd," Dr. Broaddus explained. "She is totally dedicated to our Southern cause, and absolutely fearless. She is a remarkable person, and although I admire her, I would not want my daughter to pursue such a life. She was arrested for relaying Union troop movements to Stonewall Jackson."[94]

The men were shocked. Their floor was the only part of the prison where any form of consideration or civilized decency was shown to the prisoners. This young lady was being held on one of the lower floors where harshness and crudeness prevailed. That section of the prison was full of vermin. After enduring the bugs biting them all night, at dawn each day the prisoners would kill the bugs crawling up the walls. It was said that the walls were striped with Confederate blood.[95]

As they continued down the stairs, they heard the clear, melodic voice of Belle singing, "Hurrah! Hurrah! For Southern rights hurrah! Hurrah for the bonny blue flag that bears a single star!"[96]

One day as Lewis, Mr. Roberts, Mr. Coakley, and Dr. Cooke were writing letters in their cell they heard the loud voices of John Hunter and Clay Rowe.

"You're a bunch of damned idiots!"

"If you had half a brain, you wouldn't be in the Federal Army!"

"You're fighting for the wrong side, jackass!"

"We have no intentions of moving away from this damned window!"

"You're such an ass and a coward, you couldn't hit the building, much less this window!"

Lewis threw down his paper and pencil and went running out into the hallway, with Mr. Roberts, Mr. Coakley, and Dr. Cooke right behind him. When he got to the door of Mr. Hunter's cell, what he feared was happening. The two young men were at the window daring the guards to shoot at them.

"Mr. Rowe! Mr. Hunter!" Lewis yelled. "Stop it at once!"

"Do you want to get all of us killed?" Mr. Roberts hollered frantically. He was nearly hysterical.

"Men! You must stop that at once!" Dr. Cooke sternly commanded. "This won't do!"

"If you don't care about your own safety, at least think about the rest of us—, and think about your families," Lewis said.

"Move away from that window at once!" Mr. Coakley ordered.

The two men sheepishly obeyed.

"You two need to find something better to do with your time," Mr. Roberts scolded.[97]

Later that day, as Mr. Roberts was inspecting his clothes for lice for the umpteenth time, Mr. Rowe called him into the hallway. When he returned to the room, he kept glancing sideways at Lewis but did not say anything to him. After a while, Mr. Roberts asked Mr. Coakley to walk in the hall with him. When the two men returned they looked at Lewis, but still did not say a word to him. Then Mr. Roberts asked Dr. Cooke to walk in the hall with him.

Before the day was over, Lewis observed Mr. Roberts walking up and down the hall with every member of the 'Fredericksburg elite.' Afterwards the person would keep glancing at Lewis, without commenting.

Finally, Lewis had enough. He went and found Mr. Rowe in Mr. Hunter's cell.

"I know the two of you are pulling one of your pranks," Lewis accused them. "What did you say to Mr. Roberts?"

Mr. Rowe and Mr. Hunter looked at each other and roared with laughter.

"I told Mr. Roberts a tall tale. I said you had been walking too close to the lousy soldiers in the exercise yard, and that I saw several lice crawling on your collar when we came in," Mr. Rowe finally managed to say.

Lewis nodded. "And you thought he would demand that I take my clothes off and bathe, didn't you?"

"Well, something like that," Mr. Rowe admitted.

"Why didn't he do it?" Lewis asked.

Mr. Rowe and Mr. Hunter looked at each other and grinned.

"He wanted someone else to tell you," Mr. Hunter confided.

"Well, why didn't they?" Lewis demanded.

"Well, Mr. Wrenn, it turns out that they're all afraid of you! It seems you have earned yourself a considerable reputation for being a fighting man," Mr. Rowe said.[98]

Now Lewis laughed. "So your pranks won't work on me!"

"I'm afraid not," Mr. Rowe said. "Not if they require the cooperation of the other men."

Every time the hostages thought they met the qualifications for exchange, the Federal government changed the rules.

The men were heartened to hear that the Confederates had won some recent battles in Virginia, and their hope was that they would be rescued by Stonewall Jackson taking Washington DC.[99] It looked like they had a better chance of being rescued than of being exchanged.[100]

For a few days a city policeman with a splendid tenor voice was confined to the prison. He entertained the men by singing in the passageway. After hearing him, the men from Fredericksburg decided to have Mr. Rowe write a song for him to sing, which expressed their future hopes. The song Mr. Rowe wrote was to the tune of 'Stand the Storm!'[101]

1

The hero Jackson comes, my boys
Oh! Stand the storm, it won't be long
Lift up you hearts, in song rejoice
Oh! Stand the storm, it won't be long!
He comes with sword and bay'net long
He'll lay the vandal in the dust
Oh! Stand the storm! Oh! Stand the storm!
It won't be long! It won't be long!
We'll anchor by and by.

2

Again he's swept Manassas' plain
And belching bullets thick as rain
He comes with fire and steel and flame
The despot quakes to hear his name!

3

The brutal Pope in his defeat,

Has found the line of his retreat,
And King, though man of royal name,
Deserves his fate of open shame.

4

The thund'ring shock of Southern braves,
Struck panic through the hireling slaves,
They broke, they ran, and curs'd the day
They met such men, in such a fray.

5

And now our flag from neighb'ring heights
So proudly floats, so madly frights
The tyrant and his tools of state
They tremble at their coming fate.[102]

The worst part of Lewis' confinement was the boredom of long, empty hours blending into long, endless days. He was used to working hard from dawn to dusk. Now his life consisted of eating, writing letters, and prayer meetings, with long, tedious hours in between.

His imprisonment was so intolerable that in his desperation he silently turned to God and asked, "God, have you forsaken me?"

As clear as an audible voice the answer came to him immediately, "I will never leave you nor forsake you."

"But God, I can't stand this! Not for another hour, much less another day!"

"I will never allow you to be tested beyond that which you are able to bear."

"But, You don't know what this is like!"

"I do know. When you go through the fire or the water, I am there beside you."

"I thought the occupation was horrible. This is so much worse. What if I can't handle it?"

"Stretch out your arms and I will carry you where you do not want to go."

While Lewis chaffed against the chains of injustice, he found an inner peace. The man who would leave the Old Capitol Prison would not be the same man who was incarcerated.

[1] "Journal of George Henry Clay Rowe," Ann Brown Library, Brown University, cited in "Fredericksburg's Political Hostages: The Old Capitol Journal of George Henry Clay Rowe" edited by Lucille Griffith, *The Virginia Magazine of History and Biography*, Vol. 72, No. 4 (October 1964) page 399.

[2] *The War of the Rebellion: A compilation of the Official Records of the Union and Confederate Armies* Series II, Volume IV, page 375 The order was approved by L.C. Turner, Judge Advocate, on page 366.

[3] "Journal of George Henry Clay Rowe," Ann Brown Library, Brown University, cited in "Fredericksburg's Political Hostages: The Old Capitol Journal of George Henry Clay Rowe" edited by Lucille Griffith, *The Virginia Magazine of History and Biography*, Vol. 72, No. 4 (October 1964) page 400.

[4] Ibid.

[5] Ibid.

[6] Lieutenant Colonel Henry Walter Kingsbury was in the 5th U.S. Artillery, 11th Connecticut. He was killed at Antietam.[*Battles and Leaders*, II, pages 334, 411, 651.]

[7] Clay Rowe names the order in which the men arrived at the Farmers' Bank, and gives a description of their reactions to the predicament. ["Fredericksburg's Political Hostages: The Old Capitol Journal of George Henry Clay Rowe" edited by Lucille Griffith, *The Virginia Magazine of History and Biography*, Vol. 72, No. 4 (October 1964) pages 400–402.]

[8] *Fredericksburg Ledger*, 22 Jun 1866.

[9] "E.L. Parker & Co. vs. Lewis Wren, Robertson B. Wrenn et al, 1851–August 1852", Fredericksburg Chancery Court Records, in the basement of the Fredericksburg Courthouse Annex.

[10] *30th Virginia Infantry* by Robert K. Krick, H.E. Howard, Inc. (1985) page 82.

[11] "Journal of George Henry Clay Rowe," Ann Brown Library, Brown University, cited in "Fredericksburg's Political Hostages: The Old Capitol Journal of George Henry Clay Rowe" edited by Lucille Griffith, *The Virginia Magazine of History and Biography*, Vol. 72, No. 4 (October 1964), page 401.

[12] *30th Virginia Infantry* by Robert K. Krick, H.E. Howard, Inc. (1985) page 130.

[13] *The War of the Rebellion: A compilation of the Official Records of the Union and Confederate Armies*, Vol. XII, page 88.

[14] "Journal of George Henry Clay Rowe," Ann Brown Library, Brown University, cited in "Fredericksburg's Political Hostages: The Old Capitol Journal of George Henry Clay Rowe" edited by Lucille Griffith, *The*

Virginia Magazine of History and Biography, Vol. 72, No. 4 (October 1964), page 401.

[15] "Methodist Episcopal Church, Fredericksburg Records, 1834–1852". Virginia State Library.

[16] *30th Virginia Infantry* by Robert K. Krick, H.E. Howard, Inc. (1985) page 92.

[17] *The War of the Rebellion: A compilation of the Official Records of the Union and Confederate Armies,* Vol. XII, page 88.

[18] *30th Virginia Infantry* by Robert K. Krick, H.E. Howard, Inc. (1985) page 122.

[19] "Journal of George Henry Clay Rowe," Ann Brown Library, Brown University, cited in "Fredericksburg's Political Hostages: The Old Capitol Journal of George Henry Clay Rowe" edited by Lucille Griffith, *The Virginia_Magazine of History and Biography*, Vol. 72, No. 4 (October 1964), page 401.

[20] "Journal of George Henry Clay Rowe," Ann Brown Library, Brown University, cited in "Fredericksburg's Political Hostages: The Old Capitol Journal of George Henry Clay Rowe" edited by Lucille Griffith, *The Virginia_Magazine of History and Biography*, Vol. 72, No. 4 (October 1964),, page 401.

[21] *Fredericksburg Civil War Sites: April 1861– November 1862* by Noel G. Harrison, H.E. Howard, Inc. Lynchburg, VA (1995) page 54.

[22] "The Commonwealth vs. Achilles Wrenn, unlawful gaming, July 13, 1860." Fredericksburg, Virginia Courthouse Annex Basement.

"Journal of George Henry Clay Rowe," Ann Brown Library, Brown University, cited in "Fredericksburg's Political Hostages: The Old Capitol Journal of George Henry Clay Rowe" edited by Lucille Griffith, *The Virginia Magazine of History and Biography*, Vol. 72, No. 4 (October 1964), page 401.

[24] *30th Virginia Infantry* by Robert K. Krick, H.E. Howard, Inc. (1985) page 78.

[25] "Journal of George Henry Clay Rowe," Ann Brown Library, Brown University, cited in "Fredericksburg's Political Hostages: The Old Capitol Journal of George Henry Clay Rowe" edited by Lucille Griffith, *The Virginia Magazine of History and Biography*, Vol. 72, No. 4 (October 1964), page 401.

[26] *Fredericksburg News*, 29 Jan. 1861, 2x3.

[27] "Journal of George Henry Clay Rowe," Ann Brown Library, Brown University, cited in "Fredericksburg's Political Hostages: The Old Capitol Journal of George Henry Clay Rowe" edited by Lucille Griffith, *The*

Virginia Magazine of History and Biography, Vol. 72, No. 4 (October 1964) page 401.

[28] "Journal of George Henry Clay Rowe," Ann Brown Library, Brown University, cited in "Fredericksburg's Political Hostages: The Old Capitol Journal of George Henry Clay Rowe" edited by Lucille Griffith, *The Virginia Magazine of History and Biography*, Vol. 72, No. 4 (October 1964). Pages 401–402.

[29] Ibid. Page 400.

[30] *Fredericksburg Civil War Sites: April 1861–November 1862*, by Noel G. Harrison, H.E. Howard, Inc. Publisher, pages 35–36.

[31] *The War of the Rebellion: A compilation of the Official Records of the Union and Confederate Armies*, Vol. XII, page 88.

[32] City Cemetery tombstone inscription.

[33] City Cemetery tombstone Inscription.
The Fredericksburg Artillery by Robert K. Krick, H.E. Howard, Inc. (1986) page 108.

[34] Ibid. Page 402.

[35] Ibid. Pages 402–403.

[36] *The History of the City of Fredericksburg, Virginia* by S.J. Quinn, The Hermitage Press, Inc., Richmond, Va. (1908) pages 77–79.

[37] 1860 Fredericksburg, Virginia Census.

[38] "Journal of George Henry Clay Rowe," Ann Brown Library, Brown University, cited in "Fredericksburg's Political Hostages: The Old Capitol Journal of George Henry Clay Rowe" edited by Lucille Griffith, *The Virginia Magazine of History and Biography*, Vol. 72, No. 4 (October 1964), page 403.

[39] Ibid.

[40] Ibid.

[41] Ibid.

[42] Ibid.

[43] James Lacy's real estate was valued at $140,000 and his personal estate was valued at $18,000 on the 1860 Virginia census. The 1860 Slave Schedule showed that he owned at least 39 slaves.

[44] "Journal of George Henry Clay Rowe," Ann Brown Library, Brown University, cited in "Fredericksburg's Political Hostages: The Old Capitol Journal of George Henry Clay Rowe" edited by Lucille Griffith, *The Virginia Magazine of History and Biography*, Vol. 72, No. 4 (October 1964), page 403.

[45] *Fredericksburg Civil War Sites: April 1861–November 1862*, by Noel G. Harrison, H.E. Howard, Inc. Publisher Pages 104–105.

[46] "Fredericksburg First and Last," by Moncure Conway, *Magazine of American History*, (June 1887) pages 455–456.

[47] "Journal of George Henry Clay Rowe," Ann Brown Library, Brown University, cited in "Fredericksburg's Political Hostages: The Old Capitol Journal of George Henry Clay Rowe" edited by Lucille Griffith, *The Virginia Magazine of History and Biography*, Vol. 72, No. 4 (October 1964). Page 403.

[48] Ibid.

[49] Ibid.

[50] Ibid.

[51] Ibid.

[52] Ibid.

[53] Ibid. Page 404.

[54] Ibid.

[55] "Journal of George Henry Clay Rowe," Ann Brown Library, Brown University, cited in "Fredericksburg's Political Hostages: The Old Capitol Journal of George Henry Clay Rowe" edited by Lucille Griffith, *The Virginia Magazine of History and Biography*, Vol. 72, No. 4 (October 1964). Page398.

[56] Ibid.

[57] Ibid. Page 404.

[58] William P. Wood (1820–1903) was a native of Alexandria, Virginia. He had been born a Catholic but later scoffed at orthodox religion. [Ibid.. Page 404]

[59] Ibid.

[60] Ibid.

[61] Ibid. Pages 404–405.

[62] Ibid.

[63] Ibid. Page 405.

[64] Ibid.

[65] Ibid.

[66] Ibid.

[67] Ibid. Pages 405–406.

[68] Ibid. Page 406.

[69] Ibid. Pages 407–408.

[70] Ibid. Page 405 FN.

[71] Ibid. Page 408.

[72] Ibid.

[73] Ibid.

[74] Ibid.

[75] Ibid. Pages 408–409.

[76] Ibid. Page 408.

[77] Ibid. Page 409.

[78] *Journal of Jane Howison Beale of Fredericksburg, Virginia: 1850–1862,* Historic Fredericksburg Foundation, Inc. (1979). Entry for July 23, 1862.

[79] George Rowe said that his "mess" bought a table and a chair for each, but did not mention what Lewis' "mess" did. It seems natural that they would do the same the same. [Journal of George Henry Clay Rowe," Ann Brown Library, Brown University, cited in "Fredericksburg's Political Hostages: The Old Capitol Journal of George Henry Clay Rowe" edited by Lucille Griffith, *The Virginia Magazine of History and Biography*, Vol. 72, No. 4 (October 1964). Pages 409, 413.]

[80] Ibid. Page 412.

[81] Ibid. Page 406.

[82] Ibid. Page 416.

[83] One of the people who offered his services to each of the hostages individually was Dr. James C. Hall. He was a resident of Washington, DC and a friend of many of their families.[Ibid. Page 409]

[84] Ibid. Page 409.

[85] Ibid. Page 409.

[86] "Records of the Salem Baptist Church of Spotsylvania County" in the Baptist Historical Society, Richmond, VA show that Lewis had been a member of the Salem Baptist Church.

[87] *The History of the City of Fredericksburg, Virginia* by S.J. Quinn, The Hermitage Press, Inc. Richmond, Va. Page 78.

[88] "Fredericksburg First and Last" by Moncure D. Conway, *Magazine of American History* (June 1887) page 454.

[89] "Journal of George Henry Clay Rowe," Ann Brown Library, Brown University, cited in "Fredericksburg's Political Hostages: The Old Capitol Journal of George Henry Clay Rowe" edited by Lucille Griffith, *The Virginia Magazine of History and Biography*, Vol. 72, No. 4 (October 1964) Page 408 FN.

[90] Ibid. Page 409 FN.

[91] Ibid. Page 409.

[92] Ibid. Page 410.

[93] Ibid. Page 412.

[94] Ibid. Page 410.

[95] "A Soldier's Story: Prison Life and Other Incidents in the War of 1861–'65" by Miles O. Sherrill of Catawba County, North Carolina, http://docsouth.unc.edu/sherrill/sherrill.html.

[96] "A man named Gus Williams said of Belle's singing, "I've heard 'My Maryland' sung here in the old building in a way that would make you feel

like jumping out of the window and swimming across the Potomac. When Belle was here I was on the same floor. She would sing that song as if her very soul was in every word she uttered. It used to bring a lump up in my throat every time I heard it. It seemed like my heart was ready to jump out—as if I could put my finger down and touch it. I've seen men when she was singing walk off to one side and pull out their handkerchiefs and wipe their eyes for fear some would see them doing the baby act. She left soon after I came in . . . but we all missed her, even some of the Yankees" (quoted in Williamson, Prison Life, pp. 50–51)." ["Journal of George Henry Clay Rowe," Ann Brown Library, Brown University, cited in "Fredericksburg's Political Hostages: The Old Capitol Journal of George Henry Clay Rowe" edited by Lucille Griffith, *The Virginia Magazine of History and Biography*, Vol. 72, No. 4 (October 1964) page 411FN.]

[97] "Journal of George Henry Clay Rowe," Ann Brown Library, Brown University, cited in "Fredericksburg's Political Hostages: The Old Capitol Journal of George Henry Clay Rowe" edited by Lucille Griffith, *The Virginia Magazine of History and Biography*, Vol. 72, No. 4 (October 1964) Page 417.

[98] Ibid. Page 418.

[99] Ibid. Page 420.

[100] Ibid.

[101] Ibid.

[102] Ibid. Page 421.

CHAPTER 4

ELIZA'S SECRET

After Lewis was arrested, gunfire could be heard every day. The whole town was in a state of anxiety from not knowing where the Confederate army was, what was happening, or when they would be rescued. It soon became apparent that they were under the control of Union General Ambrose Burnside.

Eliza lived in a state of apprehension, while she waited to hear of Lewis' fate. Not only was she worried about Lewis, but also she felt vulnerable with him gone. She was afraid to go to sleep at night, lest someone break into the house. She lay awake at night trying not to remember that awful incident that had happened so many years ago.[1] When she finally fell into a fitful sleep, she would awake in a panic at the creak of every board and at every little sound.

The worst part about the situation was that with stragglers all over the countryside, the criminals did not have to break in. All they had to do is knock on the front door and wait for her to open it. If she did not answer the door when Federal soldiers knocked on it, they could break it down and arrest her. Once they were in the house, there was no one to stop them from taking anything they wanted and doing anything they pleased. Anything. At least she was not alone, because Phillis was there with her, but Phillis was as fearful as she was. Thankfully, most of the time all the stragglers wanted was a little something to eat.

One sultry afternoon Eliza sat by the window trying to catch any breeze that might waft by. It rained earlier in the day, but instead of bringing respite from the heat, once the shower was over, the air seemed hotter than ever. She felt that even in this heat, she needed to be doing something productive, so she was knitting some socks for John. Like everything else, yarn was scarce, so she had ripped up her sweater and was reusing that yarn.

Sweat trickled down her neck, and she knew that her damp hair was starting to smell sour. With a sigh of anticipation, she thought of the galvanized washtub hanging on a nail on the back of the house. She would have Phillis bring in the tub and water from the pump after supper, so she could take a bath and wash her hair. She would not be able to heat the water, because firewood for the stove was scarce, but as hot as it was, even a cold bath would be refreshing. That was one luxury the Yankees had not been able to deprive her of having. As long as she had a well, and a washtub, she could take baths anytime she wished.

She would have Phillis take a bath, as well, even though it was not Saturday. Slaves got hot and sweaty, and needed baths, too.

Just then, Phillis came in the room wearing her Sunday dress. She cleared her throat and waited for Eliza to look up, before she said, "Miss 'Liza, I's done finished de work you told me to do. Would its be all right if I goes to see my girl, Nancy?"[2]

Eliza was perturbed that Phillis had changed her clothes before getting permission to go, especially since she had not had a bath yet. Now her dress would need to be washed again before Sunday, but she nodded her head in concurrence. She stopped knitting as a fleeting expression of pain crossed her face, and looked almost wistful as she said, "Nancy never comes to visit me anymore, unless I send for her. I sure would like to see her. You know I love her as much as if she were my own daughter. Tell her to please come to see me."

Phillis gave her an odd look. "You kin sees her any time you wants by jest doin' what I duz—walk up de hill to Mr. Marye's house and knock on de back door."

"I can't do that!" Eliza answered, indignant at the very suggestion. "What would people say if I went to call on a slave?"

Without thinking, Phillis blurted out, "Probably de same thing dey be sayin' all along." She immediately regretted her impudence.

Eliza dropped her knitting onto the floor. "What have they been saying?" she asked icily, tilting her head and lifting her eyebrows, her jaw set in an angry expression.

Phillis looked at the floor, and did not answer. She nervously twisted the fabric of her skirt between the thumb and finger on her right hand, knowing she had gone too far.

"What have they been saying? Eliza demanded, her voice rising and her face turning red.

Phillis stumbled over the words. "Dey say, dey say dat Nancy be lookin', lookin', more like you, den me."

Eliza gave a harsh little laugh of contempt. "How could your child look like me?" she asked in a disbelieving tone of voice. "That's silly."

Phillis eyed her cautiously, reluctant to answer.

Sensing that Phillis had more to add, Eliza demanded, "What else do they say?"

Phillis hesitated, before she continued slowly, closely watching Eliza's face for changes in her expression. "Dey be sayin' dey don't know how I be de mammy of a baby wid such white skin and wid red in her hair."

"Her skin is light because she is a mulatto! Did you tell them that she is a mulatto?" Eliza replied indignantly.

"I tells dem, but dey says ain't no mulatto be dat white. Dey says ain't even no octoroon be dat white."

Eliza glared at her for a moment, then she dismissed the subject with an emphatic, "Well, they are wrong." She was reaching for her knitting when Phillis gathered the courage to speak again.

"Kin I tells you somethin', Miss 'Liza? Somethin' I neber say afore?"

Eliza examined Phillis face, and seeing her distress, detected the gravity of the situation. All of the color drained out of Eliza face, as she forgot about the knitting, and stood up, trembling. She turned her back to Phillis, and looked out the window, not answering right away. After a few minutes she quietly asked, "What is it?" her back still turned to Phillis.

"I doesn't 'member birthin' dat chile. I wakes up one mornin', and dere she be, but I doesn't 'member birthin' her." Phillis sounded perplexed.

After a brief silence, Eliza turned to face Phillis. Her face was composed and mask-like, as she said without emotion, "The reason you don't remember having her is that the doctor gave you a drug to ease the pain of childbirth, and it wiped out your memory."

"I doesn't 'member havin' no big belly afore she was birthed, neither. Your belly be bigger than mine."

"The drug made it so you don't remember being with child, either."

"But why a white doctor be at de birthin' of a colored baby? I ain't neber heard o' dat happenin' afore."

"Do you remember how sick I had been?" Eliza patiently explained. It almost sounded as if she had rehearsed and memorized her answer. "Well, I had a large tumor in my stomach. That is why my belly looked so big. The doctor decided to remove it, but while he was here, getting ready to operate on me, you went into labor. You were hollering and carrying on so bad, that he could not concentrate on my surgery. So he took some of the drug he brought here for me, and gave it to you, so you would sleep, until after he was finished with my surgery. After he finished operating on me, he delivered your baby. That is why you cannot remember Nancy being born. The fact is, I cannot remember my operation, either, because of that drug. Nevertheless, I know it happened. Most of what I know is what Mr. Lewis and the doctor told me."

"But you 'member dat your belly be big before de surgery," Phillis answered dubiously.

"I don't really remember, but others have told me that it was, so it must be so." Phillis thought about what Eliza had said. At first, she looked dubious, but since it seemed to make sense, she nodded her head, and appeared satisfied with the explanation.

Changing the subject, Eliza said, "I wish Nancy had not gotten married so young. She is still a child. She shouldn't be married." Eliza became agitated. "Technically, as your daughter she is my property, and she should have asked for my permission, not Mr. Lewis'."

"Us colored marry young," Phillis said simply.

"But she's only thirteen!" Eliza exclaimed.

"I thought she be fifteen," Phillis answered in surprise.

"That's right," Eliza corrected herself. "She's fifteen." She looked momentarily distracted by her mistake, before she added, "But fifteen is too young, too." Her thoughts seemed to drift for a moment, then she continued, "Besides—somehow—when she was a little girl, following me around the house and chattering up a storm—and because her skin was so light—I always pictured her marrying a white man."

"How could a slave be marryin' a white man?" Phillis demanded indignantly. "She be throwed in de Fred'bu'g jail if she do dat! 'Sides, colored marry colored. Dat how it be. T'ain't no other way and you's knows it, Miss 'Liza.

Tears stung the corners of Eliza's eyes, as she began to lose control of her emotions.

"Tell her I love her, and for her to come to see me," Eliza whispered sadly, remembering the beautiful little girl, all dimples and smiles, playing in the back yard away from the eyes of prying neighbors. When the child grew into a preteen, too large to hide anymore, she was sent to Brompton to work for Mr. Marye.

"I do dat, Miss 'Liza," Phillis said as she edged toward the door. She left abruptly before her mistress could change her mind.

Eliza watched with a heavy heart as Phillis left the house, crossed the Sunken Road, and climbed the hill to Brompton. Long ago memories of the assault tried to push their way into her consciousness, but she refused to relive them again. She had already done that too many times in the past.

She had despised the baby before it was born, and never thought of it as being hers, never thought of it as even being human. "It" belonged to those two men. Lewis would not have wanted another man's baby, and who could blame him? Giving it to Phillis had seemed like the perfect solution to her at that time. She had carefully planned how it could be accomplished, so that Phillis would not realize what had happened. She hid her pregnancy, and avoided the neighbors by pretending to be sick. She spent much of the last months alone in her bedroom, even taking her meals there.

Who would have guessed that she would learn to the love the child? She certainly had never planned to do so. Now she lived with the guilt and the sorrow, and with a dreadful secret, that she could never share with anyone.

She picked up her knitting, tears rolling down her cheeks, and tried not to think about her beautiful, little daughter living as a black slave.

---

[1] The Corporation of Fredericksburg vs. Martin Spicer and Richard W. Bozel, November 14, 1847. Record in the Fredericksburg Courthouse Annex Basement

[2] The Existence of Nancy Wrenn has not been proven beyond all doubt, and the evidence is subject to other interpretations. See Biographical Sketch of Nancy Wrenn for documentation concerning her existence.

CHAPTER 5

PHILLIS' DILEMMA

The number of pickets patrolling the perimeter of the town was increased,[1] but they did not make Eliza feel safer. She knew they were there to control her, and not to help her.

Eliza knew that somehow she must keep Lewis garden going, because it could mean the difference between starvation and survival. She had never done any farming, but she had observed Lewis often enough, that she thought she could manage with help from Phillis. Besides, the neighbors would be willing to give her any advice she needed.

The day after Phillis' visit to Nancy, Eliza told Phillis that she would have to help her in the garden, but Phillis was resistant to the idea and became defiant.

"I's not a field hand," Phillis protested indignantly. "I be a house servant and I's not be workin' outdoors."

Eliza understood Phillis' dilemma. Among the 'caste' system the slaves had created for themselves, they felt that being a field hand was as low as you could go in their social strata. Phillis' dignity among her own people was at stake.

Eliza was not too proud to work in the garden, if it were necessary, but somehow she could not picture herself hoeing weeds, while Phillis watched out the window. "Well, I'm not a field hand, either," she retorted impatiently, "but I like to eat, so I'll have to work in the garden, until Mr. Lewis comes home. If you want to eat, I had better see you out there beside me, working as hard as I do."

Phillis hung her head and did not look at Eliza.. "De soldiers say you should pay me for my work,"[2] she answered sullenly.

Eliza became angry. She had warned Phillis not to talk to the soldiers, and apparently, Phillis had disobeyed her.

"Pay you? Pay you?" she loudly replied. "I do pay you! I pay you with the food you eat, the clothes you wear, and the warm, cozy bed you enjoy sleeping in so much, that's in its very own, private, cozy, little bedroom."

"De soldiers say you should give me money," Phillis insisted.

Eliza thought about the fact that she had no income, and the mortgage payments were overdue. "Did the soldiers say where I'm supposed to get the money, in order to give it to you? Have you noticed that on their orders the tavern door has been nailed shut? And have you ever seen anyone giving me any money for the work I do? I have no money!"

"Dey say if you don't give me money, for me not to work," Phillis persisted stubbornly.

Eliza glared at her. She was acting like a stubborn child. "Who are you going to listen to? Those rascals who took Mr. Lewis away, so we have to work in the garden. Or me, the one who feeds and clothes you, and treats you like a member of the family? The one who takes care of you when you are sick? The one who held your hand while you were in labor, after you went and got yourself pregnant?"

Phillis hung her head and did not answer. Eliza stared at her for a few minutes, and then tried a different tactic. Her tone softened. "Do you remember when you first came to live with me?"

"No, Ma'am." Phillis still avoided her eyes.

"Well, I do. I inherited you when my first husband, Mr. Carter, died. Do you remember how old you were?"

"No, Ma'am."

"You were six or seven years old. A little bit of thing. Do you remember how hard I made you work then?"

"No, Ma'am."

"Why do you suppose that is?"

Phillis did not answer, but continued to stare at her shoes.

"It's because I treated you like the child you were. I let you play outside with the neighborhood children every afternoon. I didn't require you to do very much at all."

"I set de table and clear de dishes," Phillis reminded her.

"And what did Mr. John have to do when he was a boy?"

"He chop de fire wood and tote de water."

"I expected more of him then, than I did of you, even though he is Mr. Lewis' son and you are a servant, because he was a boy. And how many times did I take a switch to you?"

Phillis looked up startled. "I don't 'member no switchin'," she answered indignantly.

"That's because you never got one, even when you were naughty—like the time you sold your shoes."

76

"You make me to go barefooted," Phillis complained.

"Would you rather that I had switched you?"

"No, ma'am."

"But you learned not to sell your shoes again, didn't you?"

Phillis did not answer, but looked back down at the floor.

"I didn't expect much of you when you were a child, but for heavens sake, Phillis, you are a grown woman now, and we are living in desperate times. What I'm trying to say, Phillis, is that if you were my flesh and blood daughter, I would still expect you to help in the garden."

"De soldiers say I not work 'less you pay me," Phillis persisted.

Eliza completely lost her patience and became totally exasperated. "I'm not going to pay you, and you are going to work in the garden! There will be no more discussion about this!" she said angrily.

Reluctantly Phillis followed Eliza outside and reluctantly she slowly hoed the weeds.

That afternoon, while they were working in the garden, they heard the sound of many hoof beats coming up the Turnpike from the direction of town.

Eliza and Phillis ran to the front yard and were horrified to see Federal Cavalry getting into a battle line along the turnpike and the Sunken Road.

"Oh, my God!" Eliza cried as the two women clung together. "There's going to be a battle at our doorstep!"

"What shoulds we do, Ma'am?" Phillis asked furtively.

"I don't know," Eliza answered. "All avenues of escape are cut off, except towards town. If there is a battle, it will not be safe in town, either, so let's go into the cellar."

The soldiers were angry and cursing. One of them spotted the two women in the yard and shook his fist at them.

"If we have to retreat, we're going to shell the town and your house will be burned to the ground!"[3]

Phillis became hysterical. Eliza grabbed her arm and tried to pull her towards the house.

"I'se not be gettin' in de cellar! They's gonna burn de house down on top ob us!" Phillis shrieked. She pulled away from Eliza and ran screaming out of the yard, heading towards town.

The commotion caused by the Federal Cavalry had been a false alarm. The Confederate Army never showed up, but it was two days before Phillis returned, exhausted and hungry.

While she was gone, Eliza worried about her constantly. Phillis had always been there, in the background, and Eliza had never given her much thought. During those two days without Phillis, Eliza began to realize how much she cared for Phillis and depended on her.

The next morning, when Eliza awoke, Phillis was not up. Eliza went into the little bedroom by the back door to awaken her, but Phillis was gone,[4] as were her Sunday dress, her box of trinkets, and the pillow and sheets off her bed. She had run away.

Eliza was bewildered. She had been good to Phillis. She even spoiled her. Why would Phillis desert her at the time she needed her the most? She thought about the free blacks in Liberty Town. They lived a hand-to-mouth existence, working from dawn to dusk to barely stay alive, never having enough of anything—money, food, clothing, heat, comfort. Why would Phillis choose that type of life over the relative ease Eliza provided for her?

She sat down at the kitchen table and buried her head in her hands. She tried to reason it out, but she could not. Phillis had been difficult at times. Even so, Eliza felt a bond, you might even think it was an affection, for her, in spite of the fact she was a mere slave. She had thought Phillis accepted her lot in life as one of servitude. She had thought Phillis would always be loyal to her. How could she have been so wrong?

"Should I go and look for her?" Eliza thought. She dismissed the idea—and she knew it would not do any good to report her as a runaway. To whom would she report her? Certainly not the Federal troops. They would be glad she ran away, and the civilian authorities no longer had any authority.

Eliza thought of the meager food supply she and Lewis had. There would be more for them without Phillis to feed—and Phillis had not been earning her keep. There had been precious little work for her to do since the inn was closed, and she sure did not earn her keep by the little bit of hoeing she had done in the garden.

"Yes, I'm better off without her," Eliza thought. "She was becoming a burden. I should have sold her while I had the chance." Yet, in her heart, Eliza knew she was fooling herself. She could never sell Phillis. She would sign her manumission papers before she would do that.

After a while, Eliza got up and began fixing her own breakfast.

Somehow, she knew that she would never see Phillis again. She had sometimes wondered how the parents of a poor immigrant felt, when their child got on the boat for America, knowing that they would never see each other again. Now she thought she knew.

For the first time she was glad that Nancy was married, else Nancy might have gone with her.

The house suddenly seemed so empty. Never before had she been absolutely, totally alone. She had never noticed before that her footsteps made an echoing noise. For reasons she did not understand, deep within her, she felt an intense grief—something like you experience when someone you love dies.

---

[1] *The Journal of Jane Howison Beale of Fredericksburg, Virginia 1850–1862*, Historic Fredericksburg Foundation, Inc. (1995). Entry for August 26, 1862.

[2] Ibid. Entry for May 14, 1862.

[3] Ibid. Entry for August 31, 1862.

[4] By May 1863, it was estimated that there were less than two dozen slaves left in Fredericksburg. [Letter from Sarah Ann French Alsop of Fredericksburg to her children, May 31, 1863. Virginia Historical Society, Richmond, Virginia.]

CHAPTER 6
THE GATHERING STORM

After Lewis was imprisoned, the neighbors were afraid to be seen going in and out of the tavern, so with Rev. Rowe's invitation, they moved their meetings to his basement.[1] There they had the advantage that through the street-side window, they could hear and observe any movement along the turnpike, but they could not be seen.

The next time they had one of their clandestine meetings, Mr. Marye had a curious story to tell. "I have just learned," he said, "that the Provost Marshal, General Patrick, has been charged by Secretary Stanton with showing too much leniency to the citizens of Fredericksburg and he has been removed."[2]

The neighbors were aghast. They stared at each other in disbelief.

"When have we been shown leniency by any of them?" Mr. Bozel asked, incredulously "Certainly they weren't lenient with Rev. Rowe's son, Clay, or with Mr. Wrenn, when they locked them up in prison, without charging them with a crime, or giving them a trial."

"It seems to me that the Yankees would be only too happy to watch us starve to death," Mr. Jennings added, "while they stuff themselves from the crops they steal from our farmers.[3]

"Believe it or not, but that is exactly what that villain, Pope, ordered," Mr. Marye answered. "He wants his army to subsist off our countryside, and to starve our old men, and women into submission.[4] Of course, that means all the children will starve along with them."

On August 31, clouds of smoke could be seen coming from the Union encampments across the river. In spite of the oppressive heat, Eliza walked into town to see what was going on. She found a place in the shade of a large oak tree on George Street across from the Union Headquarters at the Farmer's Bank to observe the activity. The last time she had been to the bank was to bring Lewis his carpetbag, before he was sent to prison. Baffled she watched while groups of townsfolk, as curious as she, milled about.

Cavalry officers rode up and down the street barking out orders and stirring up brown clouds of dust. Enlisted men rushed urgently back and forth jostling their way through the crowds. Wagons packed with military supplies stood with horses harnessed to them outside of the bank.

The crowd began to murmur and point in several directions. From the south, west, and north, Eliza could see companies of pickets coming in from the outskirts of town. Leaving the shade of the tree, she walked two blocks down George Street towards the river. She could see that a line of guards was drawn up at the bridge, and ambulances with the sick were slowly crossing the river leaving Fredericksburg.

The Provost Marshal rode past on his horse, giving commands. The infantry began moving down Commerce Street,[5] while the cavalry moved down George Street, passing Eliza on their way toward the bridge. There was no music and no drums playing. The only voices heard were those of the officers calling, "Forward march!"[6]

Suddenly Eliza realized what was happening. Her hated enemies were leaving! Overjoyed, she started toward home. She was halfway up Hanover Street when a tremendous explosion rattled the windows of all the houses, and caused her to clutch at a picket fence for support. Later she learned that as a final act of vengeance, the Federal Army had set off an explosion in John Scott's foundry, but luckily, most of his equipment had survived.[7] Other explosions followed as the retreating Union troops blew up the bridges. Eliza could see the smoke and flames from Williamsville Tavern. The bridges burned all night, and more explosions followed sporadically as the flames reached explosives placed under the bridges.[8]

Eliza's happiness that the occupying forces were gone was tempered by the sad fact that Lewis was still in prison. No progress had been made toward securing the release of the hostages, although petitions and letters had been sent to the authorities in Washington[9] and Richmond.[10]

In Fredericksburg, however, a new spirit of rebirth pervaded the town as supplies rolled in, along with the mail and news from the rest of the Confederacy. When the Confederate Cavalry rode into town they were received with shouts of joy, as the people of Fredericksburg lined the streets and waved handkerchiefs.[11]

Several days later, Mr. Stevens stopped by to give Eliza a letter he had picked up at the post office. It was from John. Eliza eagerly tore it open, and smiled with satisfaction to see that he still called her, 'Mama.' He was not the child of her body, but he would always be the child of her heart.

August 19, 1862

Dear Mama & Papa,

I have been so worried about you. I have heard that the folks in Fredericksburg are being treated cruelly by the Federals.

I am no longer in Goldsboro. I am back in Virginia at a place called Drewry's Bluff. It is on the south side of the James River below Richmond. We have a huge chain stretched across the water so that Union gunboats cannot go up the river. Also, our cannons are up on the bluff and pointed down at the river. Not that the 30th gets to stay at Drewry's Bluff very much. I do not think there is an inch of back roads in three counties that we have not marched over at least six times. The only thing accomplished by all this marching is that I have worn out my shoe leather.

We were sent to the Richmond area during the Seven Days Battle, but I never even got to fire my rifle. Gen. Magruder[12] nearly marched us to death. When we passed the same end of an open meadow for the fourth time one morning, I realized we were marching in great, big circles. It seems the Yanks could observe us across the meadow and thought we had thousands more troops than we did, as the procession seemed (and was) endless. Pretty clever, don't you think?

We were sent to the battle at Gaines Mills, but arrived after the fighting had ceased, then were given the "honor"?? of bivouacking on the battle field. I could scarcely find a place to put my bedroll that did not have a chunk of some kind of disgusting gore on it.

My worst experience, so far, of the whole war occurred the next night. We were marched out into the woods, God (and Robert E. Lee) only knows where, and were supposed to spend the night sleeping on knobby tree roots with the ticks and red bugs. Some of us scouted around a bit, and found an abandoned house nearby to spend the night in. I pulled a large table over to an open window, spread my bedroll on it, and was soon fast asleep. Cousin Morgan was on the floor beside the table.

In the middle of the night, I was awakened by bloodcurdling screams, and thought the Yankees had come in and were bayoneting us. Then I heard inhuman sounds, sort of a hissing, and thought for a moment they had brought their companion, the Devil, with them. Then I saw two eyes glowing in the dark and realized that a wild animal had gotten into the house. It was walking toward Morgan. My heart was beating so hard I thought it would burst. I knew if it attacked him, I would have to jump off the table and wrestle with it. The Mills' family would never forgive me if I came home without our Little Morgan! Then the most awful stench filled the air, and I realized it was a polecat! Everyone ran out of the house and either threw up or did the Virginia Quick-Step.

The rest of the men had a good laugh at our expense, but after that, I could not sleep the rest of the night—which was unfortunate, because the next day was grueling.

First General Holmes[13] marched us all over the place, and then late in the afternoon he stopped us in the road in sight of Malvern Hill. There was a report that thousands of Federal troops were retreating over the hill towards the river and we were supposed to intercept them. Richmond Wilson, a farmer from Spotsylvania, said that he wished a bombshell would come and blow him to hell, as he preferred being in hell to marching up and down this country.

We all laughed, but then a large-caliber projectile from one of the Federal gunboats on the James River exploded beside Richmond, mangling his legs and hips. His morbid wish came true, because he died that night. I am going to be careful what I wish for!

We were ordered to take cover in the woods, and spent a couple of hours being bombarded by the gunboats, with nothing but rifles with which to defend ourselves. We tried to hide behind the trees, but believe me, none of them was big enough. Fortunately, the Yankees were firing too high and were hitting the treetops. We laid on the ground and had to endure a virtual storm of leaves, tree branches, birds' nests and squirrels being rained down on us.

Then a thunderstorm broke out, and we spent a miserable night sleeping on the cold, wet ground, soaked to our skins, without our tents. The next day we were marched up and down again, but this time it was even more miserable, because it was in the mud instead of the dust. All and all we spent five days marching around and becoming acquainted with all of the flora and fauna and bugs of the backwoods east of Richmond. Old Drewry's Bluff sure looked good to me when we finally got back here.

The buzz around camp is that we will be leaving tomorrow for a long, long hike to the north. Maybe I will finally get a chance to see how well my rifle works.

Hold on, and don't let the Federals get you down. Remember that we will lick all those Yankees sooner or later. I sure hope it is sooner, and I know you do, too. I sure do miss you.

All my love,
John

P.S. Thanks for having Mr. Bozel make that extra pair of shoes for me. If it were not for them, I would be barefooted now, as I marched all the way through the soles of the first pair, to the skin of my bare-feet.

P.P.S. I met the prettiest and sweetest little gal in Goldsboro. If all goes well, I will be going back to Goldsboro after the war, to pay her a visit.[14]

Eliza's joy at receiving the letter from John was dampened by the fact that Lewis was not there to share it with her.

Less than two weeks later the news of the Confederates' second great victory at Manassas reached Fredericksburg. It was with profound relief that Eliza learned the 30th Virginia was not involved.

The days dragged on as September temperatures remained hot. One day blended into the next, with nothing but chores to distract Eliza's mind from worry.

Word reached Fredericksburg that a great battle had been fought near the little town of Sharpsburg, Maryland. The 30th Virginia had been involved this time. Two of the local boys had been killed, and 111 had been seriously wounded.[15] Eliza walked into town and anxiously scanned the casualty list. She was relieved that she did not find John's name on it.

On Friday, September 26th, Eliza answered a knock at the door and discovered a messenger from Confederate Headquarters. He brought her the news that the hostages had been released from prison and Lewis would probably be arriving home sometime during the morning.[16] Before she could leave the house, Mr. Stevens drove up in his wagon and called, "Mrs. Wrenn! I just heard that the Fredericksburg prisoners have been released from the Old Capital Prison and they are en route home now!"

Eliza rushed out of the house and climbed into the wagon, sitting on the buckboard next to Monroe. They drove to the place where Lewis had crossed the Rappahannock under arrest so many weeks ago. A large crowd had gathered. Within a short time, they spied the first of the hostages trudging towards them on the other side of the river.

The military band started playing "Dixie." The people burst into cheering, while large numbers of them waved their handkerchiefs, and a few waved Confederate flags. Tears of joy streamed down Eliza's cheeks.

It turned out the hostages had walked all the way from Marlboro Point,[17] a distance of about ten miles. Lewis was exhausted when he climbed into the wagon, but he was happy to be home. When they reached the house, he was surprised to find his garden had been so carefully tended by Eliza in his absence.

A few days later, another letter from John arrived describing his experiences at Sharpsburg.

> September 23, 1862
> Dear Mama & Papa,
>
> We are in Martinsburg, but I do not expect we will be here long, as it is getting pretty nippy, and we aren't dressed for the weather.
>
> I just wanted to let you know I am all right, in case my name appeared on any of the casualty lists from Sharpsburg. I did get my hair parted by a Yankee bullet, but it was just a flesh wound, and the good women of Shepherdstown doctored me up just fine.
>
> On the day of the battle, we left Harper's Ferry around three in the morning and marched for about six hours until

we reached Antietam Creek. By then the shooting had been going on for several hours.

Col. Manning[18] marched us to a place near a little white church, that he called the Dunker Church. Then he led us in a charge across an open area and over three rail fences, against Union forces lying protected behind a rise in the ground. There was no artillery or flank support for us, and I am very sad to report that the 30th left three-fourths of her men lying on the field dead or grievously wounded, including Col. Manning. The bullets were so thick I do not know how any of us got off the field alive. It was the worst twenty minutes of my entire life. I would rather wrestle the polecat than do that again.

Robert Mills was shot in the leg[19], but the wound was not deep, and the bullet did not hit the bone, so he will be all right. Charlie[20] and Morgan are all right. As for the neighbors, John Ennis[21] was shot in the neck[22] and is bad off, and William Jones[23] was badly wounded[24] also. Michael Ames' son, Samuel was just slightly wounded in the knee.[25]

Our neighbor, Jefferson Smith, was captured when we were fighting at South Mountain,[26] before we even got to Sharpsburg.

All of us in the 30th are in bad shape. It has turned cold and virtually everyone is barefooted, and no one has an overcoat. We were forced to sacrifice our bedrolls and other equipment on the field in front of the Dunker Church, in order to escape with our lives. To make matters worse, we do not have any tents. We sleep shivering on the ground huddled against each other for warmth. Is there anyway that you could send me a blanket and some clothes?

All my love,
John

P.S. The clothes and blanket do not have to be new.[27]

Eliza sat down and cried. Then she got the socks she had knitted for John and a shirt she had made for him from one of her old skirts, along with an old pair of Lewis' trousers. She tied them in a bundle with one of her quilts, and addressed the bundle to John. That afternoon Lewis hitched the horse to the wagon, and they carried the package to the local Confederate Headquarters.[28]

Lewis never reopened the tavern. Instead, he converted it into a grocery store.[29] He had borrowed money from Mr. Temple in order to pay his fair share of the commissary bills while he was in prison. He repaid him by selling the remainder of his stock of ardent spirits.

The biggest change in his life was that on Sunday mornings he and Eliza attended services at the Baptist Church.[30]

The neighborhood men continued meeting regularly at Rev. Rowe's house. One evening John Marye announced to the assembled group, "Now that Abraham Lincoln has decided to emancipate the slaves in the South, the Yankee newspapers are saying that we are the ones who started the war—in order to preserve slavery."

All the men in the room hooted and laughed at this foolish suggestion.

"Why would I be in favor of a war to preserve slavery when I don't even own any slaves?" Mr. Stevens asked.

"Thousands of Southerners who do not own slaves voted for secession,"[31] Mr. Marye said.

"And when did slavery become the central issue?" Lewis asked. "Abraham Lincoln said they were fighting to preserve the Union."

"That's right," Mr. Marye added. "Lincoln said that his prime objective was to save the Union. If he could do so without freeing the slaves, he would do it. If he could do it by freeing all the slaves, he would do it. If he could do it by freeing some of the slaves and not freeing others, he would do it. His motive for this war was to save the Union."[32]

"What we are fighting for," Mr. Marye reminded them, "is not whether the Negro should be freed or held in servitude, but whether the white man in the South should have the same privileges enjoyed by the white man in the North. The real question in this war in regard to slavery is not whether it should continue in the South, but whether a Southern man should be permitted to take his slaves, which he purchased almost exclusively from Northern slave traders, into the territory which is the common property of the country, without interference from the government."[33]

All those present knew that slavery was a dead issue, regardless of the outcome of the war.[34] Even without the war, slavery would not have lasted. In 1807, Congress had outlawed the importation of slaves with the approval of the Southern states, and the Confederate Constitution forbade it. The simple mathematical progression of slave ownership made it impossible for the institution to continue much longer.[35] The owners were responsible for the housing, food, clothing, medical care, furniture, bedding, and kitchen utensils for all their slaves, and long-term care of old or disabled slaves. If each slave couple produced three or more offspring—and many had large families of ten to twenty children—it only took a couple of generations before all the money produced by a plantation went to supporting the slave families.[36] Already in some cases, the white plantation owners were having to seek employment elsewhere to support their own families, while their plantations supported their slaves.[37]

The solution to the slave problem, that the men in the tavern favored, was in line with the type of work being done by the local chapter of the American Colonization Society.

The Colonization movement in Fredericksburg was started by Father John Kobler, who had been the pastor of the Methodist Church. The Society helped freed blacks by feeding them, finding housing for them, and educating them, until they could become self supporting. They taught them a trade, and then the Society raised money for their transportation to Liberia.

The goal of the Colonization Society was to encourage all slave owners gradually to free all of their slaves. They felt their policies satisfied both races. They were doing the blacks a service by training them in an occupation, then giving them the opportunity of living in their own homeland of Liberia—a place where they would never encounter racial hatred or discrimination. At the same time, they were assuaging the fears of the whites, who were concerned about having large numbers of unemployed blacks turned loose on the white population.[38]

Many of the freed slaves—who either chose to remain in Fredericksburg or were waiting for transportation to Liberia—lived in the vicinity of Liberty Town, coexisting peacefully with their white neighbors. Although they saw each other daily, the two races did not generally mix socially. A number of the other freed blacks who did not wish to immigrate to Liberia went to Chicago to live.[39]

"If the Yankees like black people so much, why don't they show a little more concern for the ones who live up North, instead of sticking their noses into our business?" asked Mr. Bozel.

"Don't be deceived," Mr. Marye added. "It's not that the rights of others are dearer to the hearts of Northerners than to Southerners. The North seems to have forgotten that they are the ones who imported the slaves. Even the pious sons of the New England Puritans owned slaves.[40] It was not until they found that the conditions of their soil and climate made Negro labor unprofitable for them, that they brought their slaves down South and sold them to us.[41] Then, after they had been paid for their slaves, they decided that slavery was immoral."

"But they had their profit first," Mr. Jennings reminded them. "Money has always been dear to their hearts."

Rev. Rowe added in a disgusted tone, "They think the only reason we have Colonization Societies is to get rid of our colored people!"

Mr. Sisson was irritated at that suggestion. "But that is not true! The only reason we send anyone to Liberia is because he wants to go, and we work hard to pay for his passage."

"I haven't seen anyone forcing the blacks to get on the boats to Liberia," Mr. Stevens grumbled.

"I have been a member of the Colonization Society since 1829,[42] and believe very much in its principles." Mr. Marye remarked, "I don't think anyone hates slavery more than I do, but it seems that my servants enjoy such a high standard of living that they consider themselves to be 'better' than the free coloreds. I feel obligated to continue providing for them, but am willing to give them their manumission anytime they ask for it."

"I wanted Eliza to free Phillis when we first got married, but she had raised Phillis from a child and was too fond of her to let her go," Lewis added.

"A number of the slaves who ran away with the Yankees are returning to their masters, saying the Yankees made them work too hard,"[43] Mr. Bozel said.

All of the men, except Mr. Ebert, had been born and raised in the midst of slavery. Since that is all they had ever known, they found it natural to accept slavery—under certain circumstances. None of them believed that slaves should be mistreated. When a slave was treated as a member of the family, and shared the fortunes or misfortunes of the family, as Phillis had, they saw nothing wrong with the institution.

Even Allan Stratton, who was a known Union sympathizer, preferred hiring slaves[44] over whites, because they were a source of cheap labor. While working for him, he taught them a trade, so when they were able to buy or were granted their freedom, they could support themselves.

"I don't believe there is a soul in the North who loves the black race more than I do," Rev. Rowe added. "I gave up a lucrative business career to become the pastor of the Fredericksburg African Church.[45]

"The whole issue, as I see it," Mr. Marye said, "is not if you are pro-slavery or anti-slavery, because there has never been a pro-slavery party. If there were, I certainly would not belong to it. It is a question of pro-constitution or anti-constitution.[46] They are calling this the War of Rebellion, and in a way, they are right. It is the North that is rebelling by not upholding the Constitution."[47]

"The Constitution should be upheld according to the plain meaning of those who wrote it, as it was plainly understood by the states that ratified it,"[48] Lewis added.

"Well, I'll tell you one thing, the abolitionist movement is pure insanity," Mr. Bozel said.

"If all the slaves were freed at once, without anyone helping them to become self-sufficient, how would they exist?" Lewis asked. "That would not be doing them a favor. It would be cruelty."

"And how safe would white people be if unemployed, hunger-crazed, freed-slaves were roaming the streets?" Mr. Stevens asked.

"Most Yankees think that white people are the only ones who own slaves." Mr. Marye said. "I read that in 1830 there were over 10,000 slaves who were owned by free blacks."[49]

"If, God forbid, we should lose this war, you will never hear any of the blacks admit to that," Mr. Bozel predicted.

All vestiges of summer quickly gave way to the crisp days of autumn, which were followed closely by the gray skies and bitter cold rains of winter.

Very early in the morning on November 9, Lewis went into town on an errand. He was suddenly startled by the sound of large numbers of horses galloping towards him. He barely had time to take refuge in a doorway, before a company of Yankee cavalry with drawn sabers went dashing by him.

The Confederates soldiers were taken completely by surprise, and before their cavalry could respond, twenty of the Southern boys were taken prisoner. The others quickly mounted their horses and skirmished with the Yankees. In a very short time, the Yankees turned around and came dashing back towards Lewis.

Lewis' stomach churned in anger. He did not know how much more he could endure from the enemy. Without realizing what he was doing, he found himself hurling rocks at the mounted force as they clattered past him. He was surprised to realize that he was not alone. A number of other people were doing the same thing, knocking one Yankee off his horse, so he could be taken prisoner.[50]

A week later, on November 17, Lewis heard that the Yankees had appeared again across the river and had planted twenty guns on the heights facing Fredericksburg. That evening the sound of artillery fire shook the house, as the Yankees shelled the city. Soon the Confederates were firing back, and an artillery dual continued until dark.[51]

Two days later a long line of Yankees came pouring over the hill at Chatham and stationed themselves in the same place they had occupied during the summer.[52] General Edwin V. Sumner gave Mayor Slaughter and the city council an ultimatum. They were to surrender the town before five o'clock that afternoon or the town would be shelled. If they did not surrender, sixteen hours would be allowed to evacuate the women, children, sick, wounded, and aged, before the shelling began.

Lewis had a sense of foreboding when he heard the news. He knew that the small garrison of 520 soldiers guarding Fredericksburg could not defend the town against 12,000[53] Union soldiers. His concern for the small Confederate force increased when he heard that General Lee had sent a telegram saying to "hold the passage of the river at Fredericksburg at all hazards."[54]

Mayor Slaughter protested that the lack of rail transportation made an evacuation impossible. General Sumner cancelled his deadline but ordered that a committee from Fredericksburg had to meet with General Marsena Patrick before nine o'clock in the morning on November 22 to finalize the surrender terms.[55]

That afternoon, Lewis heard that the 30th Virginia was on its way home to Fredericksburg. If only the army could arrive in time, the town would be defended. The next day was dark and gloomy, as rain came down by the bucketsful, and the storm continued well into the night.[56] As Lewis sat in front of his cozy fire and listened to the rain beating a tattoo on the windows, he thought about John, who was marching over muddy roads, living in the open, and sleeping on the ground. He shivered as he imagined how cold and uncomfortable he must be.

Eliza looked up from her knitting in alarm. "Are you all right, Lewis?" she asked, her brow furrowed with worry. Ever since his imprisonment, Eliza worried constantly about him.

"Oh, I'm fine," Lewis answered lightly, not wanting to share his thoughts, lest he alarm her further.

Sometime during the blackness of the night, large numbers of Confederate soldiers began converging on the town.[57]

The next morning word came that the 30th was approaching Fredericksburg. When the regiment arrived, it set up camp beside Telegraph Road below town. Many of the townspeople, including Lewis and Eliza, were waiting there with gifts of food and clothing.[58]

The reunion with John was a joyous one. John had left home a grown boy, but now he was a man, a seasoned war veteran. His slender frame had become muscular and hardened, and his previously boyish face, now half-hidden behind a shaggy beard, was lean and gaunt. The scar from his battle wound was still pink, but his unkempt hair covered it, so it was hardly noticeable.

John's regiment was being reassigned to the command of General George Pickett in General James Longstreet's First Corps.[59]

Sometime during the morning, Union General Burnside demanded the surrender of Fredericksburg. Everyone was in a state of anxiety while waiting to learn if Fredericksburg were going to be handed over to the enemy.

In the late afternoon, General Robert E. Lee arrived in town. He held a conference with Mayor Slaughter and sorrowfully told him, "It is hard that the inhabitants of a town should be subjected to the calamities of a war for which they are not responsible. For myself, I will not fire a gun on Fredericksburg under any circumstances."[60]

After the conference, Mayor Slaughter sent his reply to General Burnside, "It you want the town of Fredericksburg, come and take it."[61] Now there was no doubt. A battle for the town was impending, and John would probably be in the middle of it. To make matters worse for the townspeople, they were in the middle of a scarlet fever epidemic. Thirty-one children under the age of twelve had died from it,[62] and many more were still ill.

The next day army wagons and ambulances, supplied by General Robert E. Lee, filled with women and children began moving up the turnpike past Lewis' house, and heading out into the countryside.[63] Many left on foot and sought refuge in cabins, barns, and makeshift tents in the woods and fields.[64]

At Hamilton's Crossing, the trains filled to capacity with refugees. As the last car pulled out of the station, Union troops opened fire on it.[65] Those left in Fredericksburg were panicked by the fact that the Federals were willing to attack noncombatants.

In their home at the foot of Marye's Heights, Eliza anxiously asked, "Do you think we should leave?"

"No. We will be all right here. The battle will be down by the river. Besides, where would we go?" Lewis replied.

---

[1] William H. Reed, a Union surgeon, stated that Confederate sympathizers in the Basement of the Rowe House held secret meetings, while he was performing surgery in one of the rooms above. [*Hospital Life in the Army of the Potomac* by William H. Reed, Boston 1866.]

[2] *The History of the City of Fredericksburg, Virginia* by S.J. Quinn, The Hermitage Press, Inc. Richmond, Va. Page 80.

"Fredericksburg First and Last," *Magazine of American History* (June 1887).

The Journal of Jane Howison Beale of Fredericksburg, Virginia 1850–1862, Historic Fredericksburg Foundation, Inc. (1995), Entry for July 23, 1862.

[3] In a letter written by Commanding General Robert E. Lee to the General Commanding U. S. Army, Washington on August 2, 1862, he complains that, "A general order issued by the Secretary of War of the United States in the city of Washington...directs the military commanders of the United States to take the property of our people for the convenience and use of the Army without compensation." [*War of the Rebellion: A compilation of the Official Records of the Union and Confederate Armies*, Series II, Volume IV, Government Printing Office (1899) page 329.]

[4] *The History of the City of Fredericksburg Virginia* by S. J. Quinn, The Hermitage Press, Inc., Richmond, Va. (1908) Page 80

[5] Commerce Street is now called William Street.

[6] *The Journal of Jane Howison Beale: Fredericksburg, Virginia 1850–1862*, Historic Fredericksburg Foundation, Inc. (1995) Entry for September 1, 1862.

[7] *Fredericksburg Civil War Sites: April 1861–November 1862* by Noel G. Harrison, H.E. Howard, Inc., Lynchburg, Virginia (1995) Page 37.

[8] *The Journal of Jane Howison Beale: Fredericksburg, Virginia 1850–1862*, Historic Fredericksburg Foundation, Inc. (1995) Entry for September 1, 1862.

[9] *War of the Rebellion: A compilation of the Official Records of the Union and Confederate Armies*, Series II, Volume IV, Government Printing Office (1899) Pages 450.

[10] Ibid. Pages 860–62, 866.

[11] *The Journal of Jane Howison Beale: Fredericksburg, Virginia 1850–1862*, Historic Fredericksburg Foundation, Inc. (1995) Entry for September 3, 1862.

[12] General John Bankhead Magruder ('Prince John') was of Scots ancestry. He was born in Port Royal, Virginia on May 1, 1807, and graduated from West Point in 1830. During the Seven Days Battles, he won acclaim for his clever subterfuges, but was accused of being drunk on the battlefield. After the battles, he was transferred to the Trans-Mississippi for the duration of the war. He died in Texas on February 18, 1871.

[13] Gen. Theophilus Hunter Holmes was born November 13, 1804 in Sampson County, North Carolina. He graduated from West Point forty-fourth out of a class of forty-six. He commanded a division at the Seven Days Battles but was criticized for his poor performance. Afterwards he was transferred to the Trans-Mississippe Department, where he continued to command ineptly. He died on June 21, 1880 in North Carolina.

[14] The letter from John Kobler Wrenn is fictitious, but the events recounted in the letter are true. [30th *Virginia Infantry* by Robert K. Krick, H.E. Howard, Inc., Publisher (1985). Pages 16–19.]

[15] *The History of the City of Fredericksburg, Virginia* by S.J. Quinn, The Hermitage Press, Inc. Richmond, Va. Page 80.

[16] At sundown, Wednesday, September 24, 1862 the men were put on board a Yankee steamboat for the trip home. On Friday they reached home. ["Journal of George Henry Clay Rowe," Ann Brown Library, Brown University, cited in "Fredericksburg's Political Hostages: The Old Capitol Journal of George Henry Clay Rowe" edited by Lucille Griffith, *The Virginia Magazine of History and Biography*, Vol. 72, No. 4 (October 1964) page 429.]

It was the custom to exchange prisoners at sea. They were probably sent down the Potomac River to Fort Monroe, Virginia, where they were taken from a Federal ship and placed on a Confederate steamboat for the trip home. This was the procedure followed for releasing other prisoners, including Belle Boyd. [*War of the Rebellion: A compilation of the Official Records of the Union and Confederate Armies*, Series II, Volume IV, Government Printing Office (1899). Page 461.]

[17] "Fredericksburg First and Last" *Magazine of American History* (June 1887) page 456.

[18] Van H. Manning of the 3rd Arkansas was the senior colonel in General John G. Walker's Brigade. He led the 30th Virginia, the 46th North Carolina, and the 48th North Carolina into a booby-trap at Sharpsville (Antietam) and was severely wounded in the assault. He was wounded again and captured at the Battle of the Wilderness.

[19] *30 Virginia Infantry* by Robert K. Krick, H.E. Howard, Inc., Publisher (1985) Page 114.

[20] Charles Henry Mills was a second cousin of John Kobler Wrenn, through his mother, Elizabeth Mills Wrenn. He was born 1840, the son of Robert T. and Elizabeth Mullen Mills. He was absent on furlough January through February 1864, and admitted to Chimborazo Hospital with chronic dysentery, January 26, 1865. There are no further military records. [*30th Virginia Infantry* by Robert K. Krick, H.E. Howard, Inc., Lynchburg, Virginia, page 114.]

[21] John Innis was the son of Martha Stephens.

[22] *30th Virginia Infantry* by Robert K. Krick, H.E. Howard, Inc., Lynchburg, Virginia. Page 96.

[23] William Jones was the son of Burrell Jones.

[24] *30th Virginia Infantry* by Robert K. Krick, H.E. Howard, Inc., Lynchburg, Virginia. Page 107.

[25] *30th Virginia Infantry* by Robert K. Krick, H.E. Howard, Inc., Lynchburg, Virginia. Page 78.

[26] *30th Virginia Infantry* by Robert K. Krick, H.E. Howard, Inc., Lynchburg, Virginia. Page 127.

[27] The letter from John Kobler Wrenn is fictitious, but the events recounted in the letter are true. [30th *Virginia Infantry* by Robert K. Krick, H.E. Howard, Inc., Publisher (1985). Pages 20–30.]

[28] "The citizens of Fredericksburg and its environs put together an extensive shipment of all those goods [that the men had lost or worn out] and dispatched them to the regiment" [*The Journal of Jane Howison Beale: Fredericksburg, Virginia 1850–1862*, Historic Fredericksburg Foundation, Inc. (1995). Entry for October 4, 1862.]

[29] 1970 Fredericksburg Virginia Census.

[30] Lewis Wrenn transferred his membership from the Salem Baptist Church to the Fredericksburg Baptist Church in 1865. [Records of the Baptist Historical Society, Richmond, Virginia.]

[31] This opinion is expressed in *Defending the Southern Confederacy: The Men in Gray* by Robert Catlett Cave, Edited by Walbrook D. Swank, Burd Street Press, Shippensburg, Pennsylvania, (2001), Page 58.

[32] *Civil War Extra: A Newspaper History of the Civil War from Nat Turner to 1863 from the Collection of Eric C. Care,* Castle Books (1999) Page 312.

[33] This opinion is expressed in *Defending the Southern Confederacy: The Men in Gray* by Robert Catlett Cave, Edited by Walbrook D. Swank, Burd Street Press, Shippensburg, Pennsylvania. (2001) Pages 6, 7.

[34] This opinion is expressed in *A Diary from Dixie* by Mary Boykin Chesnut, Harvard University Press (1980) Pages 435, 512.

[35] It has been estimated that if the South had been permitted to withdraw from the Union in peace, slavery could not have been maintained in the South more than a dozen years. [*Defending the Southern Confederacy: The Men in Gray* by Robert Catlett Cave, edited by Walbrook D. Swank, Burd Street Press, Shippensburg Pennsylvania. Page57.]

[36] *A Diary from Dixie* by Mary Boykin Chesnut, Harvard University Press (1980). Page 165, 184.

[37] Ibid, Pages 163, 164.

[38] "Colonization Society of Virginia," Manuscript Mss3Am353a, Virginia Historical Library, Richmond, Virginia.

[39] *The Journal of Jane Howison Beale: Fredericksburg, Virginia 1850–1862,* Historic Fredericksburg Foundation, Inc. (1995), Entry for June 25, 1862 FN.

[40] *Defending the Southern Confederacy: The Men in Gray* by Robert Catlett Cave, Edited by Walbrook D. Swank, Burd Street Press, Shippensburg, Pennsylvania. (2001) Page 5.

[41] Ibid.
A Diary from Dixie by Mary Boykin Chesnut, Harvard University Press (1980) Page 138, 265.

[42] *Virginia Herald Dispatch,* 25 Feb 1829, 3x3.

[43] *Diary of a Southern Refugee During the War, by a Lady of Virginia,* By Judith W. McGuire, University of Nebraska Press, Page 165.

[44] 1860 Fredericksburg, Virginia Slave Schedule.

[45] *Fredericksburg Ledger,* January 26, 1866.

[46] This opinion is expressed in *Defending the Southern Confederacy: The Men in Gray* by Robert Catlett Cave, Edited by Walbrook D. Swank, Burd Street Press, Shippensburg, Pennsylvania. (2001). Page72.

[47] Ibid. Page 76.

[48] Ibid. Pages 77, 102.

[49] *Black Slaveowners: Free Black Slave Masters in South Carolina, 1790–1860* by Larry Koger, McFarland & Co. Inc., Publishers (1958) page 1.

[50] *The Journal of Jane Howison Beale: Fredericksburg, Virginia 1850–1862*, Historic Fredericksburg Foundation, Inc. (1995) Entry for November 9, 1962.
The History of the City of Fredericksburg, Virginia by S.J. Quinn, The Hermitage Press, Inc. Richmond, Va. Page 83.

[51] *The Journal of Jane Howison Beale: Fredericksburg, Virginia 1850–1862*, Historic Fredericksburg Foundation, Inc. (1995) Entry for November 17, 1862.
"Fredericksburg First and Last," by Moncure Conway, *Magazine of American History*, (June 1887) page 456.

[52] *The Journal of Jane Howison Beale: Fredericksburg, Virginia 1850–1862*, Historic Fredericksburg Foundation, Inc. (1995).Entry for November 19, 1862.

[53] *The History of the City of Fredericksburg, Virginia* by S.J. Quinn, The Hermitage Press, Inc. Richmond, Va. Page 84.
"Fredericksburg First and Last," by Moncure Conway, *Magazine of American History*, (June 1887) page 456.

[54] *The Journal of Jane Howison Beale: Fredericksburg, Virginia 1850–1862*, Historic Fredericksburg Foundation, Inc. (1995) Entry for November 19, 1862.

[55] War of the Rebellion: A compilation of the Official Records of the Union and Confederate Armies Vol. XXI, (1899) pages 783–85.

[56] *The Journal of Jane Howison Beale: Fredericksburg, Virginia 1850–1862*, Historic Fredericksburg Foundation, Inc. (1995) Entry for November 20.

[57] Ibid

[58] 30th *Virginia Infantry* by Robert K. Krick, H.E. Howard, Inc., Publisher (1985). Page 33.

[59] Ibid.

[60] "Fredericksburg First and Last" *Magazine of American History*" (June 1887) Page 457.

[61] *The Journal of Jane Howison Beale: Fredericksburg, Virginia 1850–1862*, Historic Fredericksburg Foundation, Inc. (1995) Entry for November 21, 1862.

[62] Fredericksburg Virginia Death Records, November–December 1862, Virginia Historical Society.

[63] *The Journal of Jane Howison Beale: Fredericksburg, Virginia 1850–1862*, Historic Fredericksburg Foundation, Inc. (1995) Entry for November 22, 1862.

[64] *The History of the City of Fredericksburg, Virginia* by S.J. Quinn, The Hermitage Press, Inc. Richmond, Va. Page 87.

[65] Ibid. Page 86.

CHAPTER 7

THE BATTLE OF FREDERICKSBURG

On December 3, 1862 Gen. Thomas "Stonewall" Jackson's Confederate troops arrived in the area.

Most of the inhabitants had evacuated from Fredericksburg. Only a few people were on the streets, and the shutters on most of the houses were closed.[1] The community was beginning to look like a ghost town.

Unlike the wealthier folks, who had relatives with large estates in the country to take them in, most of those who lived near Lewis had no place to go, no one to give them refuge.

In their neighborhood meeting the next day, Rev. Rowe said, "It may not be safe for us to stay in our homes. I think that each of us should be making plans to evacuate our families in case we have to."

"Jane and I are back here today because of the elections. We have already evacuated to Forest Hill to stay with her relatives," Mr. Marye commented, "and we are going to ship our furniture to Richmond for safe keeping.[2] If you have relatives in the country, you should go to them and ask for refuge."

Mr. Ebert gloomily said, "I don't have relatives in the country, where I can take my family for safety."

"You can always go to the Salem Church[3] on the Orange Plank Road and ask for sanctuary." Rev. Rowe said. "I used to be a trustee[4] there, and Mr. Wrenn was one of its members.[5] He can back me up when I say that the people there have big hearts. They will be more than happy to allow you to use their facilities, and will do whatever they can to aid you. Just do not go empty-handed. Be sure that you take blankets, tarpaulins, cooking pots, food, and everything else you think you will need to survive. Lucy and I are leaving Fredericksburg as soon as we can get packed."

"I don't like the idea of evacuating," Lewis said. "During the occupation, the homes of those who left were taken over by the Federal Army and were subjected to a lot of vandalism and thievery."

When Lewis and Eliza went to bed that night it was with the uneasy knowledge that they would be sleeping surrounded by over a hundred thousand soldiers, and over on Stafford Heights there were 147 guns[6] pointed towards them. It was a chilling thought.

The weather had been unseasonably warm, but on December 5, 1862 a cold front swept in from the north accompanied by cold driving rain. In the afternoon, the temperature dropped down low and the rain turned into sleet, freezing a layer of ice on the trees and the ground. Then a major storm left four inches of snow on the ground.[7]

In spite of the bitter cold wind, many of those who remained in the town spent their days milling about the streets, keeping an uneasy eye towards the east where clouds of smoke could be seen rising from the Yankee camps. At the riverfront, a line of Confederate soldiers with frozen beards stood facing the Rappahannock. A few of the soldiers literally froze to death while standing picket duty there.[8] Outside Confederate headquarters, wagons were being loaded and driven westward. Cavalry officers rode up and down the streets shouting out orders.[9]

Each day more families drove past the house in wagons laden with household goods. They were headed west into Spotsylvania County.

On December 10, Eliza anxiously asked again, "Do you think we should leave?"

"No," Lewis answered. "I still think that if there is a battle, it will be at the river. We will be safe here. We can always go in the cellar if the shelling gets too close."

After dinner that night, Lewis became concerned about how John and the boys in the Thirtieth were keeping from freezing to death. He decided to ride over to their camp and see for himself if they were all right.

The roads were harder to traverse than usual. All the additional traffic on the roads from the soldiers and the evacuees had churned the roads into deep, muddy ruts. For that reason Lewis was glad he had opted to ride the horse instead of driving out in the wagon.

The silver moon was high in the black sky and the stars shone like diamonds. The light reflecting off the glistening snow made it as bright as twilight. Lewis had no trouble finding his way to the campground.

When a picket at the edge of the camp stopped him, he was informed that the men had moved closer to the river. Lewis turned his horse and headed east. Soon he came to a sharp incline, and the horse carefully picked his way to the top of the hill.

At the crest, Lewis reined the horse to a stop and gazed about him in amazement. Before him were tens of thousands of campfires that had been lit by the Confederate soldiers. He could see the dark forms of men huddled close to the fires for warmth. Twinkling on the other side of the Rappahannock, Yankee campfires were visible from horizon to horizon.

He could hear some groups singing lively songs. Others were holding prayer meetings and singing hymns.

It was an awesome sight! Lewis felt a chill run up his spine. Tens of thousands of campfires were warming hundreds of thousands of the brightest and most promising young men from both nations. How many of these youthful warriors would still be alive to sit around a campfire after the battle? He shivered again, and was surprised to feel his eyes watering up, because he was not a sentimental type of person. He was too hardened by life to give in to displays of emotion. Yet, he wished he were young enough to take up a rifle and fight beside these brave, young men.

John was overjoyed to see him, but was alarmed to hear that he and Eliza had not evacuated from their home.

"You will not be safe at home," he cautioned. "You can see the Yankees are right across the river, and they have their artillery pieces placed on the heights, pointed towards the town. Their cannon balls can travel for three miles. They have brought pontoon boats down to the river in six places to build pontoon bridges. The battle is not going to be by the river. We are going to stay on the high ground behind the town, and make the Yankees come to us. When they cross the river, some of those Yankees are going to come right up Hanover Street to your house. If you stay in your house, you are going to be right on the battlefield."

"I don't know where we can go," Lewis stammered. "Most of our relatives are either refugees from Fredericksburg, or on the other side of the Rappahannock, behind enemy lines. I don't think we could even get to Marshall's house at Kelly's Ford, as the Yankees have been operating around that area for months."

"You could go to the Mills' lands around the Salem Church," John answered. "Maybe one of them will take you in."

"I hate to go to them," Lewis answered. "You know that they have never approved of your stepmother."

"Well, what about the men you were imprisoned with? Does one of them have a house in the country where you can stay?"

"Maybe Benjamin Temple would take us in," Lewis said. "I'll have to think about going there," he promised.

With a sense of foreboding, Lewis returned home. He stamped his feet to shake off the mud and snow before entering the kitchen.

Eliza was waiting anxiously for him in the sitting room where the cast iron stove was doing its best to heat the room. She jumped up and ran into the kitchen when she heard his stamping.

"He's all right," Lewis said, as he came through the door and took off his coat and hat. "I don't know how, but he says they manage to keep warm at night. They sit around a campfire in the evening, then sleep huddled against each other—he calls it 'spooning'—for warmth in their little tents. They are so active during the daylight hours that they manage to keep from freezing. They seem to be a hearty lot."

Lewis hung his things on the nail beside the back door then went into the sitting room to warm his hands over the stove, with Eliza right behind him.

"There seem to be even more soldiers about. I saw a bunch of them on Marye's Heights. The boys seem to think that the battle will be soon.

John thinks we should leave, but I think we should wait a little longer until we see what's going to happen."

Before dawn, the next day the booming of two signal guns awakened them.

"It's coming from the direction of the river," Lewis said. "I was right. The battle will be at the river."

All morning the crack of musket fire sounded in the distance. Around noon, the loud boom of cannon shook the house and rattled the windows, followed by a barrage of boom after boom from the Yankee cannons.

"I think we should get together some things, in case we have to leave," Eliza insisted. Much to her surprise, Lewis did not object, as she gathered some blankets, pillows, clothes, and food into the kitchen.

Around two o' clock, the cannon fire ceased, and for a while, it was quiet. Then the musket fire began again.

Suddenly there was a sharp rapping at the front door. Eliza jumped up in alarm. Friends and neighbors knocked quietly at the back door. They had learned from experience that no good came from loud knocking at the front door.

Lewis opened the door cautiously, and discovered a young Confederate soldier with cheeks that were rosy red from the cold. Beyond him, Lewis could see Confederate troops withdrawing up the turnpike towards Marye's Heights.

"By orders of General Robert E. Lee you are to evacuate immediately," the young man said, his breath turning to a smoky mist in front of his mouth.

"Where are we supposed to go?" Lewis asked.

"If you have friends or relatives in the countryside, and the means to travel, head for their house. If not, go to the woods beyond the town and build a campfire to keep warm."

"Wouldn't we be just as safe in our home?" Lewis asked. "We have a cellar where we could retreat for safety."

"Sir, your house will be right on the battlefield. We have our artillery on Marye's Heights, and the Yankees have almost bridged the river with their pontoons. You can see we are beginning a retreat from the town. If you don't evacuate, you will most likely be killed."

Spurred into action, Lewis closed the door, and told Eliza, "We had better take as much as we can with us, because we might not have a house when we get back. In addition to that stuff you have in the kitchen, we will take a mattress, and some pots and dishes. I can hang a couple of chairs from the tavern on the outside of the wagon.

Even if the house burns, the stove should survive the fire, but those damned Yankees just might run off with the doors and burner covers from it,—so we will take them with us—and the pump handle. I will tie the cow to the back of the wagon.

I'll go lock up the chickens in the outhouse,[10] then hitch up the carryall and bring it up to the back door. You can bring things into the kitchen, but don't block the doorway. I'll bring up a couple of food barrels from the basement through the outside cellar door, then we'll put the rest of the stuff in the wagon."

"Where will we go?" Eliza asked.

"We'll go to Benjamin Temple's place. I think he'll take us in."

A few minutes later, much to their surprise, John appeared in the doorway. "My commanding officer said that it was all right for me to come help you evacuate," he said.

It was late afternoon, before they were finished packing the wagon, and Lewis climbed onto the buckboard beside Eliza. They put a blanket over their laps, and wrapped another one around their shoulders. Huddled together under the blankets, they would not be as cold. John climbed on top of the mattress in the back.

There was a constant boom of artillery fire as they started, the vibrations of which could be felt in the wagon.

When Lewis drove out of his backyard onto the Sunken Road and headed south, there were many refugees on the road. He spied David Sisson going in the opposite direction in a wagon with his son, Landon, but his wife was not with them ."Where is Mrs. Sisson?" he called to him.

Mr. Sisson shook his head in dismay. "She refuses to leave the store.[11] She thinks she can protect it against looters. I tried to talk some sense into her, but she is determined to stay. I did not think it was right to endanger the boy's life, just because she is being stubborn, so I am taking him to safety. We've lost one child, and I don't want to lose another one."[12]

Lewis passed the intersection of the turnpike and looked down the sloping expanse of Wellford's Field towards town. Tall columns of black smoke rolled upward into the blue sky. Many of the houses were on fire. He could see the steeples of St. George's Episcopal Church and the Fredericksburg Baptist Church piercing the skyline through the smoke and flames, and wondered if they would still be there when the battle was over.

As they passed Martha Stephens' house, her disheveled form was in the doorway, her hair in wild disarray, and her notorious pipe hanging out of the corner of her mouth. They could hear her loud, coarse voice haranguing with a soldier. "I don't give a damn what anyone says, I'm not going to evacuate! I sent my daughter to safety, and that should be all that is required of me. If I die, at least it will be in my own bed and not in some damned snow drift somewhere!"

"Ma'am, my orders are to remove you from this house, by force if necessary."

Lewis chuckled to Eliza, "The Yankees will meet their match, if they have to take on ole Martha."

When they passed Henry Ebert's house, it appeared to be empty.

Large numbers of troops could be seen moving about on top of Marye's Heights and Willis Hill,[13] and along the Sunken Road. Soldiers were busy digging a trench behind the stone wall on the east side of the Sunken Road. They would be able to stand in the trench protected by the wall and rest their rifles on the top when the Yankees approached. To Lewis' dismay, he noted that many of the young men did not even have a coat to protect them against the cold, and some of them did not have shoes. They had rags tied around their feet.

Many of the refugees were on foot, and it was a pitiful sight to behold! Frightened women were carrying babies, while small children scampered beside them, clinging to their mothers' skirts and crying from the cold. Old people, who were barely able to walk, hobbled along the slippery road, some of them too feeble to carry anything, some carrying a Bible and a toothbrush in one hand and a plucked chicken and a small bag of flour in the other.[14] Their heads were bent into the icy wind. One elderly, blind, white man was being lead by an elderly black woman.[15]

Wagons creaked and groaned from the loads they carried. Perched on the very top of some of the top-heavy wagons were old people and small children.

Lewis' wagon bumped and joggled slowly along. At the end of the Sunken Road he turned onto Telegraph Road.[16] A sharp curve in the road soon put Willis Hill between them and the town. Before they drove into the deep valley of Hazel Run, John had Lewis stop the wagon. He hugged both of them, as Eliza struggled to hold back the tears.

"Don't cry, Mama," John begged her. "God willing, we'll see each other again soon."

As he started hiking down the new road that the soldiers had cut behind their lines, Eliza began to weep. She watched him until he disappeared from sight, memorizing every line and movement of his body, not knowing if she would ever see him again.

Confederate soldiers were busily preparing defenses along the ridges on both sides of the road.

As they drove into the Hazel Run valley, there were woods on both sides of the road. The trees looked like a fairyland of crystal gleaming in the remaining sunlight. How deceptive that beauty was! In this sheltered spot behind the heights, crowds of women and children had taken refuge. Many had fled in such haste that they had not brought the necessities of life with them. They were standing on the snow-covered ground, huddling around smoky campfires for warmth. The women were weeping and the children were crying pitifully. A few of the mothers had built tents by hanging a blanket or piece of old carpet on two sticks stuck in the ground. Small children were huddled under the tents, sobbing.[17]

The traffic thinned out as most of those on foot joined those women and children.

Ascending a hill on the other side of the valley, at the crest Lewis turned for a last look back at the town of Fredericksburg. Artillery guns on Stafford Heights were sending red flashes arcing into the town. The cloud of smoke hanging over the town glowed red, when the shells exploded. He could still make out the church spires piercing the sky through the thick smoke.

After driving for a few miles Lewis and Eliza came to a dirt road and made a right hand turn off Telegraph Road. After traveling a bit, they came to a neat sign that said, "Berclair." They turned west onto a narrow lane and drove through a tunnel formed by the canopy of trees. They left the noise and confusion of the exodus and found themselves in an eerie world of deep silence that was disrupted only by wagon wheels crunching through the snow. A sudden gust of wind caused the ice-laden branches to make a slight tinkling sound.

Eliza gave a startled scream when a piece of ice broke off a tree above them and fell into her lap. Then she laughed at her foolishness and put the clear, cold crystal in her mouth.

As they came into a clearing, the sun dipped below the horizon. The sky turned pink and scarlet. The pure white landscape momentarily turned blood red.

"I don't think God's earth ever looked more beautiful," Eliza murmured, "or more frightening."

On the spacious boxwood enclosed lawn ahead, they could see Benjamin Temple's rambling white house, Berclair, surrounded by large black walnut trees. Much to Lewis' consternation, he could deduce that the house was already crowded with refugees from the number of wagons around the yard and the men milling about the premises.

"They might not have room for us," Lewis warned Eliza.

Mr. Temple saw them approaching and came out of the house and greeted them warmly.

"I was wondering if we could find shelter here," Louis asked hesitantly, "maybe in the barn if your house is full?"

"Certainly!" Mr. Temple declared. "The men are sleeping in the hayloft in the barn, but Mrs. Wrenn can sleep in the house with the other women."

Mrs. Temple was delighted to see them and made them feel welcome, even though her house was already overcrowded with women and children. "Perhaps we can put Mrs. Wrenn in the sewing room with two other ladies," she said, "but I'm afraid we have run out of beds."

"We brought our own mattress," Lewis offered.

"Then that's perfect!" Mr. Temple said. "I'll have some of the boys carry it in. And we can take a bedstead from the children's room. They can put their mattress on the floor to sleep. You won't mind sharing your bed with a couple of other ladies, will you Mrs. Wrenn?"

The sewing room was barely large enough to hold the bed, a small table upon which Mrs. Temple placed a candle stand, and the two chairs that Lewis brought. On one side of the room, there were shelves with rolls of linsey-woolsey[18] and cotton cloth.

The room itself smelled like fresh, clean cloth. It was crowded, but a blessed refuge from all the commotion and confusion in the rest of the house, where children, keyed up from the break in their routine, were boisterously running and squealing in the passageways.

By bedtime, there were so many people in the house that Mrs. Temple ran out of bedclothes with which to make pallets on the floor. Some of the late comers had to sleep on the bare floor.[19]

The house was large and comfortable, with oil portraits of the Temple's ancestors hanging on the walls. In the dining room was a large mahogany table. When all the extra leafs were put into the table, twenty to thirty people could be seated around it at one time.[20]

The next morning the refugees awoke to the sound of the enemy shelling Fredericksburg with their heavy guns. A gloomy fog hung over the landscape. By the time they ate breakfast, the fog had lifted, and the day turned out to be sunny and mild.

Lewis and some of the other men walked down to Telegraph Road to find out what was going on. The firing had slowed down, so that it occurred only at distant intervals. Climbing a prominent hill, known as Telegraph Hill,[21] they met some men, who told them that the battle had not begun. They were distressed to learn that the Federal soldiers had ransacked all the homes of Fredericksburg, destroying or stealing everything in the houses.[22]

The Rappahannock River makes a sharp bend at Fredericksburg. The ground slopes gently upward in a plain for about a mile and a half back from the river, and then a ring of hills encircles the plain in an amphitheater beginning a few miles in either direction from the bend. Confederate batteries were on the crest of the hills, and their infantry was stationed at the foot of the hills in the center of the amphitheater along Sunken Road.

In the distance, Lewis could make out hundreds of blue uniforms, extending down to the river, as far as he could see in either direction.

Around noon, the men returned to Berclair and shared the sad news of the pillage of their homes with the women. A sense of gloom replaced the nervous anxiety of those in the household. The refugees knew that some of them would not have a home waiting for them, and in all likelihood, all of them had lost all of their earthly possessions.

The next morning they awoke again to the booming of artillery fire, which continued without respite for the rest of the day.

Lewis and the other men walked back to a high hill on the Howison property, near to where they had been the previous day.

On Telegraph Hill, they could clearly see the majestic figure of General Robert E. Lee on this horse, Traveler, surrounded by his staff.[23] Among them, Lewis recognized his youthful nephew, Col. Beverly Wellford Wrenn, who was detailed to work for one of Lee's staff members. All day there was a flurry of activity as messengers galloped back and forth between General Lee and the troops.

Like Lewis, most of the men with him had at least one son involved in the battle, so they had more to be concerned about than just houses and possessions.

One of Benjamin Temple's sons was a lieutenant in the 30th Virginia. Five of his other sons were serving in other Confederate units, and four sons were with units at Fredericksburg. His fifteen-year-old son, Ludwell, had run away without his consent and joined the Army. Mr. Temple had been unable to locate him, until Ludwell wrote a letter home. Then Mrs. Temple had written to General Robert

E. Lee saying that she already had six sons in his army, and that this boy was still a child. She urged him to send the boy home.

General Lee wrote her a very courteous reply, commending her on her large contribution to the army, and stating that he had ordered the boy to be released and returned home.[24]

Ludwell was with the men on the hill and very much chagrined that he was unable to be with the army.

A dense mist hung over the landscape. At ten o'clock, the fog suddenly lifted and the day became bright with the sun shining warmly. Now they could see the whole length of the battlefield from the top of this hill. Lewis felt a tightening in his stomach when a long line of soldiers came into view at the edge of town, their flags unfurled and fluttering, and their rifles glinting in the sunlight. What a grand sight they made in their neat blue uniforms. What a contrast they were to Jackson's ragged infantry, and Stuart's[25] cavalry in their soiled butternut suits.

As the Union troops began to advance across Wellford's Field, Lewis could hear them shout, "Hi! Hi! Hi!" He felt an awful dread that they might overrun the Confederate line, because there were so many of them. He watched in fascinated horror as the Confederate artillery began to shell the Federal line from their front, right, and left.

The Federals closed ranks as men began to fall and continued their advance towards Marye's Heights. When they were within range, General Cobb's[26] men behind the wall poured a sheet of lead into them.

A cloud of smoke obstructed Lewis' view for a moment, then it rose revealing the Union dead and dying lying on the field, while the survivors were running for cover. The Confederate artillery plowed through them as they retreated.

Almost as quickly as one blue line would disintegrate, another blue line would appear at the edge of town, and began its slow advance. Soon hundreds, then thousands of blue-coated bodies littered the field.

By the time they began their third attack, there were so many bodies on the field that the troops were having difficulty advancing over them.

The Federals were not the only ones suffering losses. It was not long before ambulances were seen carrying the Confederate wounded up Telegraph Road to nearby farmhouses.

The available Union troops seemed numberless. Although they were not making much headway, Lewis still feared that by their sheer numbers they would eventually overwhelm the Confederates.

Before the day was over, the women from Berclair joined them.[27] Eliza clung to Lewis' arm, her fingernails digging into his flesh, as she gasped and cried at the sight of the carnage that was unfolding before them.

A line of blue coats would advance. Then men would begin to fall. The others would close ranks and continue coming up the slope towards the Sunken Road, their rifles reflecting flashes of sunlight. Others would fall, but those still standing would keep advancing—until there was no one left. After a while, a new line of blue coats would leave the town and start across Wellford's Field, to meet the same fate as those before them. This went on all day. Lewis counted fourteen separate assaults on the Confederate position. In some places, the bodies were piled three deep.

As evening drew near and the battle began wind down, Beverly Wrenn rode his horse over to the group of civilians. "Uncle Lewis, it looks like we won today, but I don't think it's over yet," he said, directing his speech at Lewis, but talking loud enough for all to hear. "A lot of our troops, including the 30th Virginia, have not even been called into battle. We think the battle will continue on the morrow.[28]

General Cobb from Georgia was shot while standing beside Mrs. Stephen's house on the Sunken Road, and he has died. General Gregg[29] from South Carolina was seriously wounded near Hamilton's Crossing, and he isn't expected to live. We have suffered some significant losses.

There was a lot of fighting near your house, and you probably won't like what you find when you go home, but don't try to return to your house, yet, because the Yankees will probably renew their assault in the morning."

Lewis thanked him, and then commented, "I have great respect for all of our brave men, who defended our homes and our country."

Col. Wrenn smiled. "I know. I cannot express the emotion I felt when I saw our starry cross floating victorious over the battlefield."

Lewis and the others returned exhausted and hungry to Berclair only to find that the yard was full of wounded soldiers.[30]

[1] *The Journal of Jane Howison Beale: Fredericksburg, Virginia 1850–1862,* Historic Fredericksburg Foundation, Inc. (1995) Entry for December 6, 1862.

[2] "An Eye Witness Account of The Battle of Fredericksburg: From the diary of a daughter of George and Maria Hamilton of Forest Hill, Virginia," Historical Society, Richmond Virginia.

[3] Benjamin and Mildred Mills deeded to the congregation the land on which the original Salem Church was built. (Benjamin Mills was the uncle of Lewis' first wife, Elizabeth Mills Wrenn.) [Records of the Salem Baptist Church, Spotsylvania County Virginia, Baptist Historical Society, Richmond, Virginia.]

[4] *Fredericksburg Ledger,* January 26, 1866.
Minor Sketches of Major Folk, by Dord C. Jett, Old Dominion Press (1928) page 96.

[5] Records of the Salem Baptist Church in the Baptist Historical Society, Richmond, Virginia show that Lewis Wrenn transferred his membership from the Salem Baptist Church in Spotsylvania County to the Fredericksburg Baptist Church in 1865.

[6] *Battles and Leaders of the Civil War* Edited by Ned Bradford, Appleton-Century-Crofts, Inc. (1956) Page 296.

[7] *The Journal of Jane Howison Beale: Fredericksburg, Virginia 1850–1862,* Historic Fredericksburg Foundation, Inc. (1995) Entry for December 6, 1862.
Fredericksburg and Chancellorsville: The Dare Mark Campaign by Daniel E. Sutherland, University of Nebraska Press, Lincoln and London (1998) page 27.

[8] "Before the storm, peaceful interlude" by Donald C. Pfanz, *The Free Lance-Star Publishing Company,*
www.fredericksburg.com/CivilWar/Battle/0311CW.htm.

[9] *The History of the City of Fredericksburg, Virginia* by S.J. Quinn, The Hermitage Press, Inc. Richmond, Va. Page 81.

[10] *William* Kepler describes going down Hanover Avenue to the last house (which would be Lewis Wrenn's house) and finding chickens locked in the outhouse. [*History of the Fourth Regiment Ohio Volunteer Infantry* by William Kepler, Cleveland (1886) page 93.]

[11] "In Front of the Stone Wall at Fredericksburg" .by John W. Ames, Brevet Brigadier-General, U.S.V. *Battles and Leaders of the Civil War.* Volume III, The Century Co., New York, pages 122 & 124.
The Valiant Hours by Thomas F. Galway Harrisburg, PA (1961) Page 61.

[12] *Fredericksburg News* July 22, 1851, 3x1.

[13] Before the war, the part of the heights, where the National Cemetery and Montfort Academy are now located, was known as Willis Hill, because of the long occupancy by the Willis family. The ridge to the north was known as Marye's Heights. After the battle of Fredericksburg Willis Hill became known as a part of Marye's Heights.

[14] "How civilians fared during the Battle of Fredericksburg: Confederate soldier gives an eyewitness account of events here in December 1862" by Mac Wyckoff,
www.fredericksburg.com/CivilWar/Battle/civilans.htm.

[15] "Caught in the Crossfire: Civilians at Fredericksburg" By Donald C. Pfanz, *The Free Lance-Star Publishing Company*,
www.freericksburg.com/CivilWar/Battle/0407CW.htm.

[16] Telegraph Road is now Lafayette Boulevard, U.S. Route 1.

[17] *The Journal of Jane Howison Beale: Fredericksburg, Virginia 1850–1862*, Historic Fredericksburg Foundation, Inc. (1995) Entry for December 11, 1862.

[18] Linsey-woolsey was a course fabric made of wool and cotton.

[19] *The Blue Hen's Brood* by William Ludwell Harrison, chapter on "Berclair," folder on the Temple family, Virginia Rappahannock Library, Virginiana Room, Fredericksburg, Virginia.

[20] Ibid.

[21] *The Journal of Jane Howison Beale: Fredericksburg, Virginia 1850–1862*, Historic Fredericksburg Foundation, Inc. (1995) Entry for December 12, 1862.

[22] Ibid. Entry for December 13, 1862.

[23] After the battle, the hill became known as Lee's Hill.

[24] *The Blue Hen's Brood* by William Ludwell Harrison, chapter on "Berclair," folder on the Temple family, Virginia Rappahannock Library, Virginiana Room, Fredericksburg Virginia.

[25] Gen. James Ewell Brown (Jeb) Stuart was the brilliant and dashing leader of the Confederate Cavalry. He was born on February 6, 1833 in Virginia. He graduated thirteenth in a class of forty-six from West Point in 1854. He was killed at Yellow Tavern during the Battle of the Wilderness in May 1864.

[26] General Thomas Reade Rootes Cobb was born on April 10, 1823 in Georgia. He was a brilliant young lawyer who had become a successful military man despite his lack of background in that field. He was wounded in the leg, while commanding his brigade in the Sunken Road, and bled to death shortly thereafter. Cobb's mother was from the Rootes family of Fredericksburg. The general was killed within sight of her home, "Federal Hill." Tradition says that the cannon that hit him was

fired from her yard. [*The Journal of Jane Howison Beale: Fredericksburg, Virginia 1850–1862*, Historic Fredericksburg Foundation, Inc. (1995) Page 77 FN.

The Confederate General, Vol. 2, William Davis, Editor, National Historical Society (1991), page 2.

[27] Jane Beale relates that the other women went to watch the battle and she was left alone in the house. [*The Journal of Jane Howison Beale: Fredericksburg, Virginia 1850–1862*, Historic Fredericksburg Foundation, Inc. (1995). Entry for December 13, 1862].

[28] Ibid. Entry for December 13, 1862.

[29] General Maxcy Gregg was born in Columbia, South Carolina on August 1, 1814, and was a wealthy lawyer. He was mortally wounded during the Battle of Fredericksburg, and died from his wounds at 5:00 am, Sunday December 14 at Belvoir. Belvoir was the home of the Yerby family located on the south slope of the Massaponax Creek valley. ["An Eye Witness Account of The Battle of Fredericksburg" by a daughter of George and Maria Hamilton of Forest Hill, Virginia Historical Library, Richmond, Virginia.]

[30] Ibid.

CHAPTER 8

SCENES FROM HELL

Lewis awoke when the signal gun was fired on Sunday, December 14, 1862, expecting another horrific day of battle scenes like he had witnessed on the previous day. When he and the others arrived at Telegraph Hill, the Confederate troops were waiting in readiness. The mist hanging over the landscape slowly lifted and a sea of blue clad bodies lying on Wellford's field came into view. Lewis strained his eyes looking towards the town, expecting a long line of Yankees to appear in a battle line, but they never did. Although no one was shelling the town, every now and then a fire would break out, sending dense black smoke into the sky.

"The Yankees are deliberately setting houses on fire, and are continuing their vandalism," Beverly Wrenn told Lewis. "There's a rumor going around that cars have arrived at Hamilton's Crossing filled with 'campine shot' that we will use to burn the Yankees out.[1] Even if the rumor is true about the cars, I do not think General Lee will even consider using campine to burn the town. I heard him bitterly criticizing the destruction of civilian property by the Yankees. He thinks that it is absolutely cowardly to wage war against weak and defenseless civilians. He promised that he will not fire a gun on Fredericksburg, under any circumstances."[2]

The following day was a repeat of the fourteenth with only minor musket fire being heard. The scene on the field had changed, though. The day before blue clad bodies had covered the field. During the night, the blue uniforms and shoes had disappeared, and the bodies now wore only their white underwear.[3]

Early the next morning those at Berclair were awakened by the sound of troops marching past, hallooing, and shouting as they went. Lewis rushed out of the barn and heard the news that the Yankees were gone, and the Confederates were the victors.

After a quick breakfast, Lewis and Eliza set out for home.

From the top of the hill by Hazel Run, they could see that burial parties were collecting the dead from the battlefield. Beyond the battlefield, the spires of Fredericksburg's churches could be seen piercing the sky. They had survived the battle.

When they drove around Willis Hill, the Confederate soldiers looked very different from the way they looked before the battle. Many of them were wearing new, blue overcoats, and they all seemed to have shoes on their feet.

As they drove onto the Sunken Road the full horror of the scene struck them. They could see long burial trenches being dug. The ground was frozen about a foot deep making it necessary to use pick axes in order to dig the trenches. The dead were lying in rows, waiting for interment. All of the frozen bodies were nude, and were an eerie bluish color.

Lewis and Eliza were revolted by the callous way the poor, dead soldiers were picked up and thrown into the trenches three deep, without first being wrapped in a blanket or a word of prayer being said. Afterwards heavy clods of earth were thrown in on top of them.[4]

Over Wellford's field were scattered a couple of thousand other bodies that had not yet been collected. They were contorted into every conceivable grotesque posture, some with mangled or missing limbs, some with ghastly wounds to the body, and some that had been decapitated. Like the bodies by the trenches, they were all nude.

Dead horses and mules also littered the landscape.

Those employed in collecting the dead were using pick axes to dislodge the bodies, which had frozen to the ground during the night.[5]

On another area of the battlefield where Mr. Wallace's empty icehouse was located, Union soldiers were tossing bodies into the deep pit.[6]

It looked like a scene straight out of hell.

It was already common knowledge that the Union bodies closest to the wall were from the Irish Brigade. Lewis shook his head at the irony of it. He remembered that Wellford's Field had produced such a bumper crop of corn in 1847 that the greater part of the harvest had been sent to Ireland as a donation to feed the starving Irish. Now the field was being fertilized by the blood of the men who had been fed by it.[7]

"How could anyone rob a dead body of his clothes?" Eliza asked in dismay.

116

"Our boys would not rob a dead body unless they were desperate. You try living out-of-doors in the ice and snow with no coat or shoes, if you really want to know what drove them to do it," Lewis snapped angrily. Eliza looked at his reddened face and hard set jaw, and made no reply.

Lewis tried not to look at Wellford's Field, because the sight was too sickening. Even when he turned his eyes away, the images burned into his brain, and he still saw them. Despite himself, he kept looking back. His stomach felt queasy. He tried to keep his eyes on the Sunken Road, but that did not help. The stone wall was stained with huge blotches of red, that he knew was blood. Here and there were patches of crimson red snow.

As they passed Henry Ebert's house, they could see that it was bullet riddled, but still standing.

They drove on, and Martha Stephens' house came into view. She was in her yard smoking her pipe.

"Strange," Lewis thought, "she used to be the most disgusting sight in the neighborhood. Now she is a sight for sore eyes."

As they drew near she loudly boasted, "I have hundreds of bullet holes in my house and there were dead soldiers all over my yard."[8]

Lewis stopped the wagon and stared at her house in amazement. There was not a square foot that did not have at least one bullet hole in it. He looked at Mrs. Stephens quizzically, remembering her argument with the soldiers, as he was leaving town. "So where did you go, when you evacuated?" he asked.

"I didn't evacuate. I were here during the whole battle!"

Lewis looked dubious. "You must have been in the root cellar, then. I don't think a mosquito could have survived in that house."

"No, I were in the house the whole time. The bullets were whizzing by me like hornets, but I stayed to nurse the wounded."

"Nurse the wounded?" Eliza asked in disbelief. "What could you do for the wounded?"

"Why, I bandaged their wounds, and gave them water, and comforted them," Mrs. Stephens replied.

"Where did you get the bandages from?" Eliza asked skeptically.

"I tore up every piece of cloth in the house. When nothing else were left, I tore up my skirt and my petticoat, until there weren't enough of them left to even cover my knees," Mrs. Stephens declared.[9]

Lewis looked at her doubtfully. "If I remember correctly," he said, "You were wearing the dress you have on now, when we drove past on our way out of town. It doesn't look like to me it has been torn off to your knees."

"I didn't tear up this dress," Mrs. Stephens explained. "I tore up my good dress."

"Why in the world would you tear up your good dress, instead of that one?" Eliza asked.

"'Cause I were wearing my good dress. In the excitement I didn't realize what I were doing, and I tore up my good dress, 'cause that's what I had on."

"But why would you change into your good dress, when you knew a battle was about to take place?" Eliza pressed.

"I figured if I got killed, I wanted to be laid out in my good dress, so I put it on. I were still wearing it torn off to my knees, when General Lee came to thank me for nursing the wounded. I were so embarrassed to have him see me like that, but he say I should think nothing of it. He was so appreciative of what I done."

"General Lee exposed himself between the lines during the battle to thank you for nursing the wounded?" Lewis asked incredulously.

"No, he came early this morning to thank me."

"But why were you wearing your torn up dress this morning?" Eliza asked. "Why weren't you wearing the dress you have on now?"

"I guess I was so caught up in taking care of the wounded, I didn't think of changing my dress, until after General Lee came," Mrs. Stephens replied.

Lewis chuckled. "You keep telling that story, Mrs. Stephens. Sooner or later you will find some dolt head who will believe it." He flicked the reins and they drove off.

"She's as crazy as a bedbug," Eliza remarked.

"Not Martha," Lewis answered. "She's as smart as a whip. I don't know what she has up her sleeve, but she will find some people who are gullible enough to believe her, and somehow she will profit by it."[10]

After passing Martha Stephens' house, they got their first good look at their own home. There were a couple of large holes in the roof, and the two front doors and window shutters were missing, but it was still standing.

As they were drawing closer, two men came out of the house, carrying the body of a soldier. One had the arms, and the other the feet. They crossed the Turnpike, over to Wellford's field, where they placed it beside a row of other bodies.

One of the men, who was wearing a heavy blue overcoat and a new blue uniform, looked like John. The other man, a stranger, was dressed in John's old clothes.

As they pulled up at the intersection, John wiped his forehead, and walked over to them. "I had hoped we would be finished with this before you got home. This man," he nodded toward the man wearing his clothes, "was hiding in your cellar,[11] when I got here. He surrendered to me and begged me not to send him back to the Union army. I agreed to take him to the Confederate authorities, if he would exchange his nice, new clothes for mine." John opened his coat, unbuttoned a few buttons of the uniform shirt, and pulled it open exposing his under garment. "I even got new, store-bought underwear," he said with a grin. "And he's helping me clean up some before I turn him in."

"Are there anymore of them in there?" Lewis asked, nodding towards the body.

"Just one more. If you take the wagon around back, we will have him out before Mama can get out of the wagon. It is going to be hard enough on her without her seeing one of them in the house. Apparently, both armies used the house as a snipers' nest,[12] first the Rebs, then the Yankees. That is why there is so much damage on the top floor of the house on both ends. The artillerists were trying to hit the snipers. "

"What about the neighbors? Have you seen any of them?" Lewis asked before driving on.

"Nancy was here a little while ago."

"How is she? Where did she go during the battle?" Eliza anxiously asked.

"She's fine," John replied. "That girl's got a lot of spunk. She stayed in the cellar at Brompton during the battle. She says the house is badly damaged, and Mr. Marye isn't going to move back, until some repairs can be made.[13] He's staying with his wife's folks at Hamilton Crossing, but he put Nancy in charge of Brompton,[14] while he's gone."

119

"He must really trust her to put her in charge of Brompton, as young as she is," Lewis remarked.

"She always was dependable and trustworthy," Eliza said.

"She also said that the Mr. and Mrs. Stratton and their children were among those who took refuge in the Brompton cellar," John continued. "It was cold and dark in the cellar, and they could hear the house being hit with cannon balls, and were afraid the house was going to collapse on them. Mrs. Stratton became so frightened during the battle, that she apparently had a heart attack, because she died.[15] The family is really upset, and the children were hysterical."

"Oh, my goodness! I'm really sorry to hear that," Eliza said.

"So am I," Lewis added. "Mr. Stratton and I did not agree on politics, but we have known each other for many years. I certainly would not have wished that on his family. Have you seen anyone else?"

"Monroe Stevens was here checking on his house a little while ago. He says he is going to repair it and rent it out. He is going to buy a farm over in Stafford County and move there."[16]

"But Stafford County has been devastated by the enemy!" Lewis exclaimed.

"That's the point," John explained. "The people there are willing to unload their property cheap, just to get away from there. Monroe is getting a really good deal, and all he has to do is wait out the war, and he will be in a position to make a lot of money."

"What about Mr. Rowe?" Eliza asked.

"His house is not too badly damaged. He can still live in it. Mr. Stratton's house is bad shape, though, and he's going to move into one of Mr. Rowe's rental houses,"[17] John answered.

"Did Mrs. Sisson survive the battle?" Lewis inquired.

"I saw Mr. Sisson, when I first got here. He says that his wife is in a bad way. She hid in the cellar during the battle, but some Yankees found her. They dragged her out, shoved her outdoors, and made her stay outside with bullets flying all around her, until she could show them where her well is. She was frightened out of her mind by the experience. Now she keeps reliving it, cringing, shrieking, and crying, all wild-eyed. When she quiets down, she just sits and stares into space, mumbling to herself.[18] Every now and then she gets up, walks to the door, and points to the field, but she doesn't say anything."

"I guess Mr. Sisson wishes he had made her leave with him," Lewis remarked.

"He says if he had it to do over again, he would drag her out of the house." John added.

"Have you seen anyone else?" Eliza asked

"No, but Mr. Jennings house has been completely destroyed.[19] I am afraid that the Mills' family did not fare very well, either. Aunt Harriet's house[20] and Cousin Elizabeth's house[21] have both burned down. The town is in shambles. There are holes in almost every house that hasn't burned down, and the streets are littered with dead horses, smashed furniture, broken crockery, and torn-up clothes."[22]

John turned to go back to work, and Lewis drove into the yard. As they went around the house, it became apparent that, like Martha Stephens' house, their house had hundreds of bullet holes in it.[23] Only jagged pieces of glass remained in the windows, and all of the shutters were gone.

The outhouse door was missing, as were Lewis' chickens.[24] His fence had been knocked down, and many of the boards were missing. There were four freshly dug graves in his back yard. Apparently, the men had been buried where they lay, instead of carrying them to one area of the yard, and putting them in a neat row.

"Damned Yankees!" he thought to himself. "They don't even respect their own dead. Just bury them where they fall."

Lewis took Eliza by the arm and the two of them cautiously entered the gaping back entrance. His imagination could never have pictured such an awful mess. The first thing he noticed was the stench. Then his eyes adjusted to the dim light and took in the scene. There was no plaster left on the walls or ceilings. It lay in dusty chunks on the floor, mingled with shards of glass from the windows, and patches of blood.

Going into the parlor, the stench grew stronger, and it became apparent that soldiers had used the parlor as an outhouse. Though disgusting, Lewis could understand why they did it. He reasoned that they were most likely frightened young men, away from home for the first time, thrown into a worse maelstrom than they could have ever imagined. The only security they had were the four walls of his house, and that protection was illusionary.

As they went from room to room they discovered that even the inside doors were gone. Every stick of furniture and every piece of

121

glass or pottery in the house had been wantonly and deliberately broken. The prized mirror in the tavern was in a million pieces and the frame was splintered.

In Phillis' room the mattress was so soaked in blood, it would have to be burned. Upstairs in John's room, the bloody mattress looked like it had been sliced by an artillery shell.[25] Feathers were all over the place. All of their clothes, linens, and every piece of cloth in the house had been shredded deliberately and systematically. Every morsel of food they left in the house was either gone or dumped onto the floor and stirred into the plaster dust.

In the cellar all of the jars of canned foods had been smashed. Chunks of food clung to the walls and lay in puddles on the floor beneath, indicating that the jars had been deliberately hurled against the walls.

Holes in the roof meant that the upstairs rooms were unlivable, until Lewis could make repairs.

Most of the rooms downstairs had at least one large hole in the outside wall, making them unlivable also. Lewis could have easily picked up a bucket full of spent bullets from the downstairs rooms, alone.

This had been Lewis "dream" house, the one he had worked for so many years to be able to afford. It was the place where he had raised John, the place where he and Eliza had been so happy, the place with the cozy tavern enjoyed by the whole neighborhood, which had made him a respected and popular person in the community. Now it was in shambles, but he would have to clean it up, repair it, and live in it, anyway. Where else could he go? But where would he get the money?

Lewis was sixty-two years old and had been looking forward to taking things easy in his old age. That dream was destroyed. "Now I will have to work until the day I die," he thought.

"We'll have to stay in Phillis' old room and the kitchen until I can make some repairs," Lewis said unemotionally. He was in too much shock to feel anything.

Eliza, on the other hand, was sobbing, tears streaming down her cheeks. "The damages from the battle are hard enough to take, but what did we ever do to them, to cause them to be so malicious as to vandalize everything we own? We have lost everything! Absolutely everything! The filthy mess they left for us to clean up just adds insult to injury. The animals! How could they? They knew we would have to live here after they left! Filthy, nasty animals! I hate them! I despise them!" She was shrieking by the time she reached the end of her tirade.

Just then John's silhouette appeared in the doorway.

"Let's get your things unloaded from the wagon as quickly as we can," John said as he entered the house, "so I will have time to help you hunt for some doors and shutters. They were probably used as stretchers. If they have not been burned, they may be down by the millrace. I have to turn my prisoner in and be back at camp before dark, but I will have him shovel out the parlor. Mama, why don't you sweep the kitchen so we can put the barrels in there?"

[1] *The Journal of Jane Howison Beale: Fredericksburg, Virginia 1850–1862*, Historic Fredericksburg Foundation, Inc. (1995) Entry for December 14, 1862.

[2] "Fredericksburg First and last" *Magazine of American History* (June 1887) page 457.

[3] *The South: A Tour of Its Battlefields and Ruined Cities, A Journey Through the Desolated States, and Talks With the People,* by J.T. Trowbridge, Hartford, Conn.: L. Stebbins (1866) Page 107.

[4] *Battles and Leader of the Civil War, III* (1884) "Notes of a Confederate Staff Officer" by Roy W. Mason. Page 319.
"Burying the Dead at Fredericksburg" by Donald C. Pfanz, *The Free Lance-Star Publishing Company,*
www.fredericksburg.com/CivilWar/Battle/0922CW.

[5] *Battles and Leader of the Civil War, III* (1884) "Notes of a Confederate Staff Officer" by Roy W. Mason. Page 319.

[6] "Burying the Dead at Fredericksburg" by Donald C. Pfanz, *The Free Lance-Star Publishing Company,*
www.fredericksburg.com/CivilWar/Battle/0922CW.

[7] *The Journal of Jane Howison Beale: Fredericksburg, Virginia 1850–1862*, Historic Fredericksburg Foundation, Inc. (1995), Entry for December 13, 1862.
Battles and Leader of the Civil War, III (1884) "Notes of a Confederate Staff Officer" by Roy W. Mason. Page 319.

[8] "Martha Stephens: Heroine or hoax?" by Donald C. Pfanz, *The Free Lance-Star Publishing Company,*
www.fredericksburg.com/CivilWar/Battle/0728CW.

[9] Ibid.

[10] Ibid.

[11] *Voices of the Civil War: Fredericksburg*, "Letter from Edward I. Heinichen, Resident of Fredericksburg," Time-Life Books, Alexandria Virginia, Page 146, mentions that "we found numbers of Union soldiers hidden away in cellars & other out of the way places with their arms & accoutrements, who requested us, to take them prisoners."

[12] George F. Hopper to brother, December 21, 1862, George F. Hopper Letter, Vol. 123, Fredericksburg and Spotsylvania National Military Park. For Hooper's official report, see *Official Records of the War of Rebellion*, vol. 21, page 308.

[13] "Brompton: Front Door on the Battle" by Donald C. Pfanz, http://www.fredericksburg.com/CivilWar/Battle/0721CW.

[14]. "An Eye Witness Account of The Battle of Fredericksburg," From the diary of a daughter of George and Maria Hamilton of Forest Hill, Virginia Historical Society, Richmond, Virginia.

[15] *Fredericksburg Civil War Sites, Volume Two: December 1862–April 1865* by Noel G. Harrison, H.E. Howard, Inc. (1995). Pages 180–181.

[16] 1865 Fredericksburg Land Tax Records.
Stafford County Wills.

[17] 1865 Fredericksburg Land Tax Record.

[18] *Battles and Leaders of the Civil War, Volume III*, edited by Robert Underwood Johnson and Clarence Clough Buel, The Century Co. New York, "In Front of the Stone Wall at Fredericksburg" by John W. Ames, Brevet Brigadier-General, U.S.V, Page 122.
The Valiant Hours by Thomas Galway, page 61.

[19] 1865 Fredericksburg Tax Records.

[20] Ibid.

[21] Ibid.

[22] "Burying the Dead at Fredericksburg" by Donald C. Pfanz, The Free Lance-Star Publishing Company,
www.fredericksburg.com/CivilWar/Battle/0922CW.

[23] *Letters from Lee's Army* by Charles Minor Blackford, New York, Charles Scribner Sons (1947) Page 149.

[24] *History of Three Months' and Three Years' Service , Fourth Regiment Ohio Volunteer Infantry in the War for the Union* by William Kepler, PhD, Cleveland (1886). Page 93.

[25] Ibid.

CHAPTER 9
THE SECOND BATTLE OF FREDERICKSBURG

The population of the town decreased dramatically, as many residents went elsewhere for the duration of the war—some by necessity and some by choice. Those who remained, 3,000 to 4,000 in number, were mostly women, children, and the only men left were elderly or disabled.[1]

Reverend Broaddus and his wife temporarily moved to Charlottesville.[2]

Charles Wellford moved his family into his country home, a large brick house located less than a mile south of the Catherine Furnace in Spotsylvania County, not far from the Chancellorsville Inn.[3] On this lonely wilderness road, he believed that his family would find safety.

The Turnpike neighborhood had changed.

David Sisson was forced to close his store and seek work as a farm laborer.[4]

Since James Jennings house had been completely destroyed,[5] his family was forced to seek temporary accommodations in a rented house on the Turnpike, near the house rented by Allen Stratton.[6]

Monroe Stevens was able to buy the farm he had always dreamed of owning, and was living across the river in Stafford County on an estate known as Hickory Hill.[7]

Brompton had not been repaired, so John Marye was still living at Hamilton's Crossing.[8]

People in the South were outraged by the vandalism done by the Federals in Fredericksburg. They sent donations of almost $170,000 to the town to help the people recover from the shelling and pillaging of their homes. Mayor Slaughter headed the committee, which decided how the money should be distributed. None of those who lived in Lewis' neighborhood received any of the money,[9] in spite of the fact that every house facing Marye's Heights was covered with bullet marks, and the heaviest damages had occurred along the Turnpike.[10] Undoubtedly they did benefit from food and other supplies that were sent to the town.

At least one person in the neighborhood, Mrs. Martha Stephens, was not interested in repairing her home. Her damaged home became a source of income for her after the war. Veterans from both sides of the conflict gave her donations in return for her showing them the damages and telling them battle stories.[11]

Perhaps others could not, or would not, file claims, or they may have filed claims that were disapproved.[12]

Lewis did his best to make their house livable. He was able to scavenger the clapboard that was needed to repair the outside, and he had enough scrap tin in his shop to repair the roof. Glass and plaster were another matter. He did not have enough money to buy them, so he loaded his wagon with scrap tin and scavenged building supplies. He drove to William Norton's shop and was surprised to discover how haggard Mr. Norton looked.

"So many people are in desperate need of home repairs," Mr. Norton explained. "I have been working seven days a week, sun up to sun down. Unlike you, most of the men in this town do not have the skills needed to do the work themselves—and many households are totally bereft of a male presence. They consist of helpless women and small children. Ordinarily, I would not trade scrap lumber for glass and plaster, because I can drive around Fredericksburg and gather enough scrap lumber to build a mansion. I will trade with you, though, if you will help me repair some of the homes for the next couple of months. I can't pay much, but I'll send someone over to do your plaster work and will give you shutters or whatever else you need for your house."

Lewis agreed to Mr. Norton's proposal. Eliza could run the store, which was sparsely stocked in these hard times, and the extra income from Mr. Norton would help them to survive. Food was scarce and prices were inflated. Life was hard.

Spring came again and the birds were singing as in the past, but for the first time in his life spring held no magic for Lewis.

The reality of the war had replaced the initial thrill he had felt about it. Battle scenes were etched in his mind. They were so awful he wondered how a person, who saw such things, could continue to live. He tried to block them out, but every night when he closed his eyes to go to sleep, there they were tormenting him in vivid color.

The once beautiful town of Fredericksburg had become a vast cemetery, and a derelict looking one at that. There was hardly a yard that did not have at least one grave in it. Everything was in shambles. The houses bore the scars of battle, and the yards were unkempt and scruffy looking.

The most unnerving sight was the way the grass and wildflowers were growing this year. Lewis could look across Wellford's Field and identify every spot where a man had lain and bled on the ground. In that spot the grass was a darker green and the wildflowers grew more profusely.

Federal prisoners of war had buried some of the Union dead in graves that were too shallow. After a short period, parts of the bodies began showing above the ground. It was a ghastly sight. Even worse, several times while Lewis was repairing a tin roof, he looked down and saw dogs in the neighborhood taking home an arm or a leg bone.[13]

On March 27, 1863, the neighborhood was shocked and grieved to hear that Rev. Rowe's wife, Lucy, had died.[14] She had always been tiny and frail, but had been such a kindly, sweet person, that she was going to be sorely missed. Rev. Rowe was consumed with grief. "I guess I never thought of life without Lucy," he said. "My only comfort is that I know it won't be long before I will be joining her."

It became commonplace for Lewis and Eliza to hear sporadic rifle fire in the distance, mostly from the north, so much so that they learned not to panic at the sound, and just accept it as a part of their lives. Lewis became concerned, though, when he learned that his son, Marshall, had reenlisted, this time in the 4th Virginia Cavalry.[15]

"What was he thinking?" Lewis raged. "He's almost forty! And who is going to feed all those hungry little mouths if something happens to him?"

"He was probably thinking that he would rather risk death than risk living under Yankee rule," Eliza answered, "and he knows that we would not let his children go hungry."

"Does he know that the wolf is at our door? We don't have an over abundance of food, ourselves."

"Still, we would share what we have."

"You're right," Lewis answered glumly. "We'll starve to death together."

On the morning of May 1, 1863, they heard the continuous sounds of rifle and artillery fire from the north, and knew that another battle was being fought nearby. It sounded as close as the Battle of Fredericksburg did from Berclair.

Lewis rushed down the turnpike to Rev. Rowe's house where the men of the neighborhood were gathering.

"Should we evacuate again?" Mr. Ebert asked.

"Where can we go?" Mr. Sisson replied. "If we go to the Salem Church, we will be going towards the battle."

"We know the Yankees' goal is to take Richmond," Rev. Rowe contributed. "If they are able to break through the Confederate lines, they will either head towards Spotsylvania Court House to get to Richmond, in which case they will bypass us, or they will go down the Plank Road to Telegraph Road, then straight to Richmond. In that case, not only the Salem Church, but we will be in their path."

"If they go down Telegraph Road, Berclair will not be safe, either," Lewis said.

"We can't go east," Mr. Bozel said. "It is crawling with Yankees across the river."

"If we head South, we will be running in front of the enemy," Mr. Jennings remarked, "and they will be shooting at our backs."

"If seems to me," Mr. Rowe explained, "that there is no safe haven for us this time. We are boxed in on all sides. We are going to have to trust that our boys will hold their line and drive the Yankees back across the Rappahannock. We will be as safe in the cellars of our homes as any where else."

Lewis returned home, and he and Eliza waited in a state of anxiety. That evening as they lay in bed unable to sleep, they heard the popping of rifle fire far into the night.

The sounds of battle continued all the next day and into the next night.

On the third day, they were startled awake at six o' clock in the morning by the sound of cannon fire. It was coming from the direction of the river, and they realized with a sinking feeling that Fredericksburg was being shelled.

They quickly dressed, and Eliza went into the kitchen, scrambled some eggs and made a large pot of coffee.

Lewis realized that if the Yankees came, their only refuge would be their cramped little cellar. He filled some jars with water and carried them, their pillows, and a chamber pot, down into the cellar.

There was not enough room for chairs. If they had to evacuate to the cellar, they would have to sit on barrels and lean against the wall.

After eating a quick breakfast, they spent the morning frequently checking out the windows for any signs of trouble. Confederate soldiers could be seen moving about on Marye's Heights. Unlike in December, no soldiers were sent to instruct them on what to do. They were left completely on their own. At ten o' clock Lewis noticed a cloud of dust down the Turnpike towards town. Soon lines of Union soldiers could be seen coming up the Turnpike, so Lewis and Eliza quickly fled to their dark, cramped cellar.

Within minutes, they could hear the roar of cannons and the popping of rifle fire. For a while, it sounded like the battle was right on top of them. The fighting was so fierce that the vibrations from the artillery fire shook the house and rattled the jars of food on the shelves in the cellar. Dust particles, dislodged from the floorboards above them, rained down on their heads. They coughed and choked on the dust.

There is no way that Lewis could have predicted how frightening this experience was going to be. The house could collapse on top of them, or worse, catch on fire and burn down.

In mid afternoon, the firing became more distant as it moved northward. After hearing cheering, Lewis ventured out of the cellar and cautiously peeped out of a window. It was the previous December all over again. His yard, the Turnpike, and Wellford's field were strewn with blue uniformed bodies. He looked up on top of Marye's Heights, and, much to his consternation, the heights were crawling with blue uniformed Federals. Trembling, he returned to the cellar. Soon the firing seemed to be coming from Marye's Heights again. Periodically, when everything seemed quiet, he would creep upstairs to assess the situation.

Late in the afternoon, he discovered that the Confederates had recaptured Marye's Heights.

Later, when this battle was being called the Second Battle of Fredericksburg and the Battle of Chancellorsville, they learned that it was Charles Wellford's son who had guided General Stonewall Jackson on the back roads around the Federal Army making the Confederate victory possible.[16]

A letter arrived shortly after that telling them that Marshall had been very seriously wounded,[17] and would never be able to rejoin his unit. He had been maimed for life.

---

[1] *Fredericksburg: Past, Present and Future* by Robert Reid Howison, J. Willard Adams, Fredericksburg (1898) Page 31.

[2] "The Prison Diary of William F. Broaddus, edited by W. Harrison Daniel, Baptist Historical Society, Richmond, Virginia.

[3] *Chancellorsville Battlefield Sites* by Noel G. Harrison, H. E. Howard Lynchburg VA, (1990) 62–63, 83–84, 99.

[4] 1870 Fredericksburg VA Census.

[5] 1865 Fredericksburg Tax Records.

[6] Ibid.

[7] 1870 Falmouth, Stafford County Virginia Census.

[8] "Brompton: Front door on the Battle" by Donald C. Pfanz, www.fredericksburg.com/CivilWar/Battle/0721CW.

[9] *Appendices For: Gazetteer of Historic Sites Related to The Fredericksburg and Spotsylvania National Military Park*, Volume Two, Appendix I, "Typescript of Civil War Damage Inventories, Located in drawer 491 of the Office of Clerk of the Circut [sic] Court of Fredericksburg, Virginia" by Noel G. Harrison (1989).

[10] *Voices of the Civil War* "Fredericksburg, Letter from Captain Charles M. Blackford, 2nd VA Cavalry, F. Lee's Brigade", Time-Life Books, Alexandria Virginia, Page 143.

[11] "Martha Stephens: Heroine or Hoax?" by Donald C. Pfanz, www.fredericksburg.com/CivilWar/Battle/0728CW.

[12] *Appendices For: Gazetteer of Historic Sites Related to The Fredericksburg and Spotsylvania National Military Park*, Volume Two, Appendix I, "Typescript of Civil War Damage Inventories, Located in drawer 491 of the Office of Clerk of the Circut [sic] Court of Fredericksburg, Virginia" by Noel G. Harrison (1989).

[13] *Voices of the Civil War: Fredericksburg*, "Letter from Edward I. Heinichen, Resident of Fredericksburg," Time-Life Books, Alexandria Virginia Page 146.

[14] *Ancestry World Tree Project*, www.ancestry.com/tree/.

[15] *4th Virginia Cavalry* by Kenneth Stiles, H.E. Howard, Inc. Lynchburg, Virginia (1985).

[16] *Fredericksburg & Chancellorsville: The Dare Mark Campaign* by Daniel E. Sutherland, University of Nebraska Press (1998).

[17] *4th Virginia Cavalry* by Kenneth Stiles, H.E. Howard, Inc. Lynchburg, Virginia (1985).

CHAPTER 10
THE BATTLE OF THE WILDERNESS

Everyone in the neighborhood was convinced of the invincibility of the Confederate Army until the dreadful news of Gettysburg reached them. The harrowing reports of the slaughter of Pickett's men were especially hard to endure. If Pickett had not decided to leave the 30th Virginia at Gordonsville to guard the railroad crossing,[1] the casualty list would no doubt have included a lot of the men from Fredericksburg. Lewis realized that not only was Marshall grievously wounded, but he could have lost his youngest son.

In spite of Gettysburg, Lewis never lost faith that the Confederacy would ultimately win.

In the coming weeks and months, things got progressively worse for Lewis and Eliza. Hunger and fear were their constant companions. Their clothes became so shabby that they were little more than rags. Elements of the Union Army were never far away, so they never felt safe. One night they were awakened in the wee hours of the morning by pounding on the front door. Lewis' suspected that it was stragglers demanding entrance.

Their greatest fear was of stragglers. Some stragglers were soldiers who just could not keep up with their army, who just wanted a bite to eat and some water. Other stragglers were criminals. They deliberately straggled behind their units in order to plunder and terrorize the countryside. They were hated by the military as well as the private citizens.

Lewis' first instinct was not to open the door, but he knew that if he did not, they might knock the door down and kill him.

When he unlocked it, three dirty, unkempt Union soldiers with drawn guns and smelling of alcohol shoved their way inside.

Lewis tried to defuse the situation by remaining calm and speaking quietly.

"What can I do for you?" he asked.

The men looked at Eliza standing there, thin and gaunt, with her hair in braids, and loose strands of gray hair hanging limply in her face. They eyed her up and down, until she cringed under their inspection.

"She doesn't suit my taste," one of the men said with a sneer.

"Well, you can have Granny, here, fix us something to eat," another of the men demanded.

Eliza scurried into the kitchen to boil a thin gruel, scramble some eggs, and brew a pot of chicory coffee.

The men rummaged through the house, but found nothing of value. Next, they went outside and looked around.

When they returned inside, they took the plates of food and began to eat voraciously.

Lewis and Eliza silently watched them, knowing that there would be no eggs for their own breakfast.

"We can tie the chickens on the horse," one of the men remarked. Eliza quickly spoke up, "If you take our chickens we won't have anything to feed you the next time you are in the neighborhood."

"Well, that's true. We'll just take the horse."

"If you take my old, sway back horse, I won't be able to work," Lewis said.

"That's your problem, Grandpa." one of the stragglers replied, and when they left they took the horse with them.

Stragglers would show up at any hour of the night or day, and the unpredictability of their behavior and the time of their visits added to the terror. Lewis and Eliza lived in constant fear and dread of them.

The only restraint on the stragglers was the fact that there were males present in the neighborhood, although, like Lewis, they were elderly.

As the war progressed, the death rate accelerated—for military and civilians both. The soldiers were not only dying in battle, but from disease in the camps.

The civilians suffered from hunger and the lack of adequate medical supplies. In July Michael Ames' twenty-two year old daughter, Fannie Ellen, died.[2]

In the prisoner-of-war camps starvation also played a role in the high death rate. Most of the Confederate soldiers, who were taken as prisoners, absolutely refused to take the Oath of Allegiance to the United States. A small number, however, opted to take the Oath, rather than die in prison. These men were not trusted by either side and were given the derisive name of 'galvanized' soldiers.[3] Like iron or steel is galvanized by being coated with tin, they were Southerners coated with a blue uniform and sent to fight their own homeland.

The neighborhood was aghast to learn that their neighbor, Elizabeth Bayne, had received word that her son, Otho, had been galvanized. He took the Oath after being a prisoner-of-war for several months. [4]

In early August, Richard Bozel learned that his son, William was seriously ill in a Charlottesville, Virginia hospital. [5]

Then in late August, Robert Henry Mills, Elizabeth's second cousin, deserted and took the Oath. [6]

A letter from John arrived in January 1864.

Christmas Day, 1863
Dear Mama and Papa,

It does not seem like Christmas. I wish I could spend the day with you.

We have been on the move a lot. After marching to various parts of Virginia, we were put on a train and sent to Tennessee for a while. We were in some skirmishes and lost a few men, but I have not been in any great danger.

From Tennessee, we were sent to Petersburg, then back to western Virginia to Bristol to guard about 700 prisoners. Three of the prisoners were Confederate deserters, so we shot them.

There is plenty to eat in this part of the state, so I have been buying apples and peaches, and the beef is excellent. Molasses is so plentiful and issued so generously that I keep it in my canteen and drink it on marches. We have been marching back and forth a lot, first towards Knoxville, then back to Bristol, then towards Knoxville, then back to Bristol. Someone in command must have seen that a few of our men still have shoes on their feet, and he wants all of our uniforms to match. So, he is trying to wear out the remaining shoe leather.

It is cold, and on a day when there was ice in the ditches, we had to wade across a river. My legs and feet were numb when we got to the other side.

We are in Rogersville, Tennessee now, but I hope we will be returning to Virginia soon.

Love,
John[7]

On January 3, 1864, Lewis looked out on Wellford's Field and saw a large, dark, bay-colored, mare with a white spot on its side wandering aimlessly around. Approaching the horse quietly he was able to slip a noose around its neck and lead it home. Thus, he was able to replace the old, sway back horse stolen by stragglers with one that had an appraised value of one hundred and twenty-five dollars.[8]

Shortly after that, Mr. Bozel came to see Lewis and Eliza. His face was an ashen gray color, and his hands were trembling. It had been years since he had been welcome in their home, but Lewis had him sit in one of his two surviving chairs, while Eliza poured him a glass of water.

Eliza intuitively guessed what the visit concerned. "It's William, isn't it?" she asked.

With a stricken look on his face, he nodded.

He looked up at Lewis and said, "I have known for years that God was going to punish me for what I did to Mrs. Wrenn, and now He has." He glanced uneasily at Eliza. "I have wished a million times that I could take back what I did. Even spending time in jail and paying a fine has not eased my guilt. I was drunk, and I was not thinking straight. Otherwise I would never have done such a thing."

Not wishing to subject Eliza to a discussion concerning the unpleasant ordeal, Lewis changed the subject. "What happened to William?" he asked.

An anguished expression flashed across Mr. Bozel's face, and then he hung his head. "He deserted," he whispered. "He deserted and took the 'Oath of Allegiance' to the United States."[9]

"Oh, my!" Eliza blurted out.

"I am so ashamed," Mr. Bozel said. "How will I ever look anyone in the eye again?"

Eliza and Lewis glanced at each other.

"I know what you are thinking. The same way I faced people when I got out of jail," Mr. Bozel added.

"William took the coward's way out," Lewis said, "but that was his choice, not yours."

Tears welled up in Mr. Bozel's eyes. "What would you do if John deserted?"

Lewis did not answer for a few minutes. When he finally spoke he weighed his words, and they cut him like a knife, but he spoke them resolutely. "John is the apple of my eye, but if he deserted, I would disown him. We have suffered much too much for our beliefs and for our Confederacy for me to condone his being a traitor. As painful as that would be, I would have to do it."

"I think I will have to do the same thing," Mr. Bozel answered sadly. "He has brought shame to my family."

Mr. Bozel seemed older and more stooped than ever as he slowly got up. Before leaving, he looked at Eliza. "I hope someday you will be able to forgive me."

Eliza did not answer. Her thoughts turned to her secret living up the hill at Brompton. Her mouth opened as though she were going to speak, but no words came out.

Towards the end of February, another letter from John arrived.

> February 14, 1864
> Dear Mama and Papa,
>
> This has been the happiest Valentine's Day of my life! We are back in Goldsboro, North Carolina, after making a detour to New Bern, where the 30th distinguished itself in whopping the Yankees.
>
> That little girl I told you about is even prettier and sweeter than I remembered. She has promised to wait for me, so I will definitely be making a trip to Goldsboro after the war.
> Love,
> John[10]

Spring came again, but Lewis hardly noticed. The feeling of hope that usually accompanied it was missing. Lewis had more of a feeling of resignation. It did not look like the war was going to end anytime soon, but he would bide his time, until the day of victory came.

On May 5, 1864, the unmistakable sounds of battle with the booming of artillery and popping of rifle fire were heard again, coming once again from the direction of Chancellorsville.

Eliza buried her face in her hands and wept. "Not again!" she cried in anguish. "How much more can we stand?"

The battle sounds continued each day while Lewis and Eliza waited in a state of constant anxiety.

On Sunday May 8, Lewis and Eliza heard a commotion outside of their house. To their horror it was about sixty armed Union soldiers, some of whom appeared to be slightly wounded.

"It looks like stragglers fleeing from the battle," Lewis whispered.

As Lewis and Eliza cowered behind their window the stragglers passed their house and headed for town.

A few hours later Lewis and Eliza saw the stragglers heading west on the turnpike under the guard of Confederate soldiers. They had been captured and taken prisoners.[11] Lewis heaved a sigh of relief and supposed that was the end of the incident.

Eliza was afraid to go to sleep that night and slept in fits and starts, awakening at every creak and groan of the war-battered house. Towards morning she heard what she supposed was the mewing of a cat. As she lay in the dark, straining to hear the sound, so she could correctly identify its source, it very slowly became louder. It no longer sounded like mewing, but like a baby crying, but there were no infants in the neighborhood. Then the sound seemed to become that of hundreds of babies crying.

Although exhausted, she pulled herself out of the bed and got dressed. The sound had become more distinct. It was not babies crying, it was hundreds, maybe thousands, of shrieks and screams.

She ran from room to room and peered out of the upstairs windows into the dim light of first dawn. She saw some movement to the north. It was a wagon train, with some of the wagons going down the Plank Road towards town, some turning onto the Sunken Road.

She ran down the steps and peeped out of a front window. The rattle of wagons turning onto the Turnpike in front of her house caused her to shrink in fear. The other sounds were now unmistakable.

"Oh, God! Please! Please! Just shoot me and get it over with!"

"Stop! Stop! Just leave me beside the road and let me die!"

"Mama! Mama! Mama!"

"Oh God! Oh God! Oh God!"

And shrieks and screams that were indescribable.

A wagon stopped by the front door, and the driver was soon pounding on it.

By this time, Lewis had also dressed and come downstairs. He cautiously opened the door a crack and demanded, "What do you want?" He was looking into the face of an unkempt, burly, Union soldier.

"I have wounded soldiers I need to leave here."

"You can't leave them here!" Eliza emphatically cried. "I'll not have Yankees in my house!"

"I have to," the man insisted.

"We have no bed to put them in. Your men destroyed our furniture and mattresses," Lewis explained, as he tried to shut the door. "Take them someplace else."

His strength was no match for the soldier's, who pushed the door open and declared, "You two don't understand. We have at least four thousand wounded in this ambulance train, and there will probably be that many again tomorrow. We are putting our wounded in every building in this town,[12] including yours, whether you like it or not."

The man pushed them aside. They watched silently as he went from room to room, examining the house. He returned to the parlor carrying a blanket.

"Grandpa, I can see that you have very little left, and I am sorry about that, but I am still going to have to bring some wounded in here. We will make a pallet on the floor in this front room, and I will put them on it. If you had a spare bed, I could have left some officers here. As it is, you will have to take privates."

Seeing that they could not prevent their house from being turned into a hospital, Eliza demanded, "Are you going to leave medicine and bandages with them? We have no medicine and no linens with which to make bandages. Moreover, how am I supposed to feed them? We don't have enough food to hardly keep ourselves alive."

"Each of the men was issued three days rations before we left.[13] I don't have any of those other things either," the soldier said as he used a piece of chalk to mark the front door with a cross, "but one of our surgeons will check on the men as soon as he can. I had been driving these poor fellows around for two days, before I was ordered to bring them here. They are in bad shape and will be glad to have a quiet place to lie down. Lying on the floor will be far better than being jolted to death over rutted dirt roads in a wagon with no springs."

Lewis followed the man out to the wagon and peered into it.

"Dear Mother of God!" he cried when he saw the contents of the wagon. The wagon was crammed to capacity with bloody young men lying on their right sides, pressed against one another. All of them had their left legs amputated.

The muscular wagon driver scooped up one of them like a child and carried the groaning soldier into the house. He laid him as gently as possible on the blanket, but the young man shrieked with pain, beads of perspiration popping out on his forehead.

Eliza ran to get a basin of water and a rag, while the wagon driver went to get another of the wounded.

Soon Eliza was on her knees washing the faces and hands of four young Yankees. She was offended by the odor of sweat, blood, and urine that emanated from them. She looked at them in disgust and tried to hate them, but her heart broke. She saw John in each of them.

Tenderly she supported the head and shoulders of each of them against her body, as she lifted each one high enough to give him a drink of cool, refreshing water through an 'invalid feeder,' a small container with a long spout that looked somewhat like a small teapot.

She saw such gratitude reflected in their faces that tears welled up in her eyes. "I want to hate you," she gruffly told them, shaking her head, "but I can't. You're not much more than boys."

The next few weeks were a nightmare with wagons driving past at all hours of the night and day, and shrieking, screaming, and groaning the likes of which it would be impossible to describe, and sights that would rip your heart out.

Every building in Fredericksburg—residences, stores, churches, and lodge halls, were turned into hospitals under the charge of Federal surgeons.[14]

Every morning the front porch and yard would fill up with the 'walking' wounded. Some of those walking had to use their rifle or a stick to hobble along, and some were crawling on their hands and knees. The only thing Lewis could do for them was to give them water to drink and a place to rest in the shade. There were so many of them that he began to worry that they might drink his well dry.

It reached the point that Lewis and Eliza hated even to look out the windows, because they knew that they would see blood-soaked wrecks of humanity passing by in an endless parade.

Every day or so an exhausted surgeon would show up and decide who was strong enough to be moved to a hospital in

Washington, and who needed immediate surgery. Those who needed surgery were laid on the kitchen table for the operation. Their severed limbs were thrown out the back door, and when the surgeon left, Lewis and Eliza had to clean up the mess.

Wounded Confederate prisoners-of war-were driven past the house, but were never left in the homes of Fredericksburg. They were taken straight through the town to the boat landing. Those who survived the trip were transferred directly from the ambulances to a boat.[15]

Lewis and Eliza's group of wounded soldiers constantly fluctuated. As men were moved out of the house and sent north, the ambulance drivers would insist that more wounded brought from the battlefields should replace them.[16] Lewis lost count of how many soldiers he and Eliza had sheltered and nursed. This continued until the Federals departed on May 28.[17]

Eliza would rise early and take a small amount of meat and vegetables, whatever she could procure, and boil it in a pot of salted water. She strained off the broth to feed the soldiers. It was not much, but it kept them alive until they could make the trip to Washington.

Lewis would help the new arrivals to undress, and then covered them with a blanket, so Eliza could take their clothes outside and boil them, then hang them to dry.

The men had to be helped to the privy, and needed hot water to wash, and were thirsty—always so thirsty. Several buckets full of water had to be carried in from the pump every day. Since the soldiers were lying on the floor, Eliza had to get down on her knees to feed them or give them a drink of water. It was up and down, and in and out of the house all day. By sundown, Lewis and Eliza were exhausted.

On May 18, at the next neighborhood meeting, John Marye and Monroe Stevens were missing from the group. When the others had gathered, Rev. Rowe solemnly announced, "I have a couple of things to tell you. I am afraid that the first thing is really disturbing, considering what happened to Mr. Wrenn, and others, during the first occupation. I have been told that Col. Schriver has orders to arrest sixty men from Fredericksburg in retaliation for their arresting the sixty stragglers."[18]

The men reacted with anger.

"This is the thanks that the people of Fredericksburg get for turning our homes into hospitals, and our family into nurses for the Yankees?" Mr. Sisson asked in shocked astonishment.

"That's right!" Rev. Rowe replied glumly. "I've heard that they have been searching the houses in town and arresting every male they can find."[19]

"Well, the people at this end of town had nothing to do with that incident!" Mr. Bozel indignantly declared. "We've been isolated out here with no protection from anyone, and at the mercy of stragglers. I've lost count of how many times my house and shop have been ransacked."

"All the same, I would not advise any of you to go into town until after the sixty are rounded up." Rev. Rowe answered. "If you have any relatives or friends to the south of us, I would advise that you to pay them a visit and stay for a couple of days."

"How can we walk off and leave helpless wounded men in our house?" Lewis asked. "I can't do that."

"What's the other news?" Mr. Ebert asked. "I almost dread to ask."

"The second thing is that Col. Schriver has been charged with providing food to the destitute of Fredericksburg, and has been ordered to cease," Rev. Rowe continued.[20]

"That charge is hard to believe!" Mr. Jennings exclaimed. "If a Yankee with compassion for anyone exists, I sure haven't met him."

"When did Col. Schriver ever provide any food for anyone?" Mr. Sisson asked.

"As far as I can determine," Rev. Rowe answered, "never!"[21]

"If anyone had any doubt before, this certainly proves that their official policy is to starve to death the women, children, elderly, and disabled citizens of Fredericksburg. God help us! Who would have guessed that the government, that we used to revere, would turn out to be so evil?"

The next day Lewis and Eliza were startled by a loud pounding on the front door. When Lewis reluctantly answered it, his heart sank. He could see that Union soldiers had surrounded his house. He was placed under arrest and given a few minutes to pack his carpetbag.

"I don't even live downtown," Lewis protested. "I had nothing to do with the arrest of the stragglers."

"What difference does that make?" the officer in charge answered with a sneer. "You're a Southern sympathizer aren't you? Our orders are to arrest sixty men, and if we have to search every house in Spotsylvania County, we are going to arrest sixty men."[22]

"Where will he be held?" Eliza demanded. "At the Old Capitol Prison?"

"I hear he is going to Fort Delaware," was the answer.

Eliza turned ashen, and Lewis felt a shiver run up his spine.

Fort Delaware had the worst reputation of all the prison camps of both the North and South.[23] It was commonly referred to as the Fort Delaware Death Pen,[24] and it was the only prison camp where the guards were allowed to torture or kill the prisoners and could expect to be promoted, rather than reprimanded.[25]

The soldiers put him in irons, before shoving him out the door. Lewis saw that a few other men had also been arrested and were also in irons. The group of prisoners was herded down the turnpike and Hanover Street, followed by women and children who were wailing and crying, begging the soldiers not to take their men. As they passed each house, soldiers would go in and search. If there were a male inside, he was arrested.

As they progressed down the road into town, Lewis could not help contrasting the scenery to that at the time of his first arrest. Fredericksburg had been a lovely and prosperous little town, when he was sent to the Old Capitol Prison. Now there was barely a house without a hole in the roof, missing shutters or some other signs of damage in the ramshackle town. Some houses had been gutted by fire and were no longer inhabitable. Others were reduced to a pile of rubble with only the chimney to mark the spot where once a beautiful home had stood. It was a sad and dismal sight.

They passed the gutted remains of the courthouse, and by the time they reached the Chatham Bridge, the group of prisoners had swelled in number to sixty-two. Among them were Lewis' fellow-hostages from the Old Capital Prison, James Bradley, Thomas Knox, James McGuire, Michael Ames, and Abraham Cox.

The other men who were arrested were John G. Hurkamp, Councellor Cole, John J. Chew, George H. Peyton, William H. Thomas, John D. Elder, F.B. Chewning, R.B. Rennolds, James B. Marye,[26] George Aler, Charles Mander, Benjamin F. Currell, John L. Knight, William C. Smith, Joseph W. Sener, E.W. Stephens,[27]

Charles Cash, Charles B. Waite, Charles G. Waite, Jr., George W. Wroten, Thomas Newton, Robert H. Alexander, Robert Smith, Lucien Love, George F. Sacrey, Henry M. Towles, Landon J. Huffman, Lewis Moore, John T. Evans, Walter Bradshaw, Samuel D. Curtis, William White, John Solan, George W. Eve, James Mazeen,[28] William Brannan, James A. Turner, A.E. Samuel, Tandy Williams, Robert S. Parker, Christopher Reintz, Thomas F. Coleman, Patrick McDonnell, Charles Williams, William Cox, Walter M. Mills,[29] Thomas S. Thornton, John Joyce, John Miner, Richard Hudson, William B. Webb, Alexander Armstrong, William Wiltshire, Gabriel Johnston, George Mullin, and William Burke.[30]

When the men were removed from Fredericksburg, Eliza and the other women were frantic with worry. What little protection they had known was gone and they were now at the unrestrained mercy of stragglers.[31] They lived in constant fear of being assaulted. To make matters worse, the women, children, and elderly were left to care for approximately fifteen thousand sick and wounded soldiers. By the time the Federals withdrew from Fredericksburg, more than 26,000 wounded had been treated in the town.[32]

At first, it was hoped that the Federal authorities would realize that the men they arrested had done nothing wrong and release them. On May 31 the hostages still had not been released, so the Fredericksburg Common Council met and voted to send Montgomery Slaughter and John F. Scott to Richmond to appeal to the Secretary of War for help in securing their release.[33]

After the two men returned to Fredericksburg, they decided to ask Clay Rowe to go to Washington to appeal to the Federal authorities. When Mr. Rowe returned on June 20th, he reported that he had been well received by the Federal authorities. The Secretary of War had assured him that an exchange for the hostages could be carried out, if the Federal prisoners were released into his care and he escorted them through the lines.[34] After the Common Council received Mr. Rowe's report, they voted to send Mr. Rowe and Mayor Slaughter to Richmond to secure the release of the Federal prisoners of war captured by the citizens of Fredericksburg. The two men traveled to Richmond, where an order for the release of the prisoners, the necessary guard, and for two or three surgeons to accompany them was issued.[35]

The Common Council immediately issued an order authorizing Mayor Slaughter and Mr. Rowe to make the necessary plans for transportation and the release of the imprisoned citizens. The whole matter was turned over to Mr. Rowe, who arranged for the exchange of the men from Fredericksburg to take place on board a steamer under a flag of truce, with transportation being provided to Split Rock on the Potomac River.[36]

Meanwhile, while on of this was going on, Eliza received another letter from John.

> May 31, 1864
> Dear Mama and Papa,
>   I am back in Virginia. The 30th returned from North Carolina and we literally stepped off the train into a battle at Drewry's Bluff. Some of our men were wounded before we could even get into the trenches. We repelled several charges by the Yankees, and then we were told to charge. It was Antietam all over again. We had to charge across an open ground with bullets flying all around us, but this time we made it into the enemies' earth works, after clambering over some felled pine trees. We put the enemy on the run!
>   You remember Thomas Proctor, the shoemaker, whose father worked for Mr. Stratton, don't you? Well, he was shot in the shoulder during the battle.[37]
>   The other news is that I got the 'Virginia Quick Step' and have become so debilitated that I was sent to the Chimborazo Hospital in Richmond.
>   This hospital is huge and consists of many buildings. It is on top of a hill overlooking the James River[38] and the air is pure and clean. The food here is better, and I hope to be well enough to return to my unit soon.
>   Love,
>   John[39]

FOOTNOTES

[1] 30th *Virginia Infantry* by Robert K. Krick, H.E. Howard, Inc, Lynchburg VA (1985) Page 39.

[2] Masonic Cemetery tombstone.

[3] *United States Bonds, or Duress by Federal Authority: A Journal of Current Events During an Imprisonment of Fifteen Months, at Fort Delaware* by Isaac W.K. Handy, DD, of Augusta County, Va., Baltimore: Turnbull Brothers (1874), page 26.

[4] *30th Virginia Infantry* by Robert K. Krick, H.E. Howard, Inc., Publisher (1985) Page 81.

[5] Ibid. Page 114.

[6] Ibid. Page 83.

[7] This letter is fictitious but the events described are true. [*30th Virginia Infantry* by Robert K. Krick; H.E. Howard, Inc., Publisher (1985) 42–45.]

[8] "Appraisal." Fredericksburg Court House Annex Basement.

[9] *30th Virginia Infantry* by Robert K. Krick, H.E. Howard, Inc., Publisher (1985) Page 83.

[10] This letter is fictitious but the events described are true. [*30th Virginia Infantry* by Robert K. Krick; H.E. Howard, Inc., Publisher (1985) Page 46.]

[11] *History of Fredericksburg Virginia* by S.J. Quinn, The Hermitage Press, Inc. (1908) Pages 100–101.

[12] Ibid. Page 101.

[13] *The War of the Rebellion: A Compilation of the Official Records of the Union and Confederate Armies,* Series 1, Volume XXXVI, Part 2, Government Printing Office (1891) Pages 934–935.

[14] *History of the City of Fredericksburg,* Virginia by S.J. Quinn, Hermitage Press, Inc., Richmond, VA (1908) Page 99.

[15] *A Soldier's Story: Prison Life and Other Incidents in the War of 1861–'65* by Miles O. Sherrill, Catawba County, North Carolina. Page 7.

[16] *History of the City of Fredericksburg,* Virginia by S.J. Quinn, Hermitage Press, Inc., Richmond, VA (1908). Page 99.

[17] "Victims and Survivors: New Perspectives on Fredericksburg's May 1864 Photographs" by Noel G. Harrison, *Military Images Magazine,* Vol. XX, No. 3 (November–December 1998). Page 12.

[18] *The War of the Rebellion: A Compilation of the Official Records or the Union and Confederate Armies,* Series I, Volume XXXXIV, Part III, Government Printing Office (1891) Page 63.

[19] *History of the City of Fredericksburg, Virginia* by S.J. Quinn, The Hermitage Press, Inc. (1908) Page 100.

[20] *The War of the Rebellion: A Compilation of the Official Records of the Union and Confederate Armies,* Series I, Volume XLVIII, Government Printing Office (1891). Page 934.

[21] Col. Ed. Schriver stated, "The report that I have issued rations to citizens of Fredericksburg is entirely false; on the contrary I have refused every application made to me." [*The War of the Rebellion: A Compilation of the Official Records of the Union and Confederate Armies;* Series 1, Volume XXXVI, Part 2; Government Printing Office (1891). Page 934–935.]

The War of the Rebellion: A Compilation of the Official Records of the Union and Confederate Armies, Series I, Volume XXXVI, Part 2, Government Printing Office (1891). Page 527

[22] Ibid. Page 26. In this letter Col. E. Schriver states that he "was only able to round up 30 of the 60 citizens [from Fredericksburg] on account of the very few males who are now present...but I hope to send them to Washington tomorrow."

[23] "Fort Delaware: The 'Andersonville' of the North" by Al Benson, Jr., www.rebelgray.com/FortDelaware.htm.

Proof that the Northern prisons were worse than the Southern prisons was provided after the war by official reports of the Federal government. "There were sufferings in all prisons and brutalities perpetrated in this as in other wars, but proofs furnished by the evidence of General Butler, by the orders of Federal military officers, by the orders and communications of General Grant, and by the reports of Secretary Stanton, all of which are of record, fix the responsibility of this uncivilized mode of war upon the Federal administration. Secretary Stanton's report of July 19, 1866, shows that 26,246 Confederate soldiers died in Northern prisons, and 25,576 Union soldiers died in Southern prisons. Twelve per cent of the Confederate prisoners who fell into Northern captivity died notwithstanding all the facilities for receiving food, clothing, medicines and healthful conditions which the United States unquestionably possessed, while in the absence of these requisites on the part of the Confederacy the astonishing fact appears that less than per nine cent of the Union soldiers in Southern hands died in prisons. It is indisputably established that the Confederate authorities constantly pressed exchanges on equal terms, that they acceded to terms that were unequal for the sake of exchange, that they proposed many measures of relief which were denied, that at length the most pitiable and unusual of all spectacles occurred when a deputation of soldiers appeared in Washington, sent by Mr. Davis to plead for release by fair exchange, and to plead in vain." [*The Confederate Military History*, Vol. I, Chapter XX, www.civilwarhome.com/inhumanitiesofwar.htm.]

[24] *Confederate Veteran*, Vol. I (1893) page 153, Vol. III (1895) page 172, Vol. IV (1896) page 7.

[25] "*Prison Experiences*" by Randolph Abbott Shotwell, pages 344–45.

United States Bonds, or Duress by Federal Authority: A Journal of Current Events During an Imprisonment of Fifteen Months, at Fort Delaware by Isaac W.K. Handy, DD, of Augusta County, Va., Baltimore: Turnbull Brothers (1874). Pages 122,160, 236, 368.

[26] John Marye's oldest son.

[27] E.W. Stephens may have been Martha Stephens' husband, Edward N. Stephens.

[28] James Mazeen may have been Martha Stephens' future son-in-law, J.R. Mazeen

[29] Elizabeth Mills Wrenn's uncle.

[30] *History of the City of Fredericksburg, Virginia* by S.J. Quinn, The Hermitage Press, Inc. (1908). Pages 102–103.

[31] Ibid. Page 100.

[32] "Victims and Survivors: New Perspectives on Fredericksburg: May 1864 Photographs" by Noel G. Harrison, *Military Images Magazine*, Vol. XX, No. 3 (November–December 1998). Page 12.

[33] *History of Fredericksburg Virginia* by S.J. Quinn, The Hermitage Press, Inc. (1908). Page 101.

[34] Ibid. Pages 103–104.

[35] Ibid. Page 104.

[36] Ibid. Page 105.

[37] *30th Virginia Infantry* by Robert K. Krick, H.E. Howard, Inc., Publisher (1985). Page 120.

[38] *Chimborazo Hospital: That Charnel House of Living Sufferers* by Joseph P. Cullen, Richmond Historic Society, Richmond, Virginia.

[39] This letter is fictitious but the events described are true. [*30th Virginia Infantry* by Robert K. Krick; H.E. Howard, Inc., Publisher (1985) Pages 50–52.]

Confederate pay vouchers for John Kobler Wrenn.

CHAPTER 11
THE FORT DELAWARE DEATH PEN

After crossing the pontoon bridge on foot from Fredericksburg, the men climbed the stone steps leading from one weed-choked, overgrown terrace to the next, and on up to the unkempt grounds of Chatham.

The charred remains of campfires could be seen dotting what had once been a beautiful lawn. On the veranda, Lewis spied the wreck of a piano. The arbors, trellises, and flowering shrubbery had all disappeared. The large spreading shade trees were gone, with stumps marking the spots where they had once stood.

Some of the doors of the house were standing wide open, and others were completely missing from their hinges. The window panes were broken, and there was rubbish everywhere. Through the gaping doors, graffiti could be seen scribbled on the walls.[1] It was a dismal sight considering how beautiful the estate and manor house had once been.

The men were allowed to rest for about fifteen minutes, then their march resumed. Instead of utilizing the train or wagons to transport their prisoners to the river port, as the Federals had done on Lewis' journey the Old Capitol Prison, the men were marched all the way. Many of the men were so elderly and infirm, they were not up to the long march of fourteen miles to Pratt's Point.[2] Carrying luggage while wearing irons made it even harder. When they staggered or fell, they were prodded with bayonets and rifle butts to get up and continue.

The soldiers guarding them during Lewis' first arrest had been cocky and smart-alecky, strutting like peacocks and lording it over their prisoners, but these soldiers were different. They were hardened and cruel. They had no more feeling for the prisoners than they would for a herd of cattle.

All along the way, Negroes by the roadside yelled insults at them.[3] Lewis was confused by their reaction. He could not understand it, because he had treated with kindness and compassion every black he had known in Fredericksburg. He had also worked with the Colonization Society trying to secure freedom for blacks, then helping to train them, until they could earn a living. Phillis had been loved by

Eliza as though she were a member of her family. Why would the blacks harbor such hatred for all white Southerners?

When they finally stumbled the last few yards to the Point, James McGuire fainted.[4] When he came to, he was clutching his chest and gasping for breath. The men who had shared his incarceration in the Old Capitol gathered around him, and tried to help him.

"I don't think I can survive another imprisonment," Mr. McGuire panted.

"Maybe they will give you a compassionate parole, like they did before for Mr. Barton." Mr. Bradley suggested. "They know you are in ill health, and now you have fainted."

"Do you see any compassion in any of their faces?" Mr. Knox asked. "I sure don't. If those Negroes had attacked us, I think they would have stepped aside and let them kill us. The only parole they are going to give any of us is from taking the Oath."

Lewis looked at him in dismay. "I would rather die in a Union prison camp than suffer the dishonor of taking the Oath. It would be like saying that all of our Confederate dead have died for nothing! It would be telling my son Marshall that he was maimed for no purpose."

"I have three sons fighting for the Confederacy," Mr. Cox said. "I could never look them in the face again, if I took the Oath."

"My only son is in the Confederate army," Mr. McGuire replied. "I do not want to take the Oath, either, but I want to live to see him again. I don't know what I am going to do. I hope they will agree to parole me."

John Hurkamp overheard their conversation and spoke up, "I have a letter with me from Union General John Sedgwick stating that I treated him and his staff kindly, when he made his headquarters in my house, and he hopes to return the favor someday.[5] I fully intend to use that letter to try to obtain my release."

Lewis stared at him in disgust. "I would burn my own house to the ground[6] before I would give aid and comfort to the enemy," he declared. He had more respect for Benjamin Temple who refused to let the Union soldiers use his well or sit on his porch, than he did for Mr. Hurkamp, who treated the Union soldiers 'kindly.'

After they arrived in Washington, D.C., the men were transported to the Old Capital Prison in carriages. When they got there, Lewis looked at the old building with resignation. If possible, it looked even more derelict than the last time he had seen it.

The prisoners lined up, and one at a time, the men went into the commandant's office to give his name and answer if he would take the Oath.

Afterward it was announced that James McGuire, James Bradley, Thomas Knox, Michael Ames, John Hurkamp, Councellor Cole, John Chew, George Peyton, William Thomas, and John Elder would be released.[7]

While they were waiting to be released, the men, who had shared the earlier incarceration, gathered around Lewis and Mr. Cox.

"I brought stamps and stationery with me," Mr. McGuire said. "I want to give them to you, along with a list of addresses of my friends in the North. When you get to Fort Delaware, write them immediately, and ask them to help you. Tell them that you are a friend of mine, and I am sure they will help to provide some food and other necessities for you."

The others also gave them stationery, stamps, and a list of names.

"When we get back to Fredericksburg," Mr. Knox promised, "we will do everything in our power to get you released."

"Is there anything you need?" Mr. Bradley asked. "Socks? Underwear? I'll gladly give you anything that I brought with me."

"I have everything I need," Lewis answered. "I don't want to take too much, since we have to carry our own luggage."

"I'm fine, too," Mr. Cox added.

"I have something you can use," Mr. Ames said as he pressed some money into Mr. Cox' hand. "The two of you use this to help buy food from the commissary until you start getting aid from the outside."

The other three men also gave them some money to be shared between them.

When the escort arrived for the men being released, the friends quickly said their good-byes. Although he had not asked, Lewis suspected that, with the possible the exception of Mr. Hurkamp, all of them had taken the Oath.

Then the men who remained were taken to some large, filthy, bug infested holding cells.

Before the hostages left Washington for Fort Delaware, William Lange,[8] Thomas Manuell, Joseph Hall, William Jones,[9] and Wyatt Johnson were arrested in Fredericksburg to replace those who had been released, and they joined the other hostages from Fredericksburg.[10]

A few days later, they were herded onto a crowded steamboat along with ragged prisoners of war, other political prisoners, and criminals. Among the political prisoners were judges, businessmen, clergymen, doctors, and editors. Many of them did not even know why they had been arrested. They had not been given the benefit of a trial and no charges had been brought against them.[11]

The political prisoners and hostages were allowed to stay on the deck, but the prisoners of war were locked in the hold.

Although Lewis had been depressed and anguished over his earlier incarceration, he was really nervous this time. All ruminants of civility were missing from these guards. They treated the hostages as though they were animals.

Abraham Cox stood dejectedly beside Lewis at the rail on the deck, apparently lost in his own depression. They would not be enjoying a fine last dinner in the dining hall on this trip, and there would be no boisterous picnickers to annoy them. All the passengers were either prisoners or guards.

As he stood there, exhausted and weak, Lewis watched the dark water churning beneath the boat. Dense fog surrounded the boat turning everything he could see into a drab, lifeless gray color. Lewis did not know if he would ever set foot on the sacred soil of Virginia again, and that thought brought him great sorrow. He closed his eyes for a moment. The picture flashed in his mind of Virginia in the spring, before the roar of cannons, hordes of invading armies, grotesque, swollen bodies, and horribly wounded men had robbed her of her beauty. He could see the dogwoods and red buds in bloom, and the red-breasted robins in the emerald green trees. It was almost too painful to think about, so he opened his eyes again and stared into the nothingness before him. After a while, a dark, formidable, pentagon-shaped fort began to emerge from the fog that surrounded Pea Patch Island. It was made of granite and its walls were thirty-two feet high. Three tiers of guns pointed towards the water.[12]

Pea Patch Island was a muddy shoal in the middle of Delaware Bay, three-fourths of which was useless bogs. The island had been created when a ship in the seventeen hundreds, loaded with peas, had foundered on a sandbar. The peas sprouted and drifting debris and sediment were caught in the sprouts. Over a period of many years the island was formed.[13] When their ship moored at the wharf, the guards used rifle butts to hurry the political prisoners and hostages off the boat.

Lewis felt like he was stepping into the nether world. The water around the wharf was green with slime, while the stench of unspeakable filth, disease, and death nearly choked him.

He could hear the echoing sound made by the tread from scores of sentries pacing back and forth on top of the walls, and through the fog, he could see the numerous guards along the pier. It was a sight that was intended to instantly overwhelm the prisoners and eradicate all hope of escape.

The next thing Lewis was aware of was that he was being attacked by swarms of hungry mosquitoes from the surrounding swamps. They were buzzing in his ears, and biting his face and hands. He tried to brush them away, but with a carpetbag in one hand and his bedroll in the other, the only way he could reach his face was to lean over. He soon gave up and endured the stinging as he crossed the thirty-foot moat and entered the fort through its massive wooden doors.

When Lewis' turn came to give the commandant his name, he was asked once again, "Will you take the Oath?"

Lewis gave the man a withering look of contempt. "I would rather be dead," he icily answered. "I would much prefer death to the dishonor of taking your Oath."

Lewis and the others from Fredericksburg were escorted to the twelve-foot wide sally port, where a new horror assaulted their eyes. Close to one wall, half of a dozen prisoners were strung up by tight straps wound around their thumbs. Their toes were barely touching the ground. The men's faces were contorted and they were screaming in agony. The tight cords had caused some of the men's thumbs to burst, maiming them for life, and one of the men had urinated on himself. An armed guard stood nearby to prevent anyone from interfering.[14]

With the sound of the screams echoing in his brain, Lewis followed his escort up the stairs of a large building where they were to be housed. There were seven stifling rooms opening onto a wide, dark, central hallway.[15] In each room there were tiers of double, board bunks.[16] Some of the bunks were already occupied.

As they entered the hallway, the guard called out, "Fresh fish! Fresh fish!"[17] Curious inmates clustered in the doorways to gape at the new arrivals.

"Pick a bed," they were told.

Lewis hurried into a room and chose an empty bunk, and then invited Abraham Cox to share the bunk with him. If he had to share a bed with someone, he wanted it to be the person of his choosing.

In the room, there was a table by the window, shelves for tableware and provisions, and nails for them to hang their clothes on. A previous tenant had strung a clothesline for them to hang their wash on.[18]

After Lewis and Mr. Cox had unpacked and arranged their belongings, they urgently began writing letters, appealing for help. It was not until they had finished the letters that they took a closer look at their surroundings.

There were bars across their open window, which faced the southwest. When they looked out, they could see the river flowing past the island, and a boat passing by. Although trees obstructed the view, they could make out Delaware City on the far shore.

Looking down on the grounds around the fort, Lewis could hardly assimilate what he saw. Prisoners of war were kept in two pens, one for the officers, and one for the privates. Lewis could see over the barricade into the private's pen. As the new prisoners-of-war were led into the pen, they were met by hundreds of hollow-eyed skeletons of half-naked men with bony hands attached to bony arms. The hands were reaching out to grab a blanket, or whatever else, the new arrivals carried with them. The clothes on the living skeletons were literally rags,[19] and sores covered their bodies, no doubt from lice and other vermin. Lewis had seen what lice could do at the Old Capitol. It caused him agony to know that these pitiful, abused men were Confederate heroes, revered by the people in the South. He knew that most of them were captured at Gettysburg.

There were not enough barracks in the private's pen, so housing was supplemented by crudely constructed 'shebangs,' shacks made of upright boards, nailed together with large cracks between the planks, giving very little protection from the elements.[20]

As Lewis and Mr. Cox watched, they heard voices from the top of the wall surrounding the pen calling, "Rat call! Rat call!" followed by maniacal laughter.

From their miserable shebangs, hundreds of desperate men hobbled toward the wall, where Union soldiers started throwing something down into the mob.[21]

"What is it that they are throwing to the prisoners?" Mr. Cox asked. "Is it meat?"

"No. It's rats!" Lewis answered in disgust.

The two men watched in horror as prisoners pushed and shoved one another to have the good fortune of being one of those who got a rat.

Soon afterward, the air that drifted through the bars of their window mingled the smell of fried rats with the pervading odor of urine, disease, and sewage.

"I don't think we will be treated as the 'elite from Fredericksburg' in here," Mr. Cox glumly remarked.

"We'll be lucky to get out of here alive," Lewis dejectedly answered. He hoped that some of their letters would be answered before they, too, were reduced to eating rats.

On the grounds beneath them, they could see prisoners of war carrying boards, rolling barrels of flour, pushing wheelbarrows, and pulling horse carts filled with water, beef, bread, shingles, and other stuff.[22]

"I thought it was a war crime to use prisoners of war as slave labor," Mr. Cox remarked.

"So did I," Lewis answered.

Another political prisoner, who overheard their conversation, explained, "The prisoners of war only get two sparse meals a day. If they volunteer to do slave labor, then they are given a third meal.[23] Much of the labor that would ordinarily be done by oxen or mules is done by prisoners.[24] Their regular rations are one cracker and a cup of poor coffee in the morning, and a small piece of meat with a cup of soup at dinner.[25] It is not enough to keep a man alive."

"According to the laws of war," Mr. Cox expounded, "prisoners captured in an armed contest must be protected, provided with proper quarters, clothing, bedding, and camp equipment. He is to be fed the same rations as his captors, and not required to labor on military works or menial jobs."[26]

"Do you see any of those laws being enforced here?" the man replied. "I sure don't. Just look over there. Those men probably tried to escape."

Lewis looked in the direction he was pointing and saw two men chained together. Each man had both of his hands chained to the other man's hands, making it difficult for them to perform the simplest action.[27]

"And down there." The man pointed in another direction. "That's a popular punishment for the slightest infraction."

Following the man's pointed finger Lewis saw a number of men with a heavy iron ball attached to their ankles by a heavy chain.[28]

"And over there. Perhaps that man at least deserves his punishment."

A man was being paraded barefooted through the fort yard and around the barracks with a barrel over his head. There was a sign on the front of the barrel that said, "Thief." A drummer was marching in front of the man, and a soldier with a musket was following him.[29]

"And over there."

Lewis saw a man was strung up with his hands tied by a rope and his arms above his head. He was suspended in the air, with no chance to rest, even for a moment. The end of the rope was tied to a branch of a tree.[30]

Lewis found that the hostages had free access to anything on their floor, but there was a guard to prevent them from leaving the floor. A number of the men had already gathered in the hallway to play cards and gamble. Others were reading or writing letters in their rooms.

The men had a water closet on their floor that they shared as a group. From his window, Lewis could plainly see that this was not the case in the pens. Sinks [latrines] had been constructed for the prisoners of war. He soon learned that there were thousands of prisoners of war, who had to use the prison sinks. Although the number fluctuated from time to time, only two men were being admitted at a time. It was not unusual for him to see upwards of five hundred men standing in line to use them. No wonder the prison camp smelled so foul! Men, who could no longer wait, were relieving themselves on the ground.

Lewis quickly understood the depth of the inhumanness of the 'only two men in the sinks' policy. Within a couple of days, he and all of the party from Fredericksburg had diarrhea. They soon learned that it was called the 'common complaint' of Fort Delaware.

It was not unusual in the morning to see the body of some poor, sick soldier who had died with diarrhea streaming down his legs, while attempting to crawl to the sinks during the night.[31]

The soldiers guarding the sinks could be especially cruel. To keep the line moving, they would order the men to run down the walkway leading from the sinks, even if the men were lame. A number of the prisoners had only one leg, or were on crutches due to war wounds.

One day an event occurred that had all the prisoners in the fort upset. Around dusk, they heard the crack of musket fire. Before bedtime, the details were known throughout the prison. A thirty-year-old, crippled prisoner named Col. Edward Pope Jones had been shot and was not expected to live—executed because he was not able to run! He had been hobbling along, wearing one shoe, and carefully stepping down a rough place in the walkway. Without even calling out a warning, the guard had shot him.[32]

Later the news circulated around the prison that the guard, Bill Douglas, who murdered the crippled man, was not even punished. He was promoted to corporal, instead.[33]

Afterwards, orders in frames covered with glass were posted in various places authorizing the sentinels to shoot anyone who disobeyed a challenge.[34]

The guard on Lewis' floor complained to the men, "You political prisoners are really lucky to be treated so well by us. You know our soldiers just shoot some of our prisoners of war. They have the new group draw tickets to see which ones will be shot, and which ones will live.[35] I think we should do that with political prisoners, too. It would reduce the crowding and save the government money."

Those who shared Lewis' room examined their clothing and each other's hair for nits and lice, before they went to bed each night, and were very careful about bathing every day. Each day they sat by the window and carefully picked nits off their clothes. Lewis quickly learned that no amount of vigilance could keep the lice off of them, because there were men on their floor who did not pay attention to their personal hygiene, and left vermin behind in every room they entered.[36]

In spite of his many precautions concerning lice, Lewis spent restless nights being eaten alive, not by lice, but by mosquitoes and bedbugs.

The moment the lights were extinguished each night, the bedbugs would go to work. Tiny ones would bite his hands producing an almost intolerable burning sensation. Larger ones would drop out of the cracks of the bunk above, and go to work on his face and neck. Their crawling, biting, and offensive odor made sleep almost impossible[37] for him.

Lewis resorted to rubbing oil of cinnamon on his body before retiring in hopes of discouraging the bedbugs.[38]

Within a week, many of the men from Fredericksburg had large open sores on their bodies. It was the common witticism that a man in Fort Delaware had more life on him than in him.[39]

Getting a good night's sleep was very difficult. Besides the pain and nuisance of insect bites, it was oppressively hot, and did not begin to cool off until about two o'clock in the mornings. The room was crowded with three tiers of double bunks along three sides of the room. When that many elderly men fell asleep, the noise level from snoring was unbelievable. In addition, there was the noise created by the younger men who stayed up late playing cards and gambling in the hall, and the footsteps of those shuffling back and forth to the water closet. Lewis felt sleep deprived the whole time he was at Fort Delaware.

During the day, there was also a lot of racket and confusion because a few noisy men were always swearing, arguing, or horsing around in the hallway.[40]

On the first day, Lewis went to the dining hall with the others for dinner. The food had been put onto the disgustingly dirty tables beforehand. There were no plates, knives, forks, or spoons. Each man had a small piece of beef, which had been boiled without any seasoning, a piece of coarse bread, and a bowl of rice soup.[41] There were flies and dirt in the soup,[42] so Lewis did not attempt to eat it. The cup of coffee that was provided was muddy and awful. The cooks looked so filthy that Lewis decided not to go back.[43] After that, Lewis and Mr. Cox just got their bread allowance of a loaf each every other day[44] from the baker, and used the money they had been given to buy food in the sutler's store to prepare their own meals. The sutler's shop was stocked with cheese, butter, eggs, etc.[45] and many articles needed for comfort, that were not available anywhere else on the island, but the prices were exorbitant.[46]

Their water came from a cistern on top of the building and was tolerably clear. It could be obtained by turning a cock at the head of the stairs.[47] This made it easy to take a bath each day, something that was necessary to remove nits.

They were astonished to learn that there was a barroom in the sutler's store, and there was always a crowd of from fifty to one hundred men hanging around the door waiting for his turn to buy a drink. Only two men were allowed in the barroom at a time, with the men entering by one door, and exiting by another. Liquor was supposedly a contraband article, and any prisoner discovered to be drunk was severely punished. Yet, the guards were frequently drunk and staggering around the island, and liquor was openly sold to anyone who had the price of a glass.[48]

A few days after their arrival, a pompous-acting guard came into the hallway and bellowed, "Roll out! Roll out, all you that want to take a walk, and be in a hurry about it, too!"[49] The men were escorted outside for twenty minutes. They walked to the wharf where they stood around, until escorted back inside. Although there were Confederate prisoners in the vicinity, they were forbidden to speak to them.[50]

Several days later, they were taken for another walk but were allowed a wider range of movement. Some of the men went in swimming in the river, while others enjoyed the shade of a willow tree.[51]

During good weather, the men were supposed to be allowed two hours a day outside in the fresh air, one hour in the morning and one in the afternoon. Often this did not happen, and sometimes they were scarcely outside fifteen minutes, before the guard ordered their return.[52]

Within a few weeks parcels began to arrive addressed to Lewis or Mr. Cox, and they were able to eat an adequate diet and share some of their food with the others in their room. However, they were distressed to learn that their packages had been opened and sundry articles had been removed. What was done with the stolen merchandise, they never learned.[53]

Lewis' constant concern was for the young men in the pens. When the weather turned rainy and cold, he heard that there was water standing on the floors of the shebangs and officer's barracks.[54]

Each morning he would see about a dozen,[55] rough, ill-made coffins lined up on the wharf, waiting to be transported to the Jersey shore for burial.[56] He learned that when a prisoner died, his naked body was stored in the Dead-House, until a coffin could be built for him. The prisoner was then buried completely nude, without even a blanket to cover his body.[57] Lewis could not understand how a so-called Christian nation could engage in such barbaric practices.

"I'm glad he's not here with us, but I sure do miss Rev. Broaddus," Mr. Cox had told Lewis on their first day at Fort Delaware.

Both men knew that the prayer meetings they held in the Old Capital Prison were the only thing that had sustained them during that incarceration. Their circumstances were worse at Fort Delaware, making it even more imperative that they have prayer meetings.

Since Mr. Cox was a Sunday school teacher, it was decided that he should lead the prayer meetings, and they would be open to anyone on the floor. Each night their room was filled with men who spent the evening on their knees.

One of the guards told them that a Rev. Isaac Handy held church services outdoors on Sundays, and anyone of the political prisoners could get permission to attend.

After that, most of the men from Fredericksburg attended the Sunday services conducted by Rev. Handy in the officer's pen.

Lewis discovered that Rev. Handy was also a political prisoner.

"I'm from Portsmouth, Virginia," Rev. Handy explained. "My family and I were visiting my wife's family in Delaware about a year ago. The trip had been very difficult to arrange, but my wife had not seen her family for over five years, and she and her mother both were in ill health. She wanted to see them very badly, so, I arranged with Richmond and Washington to get the necessary travel passes. The second night that we were in Delaware, we attended a private dinner party in the private home of one of my wife's relatives. Everyone was questioning me about what it was like living in the Confederacy. Someone asked me about my feelings of loyalty to the United States' flag. I honestly stated that I no longer feel any loyalty to the United States' flag. I was arrested in Bridgeville, Delaware for making that remark, and I have been here ever since. I have in my pocket, as we speak, a pass issued to me by the officials in Washington stating that I am guaranteed safe passage to return to the South—but here I am in prison. I have not seen my children since my arrest, and I have seen my wife only a couple of times."[58]

"Were you given a trial or some sort of hearing?" Lewis asked.

"No, I've never been accused of a crime," Rev. Handy answered. "This prison if full of men who were suspected of thinking disloyal thoughts, who were never given a trial. They are not suspected of committing disloyal acts, but thinking disloyal thoughts. They are Northerners who disagreed with Lincoln's policies, sympathized with the South, or disagreed with the war, or maybe someone just thought they disagreed with Lincoln's policies, sympathized with the South, or disagreed with the war.

The Union army is supposedly fighting 'to set men free' when their right to 'free thoughts,' not to mention 'free speech' and other freedoms, no longer exist. If you are even suspected of disagreeing with Lincoln or his policies, you are sent to prison without trial for an undetermined length of time. At least I know why I am here. Many of the political prisoners have no idea why they are here. They have just been told that it is for the good of the country. A person has no right to any views except those prescribed by the administration, however corrupt they may be.[59]

Once you are imprisoned, there are no prospects of relief, until you are completely broken down and cowed, or are willing to be a hypocrite and take the Oath. If you have powerful friends, they might be able to arrange a pardon for you. I have found that most friends will sympathize or pray for you, but they will not publicly defend you, lest they, too, be thrown in prison. There are men in here who have not even received a letter from their parents in months, or, worse, they have received abusive letters from siblings, who are fearful for their own safety."[60]

"Glory, glory, halleluiah," Mr. Cox remarked.

"Right! Glory, glory, halleluiah!" Rev. Handy answered.

"White people are not the only ones being duped," Lewis remarked. "The blacks, who think the Federal government is going to bring them freedom, are being the duped also. My son, John, tells me that when the Thirtieth Virginia was at the Seven Days Battles, they found that the Federal troops had used blacks as human shields at

Seven Pines," Lewis said. "It is really pathetic that the blacks thought that the Federal troops were going to free them, then they were used as human shields. He said their bodies filled up four ice houses."[61]

"If the world only knew," Mr. Cox remarked.

Lewis asked Rev. Handy about the couple of hundred Confederate prisoners that he had seen marching around in old Union uniforms ."They took the oath," Rev. Handy explained. "Neither side trusts or respects them, but they are to be pitied. They have been on short rations ever since they got here, and have had to drink water from the moat, which is contaminated with excrements. They took the oath out of desperation."[62] The Union has the money and the resources to provide all the prisoners here with an adequate diet, clothing, blankets, medicine, and medical care. They deliberately withhold those things out of pure malice."[63]

As the weather got hotter, the prison became more unbearable. There were times that the men spent the whole day sitting on the windowsills, hoping for a breeze. However, the river was as smooth as glass, and there was not a leaf stirring.[64]

One day when several of them were sitting on the sill, one of the guards ordered the men to take their arms away from the window. Mr. McGruder, one of the political prisoners in Lewis' room, refused to do so. The guard took aim with his musket, and the men hastily moved away from the window. A few minutes later a guard came into the room and took Mr. McGruder to the guard house.[65]

"I can't believe, as hot as it is, that they won't even let us sit unmolested in the window," Mr. Walter Mills complained.

"They would not let us touch the windows at the Old Capitol," Mr. Cox replied. "It's not fair, but if you value your life, you had better do as they say."

"Look what happened to that poor Col. Jones," Lewis added. "They have the authority to shoot you any time they choose."

Lewis and the others spent one and a half months in Fort Delaware, while Clay Rowe worked diligently for the release of those from Fredericksburg in exchange for the release of the sixty stragglers.[66]

On July 2, 1964,[67] when Lewis and the others were released from Fort Delaware, they were marched to the wharf, where two tables had been set up. The Commission of Prisoners, certain officers, and several guards were there at the head of the wharf. When his name was called, Lewis carried his carpetbag on board the steamer.[68]

The hostages were exchanged at sea into the custody of Clay Rowe. When his formal exchange was made, Lewis and Mr. Rowe embraced each other. Memories of their earlier, shared incarceration flooded Lewis' mind. A band on the Weycomoke began to play 'Dixie' as the men boarded the steamer for their trip home. Tears welled up in Lewis' eyes at the sound of his national anthem, and he joined in the jubilant cheering. They were transported to Split Rock, twelve miles from Fredericksburg, and put ashore. Carriages and wagons were waiting to transport the sick, but most of the men walked home.

Upon arriving in Fredericksburg the hostages were greeted with shouts of welcome. The men, tired but happy, courageously began singing, "There's no place like home," and the townsfolk joined in.[69]

---

[1] *The South: A Tour of Its Battle-fields and Ruined Cities* by J. T. Trowbridge, L. Stebbins, Hartford, Connecticut (1867) Page 113.

[2] "An Account of the Reign of Terror" by Sarah Ann French Alsop, Fredericksburg, VA, Virginia Historical Society, Richmond, Virginia.

[3] Ibid.

[4] Ibid.

[5] "Walk Through History...Hanover Street" www.historypoint.org.

[6] Some Southerners, when given the choice, did burn their homes to the ground rather than allowing Union officers to use them. An example was the manor house at Powhatan Plantation in Williamsburg, Virginia.

[7] *History of the City of Fredericksburg, Virginia* by S.J. Quinn, The Hermitage Press, Inc. (1908). (Hereafter referred to as Quinn) Page 102

[8] William Lange may have been a relative of Henry Ebert's wife, Sophia (Lange) Ebert.

[9] This William Jones may be the William Jones of the 30th Virginia who was badly wounded at Sharpsburg (Antietam).

[10] Quinn, Page 103

[11] "Fort Delaware: The 'Andersonville' of the North" by Al Benson, Jr., www.rebelgray.com/FortDelaware.htm.

[12] "Welcome to the Official Fort Delaware Society Webpage" www.del.net/org/fort/.

"Fort Delaware Prison" www.censusdiggins.com/fort_delaware.html.

United States Bonds, or Duress by Federal Authority: A Journal of Current Events During an Imprisonment of Fifteen Months, at Fort

Delaware by Isaac W.K. Handy, DD, of Augusta County, Va., Baltimore: Turnbull Brothers (1874).

[13] *W.P.A.* New Jersey, New York Viking Press (1939) page 632.

[14] *United States Bonds, or Duress by Federal Authority: A Journal of Current Events During an Imprisonment of Fifteen Months, at Fort Delaware* by Isaac W.K. Handy, DD, of Augusta County, Va., Baltimore: Turnbull Brothers (1874). Page 189.
Confederate Veteran, Vol. XIII (1905) page 107.
The Amazing Civil War by Webb Garrison, Rutledge Hill Press (1998), page 15.

[15] *United States Bonds, or Duress by Federal Authority: A Journal of Current Events During an Imprisonment of Fifteen Months, at Fort Delaware* by Isaac W.K. Handy, DD, of Augusta County, Va., Baltimore: Turnbull Brothers (1874), page 24.

[16] Ibid. Page 15.

[17] Ibid. Page 85.

[18] Ibid. Page 34.

[19] "War Department policy, as expressed by the Commissary General, was 'to provide as little clothing for them as possible.'" Article on Fort Delaware by James A. Cox in *Civil War Times*, July–August 1993 quoted in *"Fort Delaware: The 'Andersonville' of the North"* by Al Benson, Jr. www.rebelgray.com/FortDelaware.htm.

[20] *United States Bonds, or Duress by Federal Authority: A Journal of Current Events During an Imprisonment of Fifteen Months, at Fort Delaware* by Isaac W.K. Handy, DD, of Augusta County, Va., Baltimore: Turnbull Brothers (1874), page 34.

[21] "John S. Swann, Prison Life at Fort Delaware" transcribed by Neil Allen Bristow,
http://freepages.genealogy.rootsweb.com.
/~greenwolf/coombs/swann-js.htm?sourceid=002246989974706.

[22] *United States Bonds, or Duress by Federal Authority: A Journal of Current Events During an Imprisonment of Fifteen Months, at Fort Delaware* by Isaac W.K. Handy, DD, of Augusta County, Va., Baltimore: Turnbull Brothers (1874), page 15.

[23] Ibid. Page 16.

[24] Ibid. Page 501.

[25] Ibid. Page 88.

[26] The Confederate Congress passed an act stating these same humane laws would be adhered to on May 21, 1861. *The War of the Rebellion: A Compilation of the Official Records of the Union and Confederate Armies*, Ser. II, Vol. VIII, page 345.

[27] *United States Bonds, or Duress by Federal Authority: A Journal of Current Events During an Imprisonment of Fifteen Months, at Fort Delaware* by Isaac W.K. Handy, DD, of Augusta County, Va., Baltimore: Turnbull Brothers (1874). Page 111.

[28] Ibid.

[29] Ibid. Page 114.

[30] Ibid. Page 154.

[31] Ibid. Pages 202, 482.

[32] Ibid. Pages 473–474.

[33] Ibid. Pages 475, 481.

[34] Ibid Page 478.

[35] An incidence where this occurred was described in the *Confederate Veteran*, page 315, July 1898.

[36] *United States Bonds, or Duress by Federal Authority: A Journal of Current Events During an Imprisonment of Fifteen Months, at Fort Delaware* by Isaac W.K. Handy, DD, of Augusta County, Va., Baltimore: Turnbull Brothers (1874). Page 30.

[37] Ibid. Page 347.

[38] Ibid. Page 375.

[39] "Fort Delaware Prison, www.censusdiggins.com/fort_delaware.html.

[40] *United States Bonds, or Duress by Federal Authority: A Journal of Current Events During an Imprisonment of Fifteen Months, at Fort Delaware* by Isaac W.K. Handy, DD, of Augusta County, Va., Baltimore: Turnbull Brothers (1874). Page 102.

[41] Ibid. Page 445.

[42] Ibid. Page 451.

[43] Ibid. Page 23.

[44] Ibid. Page 336.

[45] Ibid. Page 425.

[46] Ibid. Page 110.

[47] Ibid. Page 18.

[48] Ibid. Pages 141, 430.

[49] Ibid. Page 63.

[50] Ibid. Page 34.

[51] Ibid. Page 40.

[52] Ibid.

[53] Ibid. Page 447.

[54] Ibid. Page 435.

[55] Ibid. Page 119.

[56] Ibid. Page 115.

[57] Ibid. Page 142.

[58] *United States Bonds, or Duress by Federal Authority: A Journal of Current Events During an Imprisonment of Fifteen Months, at Fort Delaware* by Isaac W.K. Handy, DD, of Augusta County, Va., Baltimore: Turnbull Brothers (1874). Pages 1–12, 484.

[59] Ibid. Page 315.

[60] Ibid.

[61] Manuscript by James Jackson Broaddus, Virginia Historical Society, Richmond, Virginia.

[62] *United States Bonds, or Duress by Federal Authority: A Journal of Current Events During an Imprisonment of Fifteen Months, at Fort Delaware* by Isaac W.K. Handy, DD, of Augusta County, Va., Baltimore: Turnbull Brothers (1874) page 26.

[63] "Fort Delaware: The 'Andersonville' of the North" by Al Benson, Jr., www.rebelgray.com/FortDelaware.htm.

[64] *United States Bonds, or Duress by Federal Authority: A Journal of Current Events During an Imprisonment of Fifteen Months, at Fort Delaware* by Isaac W.K. Handy, DD, of Augusta County, Va., Baltimore: Turnbull Brothers (1874), Page 44.

[65] Ibid. Page 461.

[66] Quinn, page 105.

[67] *United States Bonds, or Duress by Federal Authority: A Journal of Current Events During an Imprisonment of Fifteen Months, at Fort Delaware* by Isaac W.K. Handy, DD, of Augusta County, Va., Baltimore: Turnbull Brothers (1874) page 467.

[68] Ibid. Page 144.

[69] Quinn, Pages 104–106.

CHAPTER 12
THE WORLD SHALL YET DECIDE

L ewis was surprised to see how much older Eliza looked. She had been a buxom, comely woman at the beginning of the war, but now she was extremely thin, her hair was completely gray, and her skin was lined with fine wrinkles. He knew that the Yankees had made life hell for her and the other women of Fredericksburg. He seethed with hatred for them, and each night on his knees he asked God to help him somehow to forgive them.

Lacking other ways to earn a living, Lewis scavenged military refuse from the battlefields, which he sold to dealers in Richmond and Washington.[1]

In September, Lewis and Eliza received a letter from John.

Richmond, Virginia
September 1864
Dear Mama and Papa,
    Since the last time I wrote you, Thomas Proctor was captured at Totopotomoy Creek. I hear he was sent to Elmira Prison.[2]
    The 30th Virginia is camped on the Hewlett line between the James River and the Appomattox River. It is really hot here. The ground has been tromped on until there is scarcely a blade of grass to be seen, and dust arises in clouds from under your footsteps. We breathe dust all day long. Life in the bomb-proofs and trenches is hot, boring, and miserable.
    We were given a really poor place to camp, next to a mill pond that the Yankees had drained, turning it into a swamp. It is swarming with mosquitoes.
    I have malaria. I think it was caused by the bad air from the swampy mill pond. Anyway, I am at the Chimborazo Hospital[3] again, which is a lot more pleasant than the miserable shebang I had been occupying.
    I was sent here with another man who also has malaria. His name is Milton Dudley[4] and he is in the

29th Virginia.[5] The 29th is camped next to the 30th by the mill pond.[6]

As luck would have it, our malaria is following the same schedule. We have the 'shakies' on the same day, shaking until our bones ache, and our teeth chattering, until its a wonder they don't break, then we are well on the same day. I can't enjoy my well day knowing that I will have the 'shakies' again on the morrow, but having Milton for a friend has made it more tolerable.

The 29th is from the Appalachian Mountains of southwestern Virginia, and most of the men are really wild and uneducated. They do not cotton much to military discipline, but they are fearless, and I think they will do well in a battle. The funny thing about Milton is that he is not like the others. He is well educated. He says his father is a schoolteacher from Maine.[7]—Imagine that! A schoolteacher from Maine is living in the Appalachian Mountains of Virginia!

Anyway, Milton reads all the time, and on his well days, he reads stories to the men in our ward. I am not the only one from the 30th who has malaria. Robert and William Berrey, John Temple,[8] and over one hundred others that you may not know also have it. We are being given quinine and I hope to be well again soon.

I am glad that Papa is home. The next time I meet the Yankees on the battlefield, I will remember what they did to him, and make them pay dearly for it.

I will write again, when I feel better.

Love,
John[9]

As the war dragged on, living conditions continued to grow worse for Lewis and Eliza. The winter of 1865 was so bad, that Lewis did not know if he and Eliza could survive another such winter. There were days when all they had to eat was a thin gruel made of flour, and they would not have had that, if it were not for the generosity of John Marye.[10] Firewood was hard to obtain, as the countryside was stripped bare. Loose boards from destroyed houses had been scavenged until none was left. Now ruined houses were being disassembled piece by piece with pry bars and sledge hammers to get firewood.

All of this could have been endured, if it were not for the depressing reports of the deplorable condition of the Confederate Army—starving, barefooted, nearly naked, their numbers dwindling daily. Yet, Lewis and Eliza still clung to their hopes for a Confederate victory.

They were saddened to hear that John Marye's son, Ned, who was in the Fredericksburg Artillery, had died from disease.[11] He was only twenty-nine years old.[12] They were all the more thankful that Lewis' sons were still alive.

On March 6, 1865, Federal troops came up the Rappahannock River on boats and landed at the Fredericksburg wharves. They destroyed the train depot and rail cars at Hamilton's Crossing, then captured the home guard. After confiscating the quartermaster's supplies, they showed mercy on the people of Fredericksburg, perhaps for the only time during the war, and distributed food to them. The next day they left again.[13]

Once more spring came, but instead of hope, it brought the feeling of impeding doom.

Lewis knew that the Union army far outnumbered the Confederate army and they seemed to have an unlimited supply of men for replacements. He also knew that the resources of the North far exceeded that of the South. Yet, he clung to hope for the Confederacy.

One balmy day, when the sun was shining, and the cloudless blue sky seemed so far away, Lewis sat on his back steps and gazed at what had once been his garden. Weeds were growing where the neat rows of vegetables used to be. There was no use in his planting another garden. The Yankees would just steal everything he grew. Those in town had communal gardens,[14] but those who lived out on the Turnpike had no security against stragglers. Even his fence was gone. The last remains of it had been burned for firewood. He thought of the condition of Fredericksburg and felt sad. It once was so beautiful, but the derelict town was now in ruins.

As he sat there feeling blue, his attention was drawn to a red-breasted robin hopping around the yard. He looked around and found the rusty-colored mate nearby. Then he noticed that the red bud tree was in bloom again, and emerald green blades of green grass were pushing their way up through the soil.

"Odd, isn't it?" he thought. "No matter how bad things get, the sun still rises in the east, and sets in the west, and the robins return each spring. In spite of all I have been through, I am still here, and I have survived. God is still in His heaven, and He will help me through whatever the future holds."

Suddenly a feeling of peace came over him, and he knew that no matter what happened, life would go on.

When the news arrived that Lee had surrendered, it was a bitter pill to swallow. Lewis felt like the life had been crushed out of him.

"How could God let it happen?" Eliza cried.

Lewis sadly told Eliza, "You can't judge the merits of a cause by its success. Just remember that an evil man named Herod was sitting on the throne at the same time our Savior was being crucified. Truth will someday triumph. Our boys were poorly equipped, poorly clad, poorly fed, and virtually without pay. At times, they had to eat weeds and grass to survive. Many of them were bare-footed as they marched over frozen ground or burning highways. They were outnumbered three to one, yet they held out for four years against an army that was well equipped, well clothed, well fed, and well paid. They willingly fought to the death, when it was necessary, for the cause they loved.[15] It took two million, eight hundred thousand Union troops four years to defeat our six hundred thousand men."[16]

Lewis tried to pick up the pieces of his life. When goods became available again, he reopened his store,[17] and he was able to make a modest living.

John came home in rags. He had been at the Chimborazo Hospital in Richmond, when on April 2, 1865 news came that the Yankees were approaching, and Richmond was being evacuated. The patients panicked, as the nurses, cooks, and other attendants abandoned their duties and fled. Close to a thousand sick or wounded soldiers—all of those who could either walk, hobble, or crawl—fled the hospital, rather than risk being captured in their beds, and sent to the prisoner of war camp in Newport News.[18]

After fighting for the Confederacy for four years, John had been captured in Richmond on April 3, 1865,[19] and had been paroled on April 17.[20]

With no transportation available, he had walked from Richmond to Fredericksburg, an easy task for a man who had marched a couple of thousand miles in the past four years.

He stayed with Lewis and Eliza until the weather turned cool in the fall, then he started out on another long walk. This time he walked from Fredericksburg, Virginia to Goldsboro, North Carolina,[21] where he married Martha Elizabeth Phillips on January 4, 1866.[22]

Martha was fifteen years old at the time of their marriage.[23]

The very thing that the neighborhood men had feared before the first occupation came to pass. The slaves were set free without any provision being made for them to have a way to support themselves. Denied the food and lodging formerly provided by their masters, and lacking the skills to earn a decent wage, some of them were forced to steal to exist. Many of the citizens of Fredericksburg became the victims of robberies. Michael Ames' blacksmith shop was broken into and robbed twice.[24] James Bradley's store was also broken into and robbed twice.[25] John Marye's meat house was robbed of its entire content of edible foods.[26] James McGuire was robbed twice.[27] Thieves carried off all of David Sisson's beehives, except one, which was too large to be easily carried off. The beehives were abandoned when the thieves could not figure out how to get the honey out of them.[28]

In an incident that was probably just a prank, Montgomery Slaughter's gate was removed and carried to another part of town.[29]

A worse incident, however, happened to Charles Wellford, and had nothing to do with former slaves. He was assaulted and beaten by soldiers of the occupying army, while standing in front of his own home. After he was hit in the head three or four times, his son, Thomas, came to his aid. Thomas was also attacked and severely beaten.[30]

As time passed, a sense of normalcy began to return to Fredericksburg, but the old neighborhood had been irrevocably changed. New houses with new families were occupying lots that used to be empty. Monroe Stevens never moved back to the neighborhood. He was living in Stafford County.[31]

John Marye repaired Brompton and moved back into it, only to die shortly thereafter.[32]

George Rowe,[33] Richard Bozel,[34] James Jennings,[35] and John Bryce[36] all passed away.

169

Henry Ebert was operating a tavern,[37] and David Sisson was working as a laborer.[38]

Allan Stratton had moved to Washington, D.C.[39]

Of the men incarcerated in the Old Capitol Prison with Lewis, Michael Ames,[40] James Bradley,[41] Rev. Broaddus,[42] John Coakley,[43] James Cooke,[44] John Roberts,[45] John Scott,[46] Benjamin Temple,[47] and Charles Wellford[48] had all died.

Beverly Gill had moved to Baltimore and had died there.[49]

Saddest of all, the brilliant, mischievous, mercurial Clay Rowe had gone insane at the age of thirty-nine, and was at the state mental hospital in Williamsburg.[50]

Lewis made his peace with the United States. It became apparent to him that the Union after the war was very different from the Union from which they had seceded. Before the war, he thought of himself first and foremost as being a Virginian, and second of all as being an American. After the war, he considered himself an American first and a Virginian second.

He began to think that this might be a better way, and after a while, he once again found pride in being an American.

Yet, he could not forget that the American flag had hung above the courthouse, when the people of Fredericksburg were being systematically starved. Union soldiers had carried that flag up Hanover Street when they wantonly vandalized, stole, or destroyed everything that he owned. He had walked behind that flag in irons, when he was forcefully removed from his hearth and home, and sent to the Old Capitol Prison and the Fort Delaware Death Pen to be used as a pawn by the United States government.

He always clung to the belief that the war was not only immoral, illegal, and wrong, but worse, it was also unnecessary. It had been a sin against God and man to purchase with blood soaked fields and shattered lives, that which could have been settled in a court of law. He considered Abraham Lincoln to be the most evil American who had ever lived. He had sacrificed the lives of 500,000 American soldiers, and shattered the lives of hundreds of thousands of others, because he knew he was wrong and could never win in a court of law. Nearly 100,000 of those soldiers died within thirteen miles of Lewis' front door.[51]

Lewis distrusted the Yankees, who in their sanctimonious way had hated everyone who did not share their beliefs. They had killed, burned, and destroyed in their attempt to wipe Southerners off the face of the earth. Their invasion of the South had been brutal and barbaric. With their remorseless plans for extermination, they had inflicted untold cruelties on women and children, and had caused the deaths of untold numbers of them. They left behind them a legacy of hatred[52] that would last for generations.

They created animosity between the black and white races, which had not existed in the South before the war.

To the South's honor was the fact that they refused to make war upon the weak and defenseless. When they marched through their enemy's country, they did not lay waste to their fields, rob the families of their sustenance, or burn their homes, in spite of the fact that their own families were insulted, tormented, and robbed.[53]

One Pennsylvania farmer was quoted as saying, "I must say they acted like gentlemen, and, their cause aside, I would rather have forty thousand Rebels quartered on my premises than one thousand Union troops.[54]

Lewis longed to visit his sons and grandchildren before he died, especially John in Goldsboro.

On hot summer nights, when the neighborhood was quiet, and the only sound was a dog barking in the distance and the rhythmic clicking of Eliza's knitting needles, Lewis' mind would drift back to that time when the Williamsville Tavern had been the center of activity for the neighborhood. In his mind's eye, he could see Rev. Rowe eating a piece of apple pie, while Mr. Marye sipped his glass of whiskey. Monroe Stevens would be playing checkers with Mr. Bozel or Mr. Stratton. Mr. Marye would be leading a discussion on some bit of important news, while Mr. Sisson, Mr. Ebert, and Mr. Jennings joined in with the others in the discussion.

With the exception of Mr. Stratton, they had all been loyal to the starry cross.

Then the words of a poem by Father Ryan would drift into Lewis' mind.

"Might! sing your triumph songs!
Each song but sounds a shame.
Go down the world in loud-voiced throngs
To win from the future fame.

> Our ballads, born of tears,
> Will track you on your way,
> And win the hearts of the future years
> For the men who wore the gray.
>
> All lost! but by the graves
> Where martyred heroes rest
> He wins the most who honor saves—
> Success is not the test.
>
> The world shall yet decide
> In truth's clear, far-off light
> The soldiers who wore the gray and died
> With Lee were in the right."

and he would wonder how many generations would have to pass before his story could be told.

Lewis died on August 19, 1877 while visiting John in Goldsboro.[55] His obituary said, "He was a good man full of faith and the Holy Ghost."[56]

---

[1] Fredericksburg Civil War Sites: April 1861–November 1862 by Noel G. Harrison; H.E. Howard, Inc (1999) Page 23.

[2] *30th Virginia Infantry* by Robert K. Krick; H.E. Howard, Inc., Publisher (1985). Page 120.

[3] Ibid. Page 136.

[4] When the author, a descendent of John Kobler Wrenn, married a descendent of Milton Lowry Dudley, they were amazed to learn that their ancestors had been sent from Petersburg to the Chimborazo Hospital in Richmond on the same day with the same diagnosis. It is possible that John Kobler Wrenn and Milton Lowry Dudley shared the same room.

[5] 29th Virginia Infantry by John Perry Alderman; H.E. Howard, Inc., Publisher (1989). Page 102.

[6] Ibid. Pages 48–53.

[7] 1860 Tazewell, Virginia Census.

[8] *30th Virginia Infantry* by Robert K. Krick; H.E. Howard, Inc., Publisher (1985). Pages 82, 130.

[9] This letter is fictitious but the events described are true.
Ibid. Pages 55–61.

Confederate pay vouchers for John Kobler Wrenn.

[10] John Marye helped the people of Fredericksburg to survive by supplying them with flour from a mill he owned. [*Virginia Herald Dispatch* 27 Jul 1868, 3x1.]

[11] *The Fredericksburg Artillery* by Robert K. Krick; H.E. Howard, Inc. (1986) page 106.

[12] *Ancestry World Tree Project*, www.ancestry.com/tree/.

[13] Fredericksburg Civil War Sites: April 1861–November 1862 by Noel G. Harrison; H.E. Howard, Inc. (1999) Page 23.

[14] Ibid.

[15] This opinion is expressed in Defending the Southern Confederacy: The Men in Gray by Robert Catlett Cave, edited by Walbrook D. Swank, Burd Street Press, Shippensburg, Pennsylvania (2001). Pages 14–15.

[16] Ibid. Page 41.

[17] 1870 Fredericksburg, Virginia Census.

[18] *Chimborazo Hospital: That Charnel House of Living Sufferers* by Joseph P. Cullen, Virginia Historical Society, Richmond VA Page 42.

[19] *30th Virginia Infantry* by Robert K. Krick; H.E. Howard, Inc., Publisher (1985). Page 136.

[20] Confederate Service Record of John Kobler Wrenn.

[21] Family lore passed down from John Kobler Wrenn.

[22] Wayne County North Carolina Marriage license.

[23] Calculated from date of birth on her tombstone in Willow Dale Cemetery, Goldsboro, North Carolina.

[24] Fredericksburg Ledger, 8 Nov. 1870.

[25] *Fredericksburg Ledger*, 12 Dec 1865, 4 Dec 1866.

[26] Ibid. 20 Aug 1867.

[27] Ibid. 17 Sept. 1867, 16 Mar 1869.

[28] Ibid. 6 Aug 1869, 3x1.

[29] Ibid. 21 Nov. 1873.

[30] Ibid. 7 Jun. 1865.

[31] Will of Monroe Stevens dated February 3, 1912.

[32] *Virginia Herald Dispatch*, 27 July 1868, 3x1 and 2x6.

[33] *Minor Sketches of Major Folk* by Dora C. Jett; Richmond Old Dominion Press (1928) pages 96–97.

[34] 1875 Fredericksburg Tax Records.

[35] *Virginia Herald Dispatch*, 5 Jun 1876, 3x2.

[36] *Fredericksburg News*, 27 Apr 1874, 2x5.

[37] *Virginia Herald Dispatch*, 17 Apr. 1873, 3x2.

[38] 1870 Fredericksburg Virginia Census.

[39] 1866 Fredericksburg Land Tax Record.

[40] *Fredericksburg News*, 31 May 1875, 2x5.

[41] Confederate Cemetery Tombstone Inscription.

[42] City Cemetery Tombstone Inscription.

[43] St. George's Cemetery Tombstone Inscription.

[44] Fredericksburg, Virginia Death Record.

[45] *Fredericksburg Ledger*, 3 Dec 1872.

[46] City Cemetery Tombstone Inscription.

[47] Tombstone Inscription, Fredericksburg City Cemetery.

[48] *Ancestry World Tree Project*, www.ancestry.com/tree/.

[49] *Virginia Herald Dispatch*, 14 Aug 1876, 3x1.

[50] 1870 Fredericksburg, Virginia Census.
Fredericksburg News, 14 Mar 1878.

[51] They died in the Battles of Fredericksburg, Chancellorsville, The Wilderness, and Spotsylvania Courthouse.

[52] This opinion is expressed in *United States Bonds; or Duress by Federal Authority: A Journal of Current Events During an Imprisonment of Fifteen Months, at Fort Delaware* by Isaac W.K. Handy, DD, of Augusta County, Va.; Baltimore: Turnbull Brothers (1874) page 384.

[53] This opinion is expressed in Defending the Southern Confederacy: The Men in Gray by Robert Catlett Cave, edited by Walbrook D. Swank, Burd Street Press, Shippensburg, Pennsylvania (2001). Page17.

[54] Ibid. Page 17.

[55] Wayne County North Carolina Death Certificate.

[56] Goldsboro Messenger, 30 Aug 1877, page 3.

CHAPTER 13

BIOGRAPHICAL SKETCHES

Michael Ames

Michael Ames was born circa 1806 in Virginia, and worked as a blacksmith.[1] He was an Old Line Whig,[2] and a member of Sons of Temperance.[3]

On October 20, 1827, he married Snowey [Snnoy] English, daughter of Elizabeth English.[4] They had five children.[5]

1. Bettie Ames, b. ca. 1832
2. Frances Ellen (Fannie) Ames, b. ca. 1838, d. 10 July 1863[6]
3. Samuel S. Ames, b. ca. 1843
4. Parmelia Ames, b. ca. 1845
5. George M. Ames, b. ca. 1848

Michael Ames son, Samuel S. Ames enlisted in the 30th VA, Co. B on April 22, 1861. He was later promoted to corporal. He was 'slightly' wounded in the knee at Sharpsburg on September 17, 1862. The roster showed that he was still absent because of the wound in July 1864, and then there is no further record of him. He may have died from the wound.[7]

Michael Ames was one of the citizens of Fredericksburg who was arrested as a hostage and incarcerated in the Old Capitol Prison in Washington, D.C. in the summer of 1862.[8]

He was arrested again as a hostage by the Union troops in May

---

[1] 1860 Fredericksburg, Virginia Census.
[2] *The History of the City of Fredericksburg Virginia* by S.J. Quinn, The Hermitage Press, Inc., Richmond, VA (1908) page 793.
Fredericksburg News, 25 Oct. 1852, 2x3.
[3] Ibid. 30 Jun 1848, 3x1.
[4] Fredericksburg Virginia Marriage Register.
[5] 1860 Fredericksburg, Virginia Census.
[6] Masonic Cemetery tombstone.
[7] *30th Virginia Infantry* by Robert K. Krick, H.E. Howard, Inc., Publisher (1985) page 78.
[8] *The War of the Rebellion: A Compilation of the Official Records of the Union and Confederate Armies,* Series II, Vol. IV, Washington: Government Printing Office (1899) Pages 366, 376, 861, 866.

1864, but was released after he was taken to Washington, D.C.[9]

Between 1860 and 1870, Michael Ames' real estate decreased in value from $2,000 to $0, and his personal property decreased in value from $6,000 to $250.[10]

After the war, Michael Ames was one of the many victims of robbery in Fredericksburg, when his blacksmith shop was broken into twice in 1870.[11]

Michael Ames died in May 1875. He was 73 years old.[12] On May 13, 1877, his wife, Snowey English Ames, died at the age of 74.[13]

Thomas S. Barton

Thomas S. Barton was born circa 1833 in Virginia and was a clerk.[14] He was the son of Thomas B. and Susan Catherine (Stone) Barton.[15] He was one of the citizens of Fredericksburg who was arrested as a hostage in the summer of 1862, but because of his ill health, he was paroled to friends in Baltimore.[16]

Elizabeth Bayne

Very little is known about Elizabeth Bayne, except that she was born circa 1806 in Virginia, and lived on the Turnpike.[17] Her son, Otho, enlisted in the 30th Virginia, Company I on July 25, 1861 and reenlisted on March 4, 1862

Correspondence between Elizabeth Bayne and the Federal government after the war indicated that Otho was taken prisoner in the spring of 1862. He took the Oath and enlisted in Baker's District of Columbia Calvary in July 1863, and was sent to Fortress Monroe in

---

[9] *History of the City of Fredericksburg, Virginia* by S. J. Quinn, Hermitage Press (1908) page 102.

[10] 1860 & 1870 Virginia Censuses.

[11] *Fredericksburg Ledger*, 8 Nov 1870.

[12] *Fredericksburg News*, 31 May 1875, 2x5.

[13] Ibid. 17 May 1877, 3x6.

[14] 1850 Fredericksburg, Virginia Census.

[15] Ibid.

[16] *The War of the Rebellion: A Compilation of the Official Records of the Union and Confederate Armies*, Series II, Vol. IV, Washington: Government Printing Office (1899) Page 861.

[17] 1860 Fredericksburg, Virginia Census.

April 1865. No further trace of Otho has been found.[18]

John Jamison Berrey

John Jamison Berrey was born February 13, 1812 in Madison County, VA, the son of Abner and Lucy Berrey.[19] He was a merchant.[20]

He moved to Fredericksburg in 1828 and went into the hardware business with various partners. At the time of the war, he was connected with the hardware business of English, Spindle, and Co.,[21] was an Old Line Whig,[22] and a member of the Fredericksburg Methodist Church.[23]

On February 3, 1835, John J. Berrey married Mary W. Lucas.[24] They had eight children.[25]

1. Mary L. Berrey, b. ca. 1837
2. Robert Banks Berrey, b. ca. 1838
3. Lucy Berrey, b. ca. 1840
4. John Jamison Berrey, Jr. b. ca. 1841
5. William Henry Berrey, b. ca. 1843
6. Bettie C. Berrey, b. ca. 1844
7. Zachy Taylor Berrey, b. ca. 1848, d. before June 1866[26]
8. James R. Berrey, b. ca. 1850

Four of his sons were in the Confederate Army.[27]

His son, Robert Banks Berrey, enlisted in the 46th Virginia Infantry, Company A in May 1861, and in the 30th Virginia, Company A on February 18, 1862. He was promoted to corporal on May 16, 1864 and to sergeant on November 1, 1864. He was hospitalized with malaria January through March 1865. There is no further record of

---

[18] *30th Virginia* Infantry by Robert K. Krick, H.E. Howard, Inc., Publisher (1985) Page 81.

[19] Fredericksburg Virginia Death Record.

[20] 1860 Fredericksburg, Virginia Census.

[21] Star, 30 Nov 1892, 3x4.

[22] *The History of the City of Fredericksburg Virginia* by S.J. Quinn, Hermitage Press, Inc., Richmond, VA (1908) page 79.

[23] *Steward's Book*, Fredericksburg Methodist Church.

[24] Virginia Marriage Register.

[25] 1860 Fredericksburg, Virginia Census.

[26] *Fredericksburg Ledger*, 22 Jun 1866.

[27] *Star*, 30 Nov 1892, 3x4.

him.[28] Perhaps he was one of the 'walking wounded who was able to escape from Chimborazo Hospital just before Richmond fell, and managed to make it back to Fredericksburg without being captured.

John Berrey's son, John Jamison Berrey, Jr. enlisted in the Fredericksburg Artillery on July 16, 1861. He was paroled at Appomattox.[29]

Another son, William Henry Berrey, enlisted in Company B, 30th Virginia on April 22, 1861. He was promoted to corporal December 12, 1861, and to sergeant November 1, 1863. He was hospitalized with malaria, March 10, 1865. He signed a parole in Ashland, Virginia on April 29, 1865.[30] There is no explanation of why he was in Ashland. Perhaps he was one of the 'walking wounded who was able to escape from Chimborazo Hospital just before Richmond fell, and was captured in Ashland.

In June of 1866, the remains of John Berrey's son, Zack, arrived at the train depot and were buried in Fredericksburg. Apparently, he had been killed during the war.[31]

John Berrey was one of the citizens of Fredericksburg who was arrested as a hostage and incarcerated in the Old Capitol Prison in Washington, D.C. in the summer of 1862.[32]

He was elected to the common council in Fredericksburg in July 1865.[33]

Between 1860 and 1870, John Berrey's real estate had decreased in value from $2,000 to $0, but his personal property had increased in value from $8,800 to $10,000.[34]

After the war, he continued to work in the hardware business, and then a few years before he died, he took a job as bookkeeper for

---

[28] *30th Virginia Infantry* by Robert K. Krick, H.E. Howard, Inc., Publisher (1985) page 82.

[29] *The Fredericksburg Artillery* by Robert K. Krick, H.E. Howard Inc. (1986) page 97.

[30] *30th Virginia Infantry* by Robert K. Krick, H.E. Howard, Inc., Publisher (1985) page 82.

[31] *Fredericksburg Ledger,* 22 Jun 1866.

[32] *The War of the Rebellion: A Compilation of the Official Records of the Union and Confederate Armies,* Series II, Vol. IV, Washington: Government Printing Office (1899) Pages 366, 376, 861, 866.

[33] *Fredericksburg Ledger,* 20 Jul 1865.

[34] 1860 & 1870 Virginia Censuses.

the Eagle Shoe Company.[35]

John Jamison Berrey died of pneumonia on November 28, 1892. He was 80 years old.[36] His obituary said that he "was a kind-hearted Christian and was greatly esteemed by all who knew him." Montgomery Slaughter was one of the honorary pallbearers at his funeral.[37]

Richard W. Bozel, Jr.

Richard W. Bozel was born circa 1820 in Virginia, and was a shoemaker.[38] He bought his property on the Turnpike from John L. Marye on June 1, 1841.[39]

Richard Bozel and his wife, Maria had five children.[40]

1. William M. Bozel, b. ca. 1844
2. Emmett Bozel, b. ca. 1852
3. Eugene Bozel, b. ca. 1854
4. Lawrence Bozel, b. ca. 1856
5. Ernest Bozel, b. ca. 1862

On November 7, 1848, Richard W. Bozel along with Martin Spicer assaulted Eliza Wrenn. The testimony at the trial concerning the assault was not recorded, but the men were found guilty of "striking, bruising, wounding, ill treating, and other wrongs," and doing "great damage" to Eliza C. Wrenn.[41] The word "rape" is not mentioned, but it is not likely that Eliza Wrenn would testify in open court that she had been raped, considering the stigma and shame directed against the victims of rape at that time. The use of the word "damage" is interesting, in that it suggests harm that cannot be undone.

Richard Bozel's son, William M. Bozel, enlisted in the 30th Virginia, Company A, on March 4, 1862. He was admitted to a Charlottesville Hospital seriously ill on July 27, 1863. He deserted and took the oath between December 16 and December 29, 1863.[42]

---

[35] *Star*, 30 Nov 1892, 3x4.
[36] Fredericksburg Death Record.
[37] *Star*, 30 Nov 1892, 3x4.
[38] 1860 Fredericksburg, Virginia Census.
[39] Fredericksburg Deed Book M, Page 166.
[40] 1860 & 1870 Fredericksburg Censuses.
[41] Commonwealth vs. Martin Spicer and Richard Bozel, 1849, Cr-HU-R, 470-283.
[42] *30th Virginia Infantry* by Robert K. Krick, H.E. Howard, Inc., Publisher

Between 1860 and 1870, Richard Bozel and Maria sustained a real estate loss from $800 to $500 and a personal estate loss from $50 to $0.00[43]

Richard Bozel apparently died before the 1875 tax records, when his name was dropped and Mrs. Bozel was listed as the owner of their property.[44]

Maria Bozel was last listed on the tax records in 1878.[45]

Starting in 1879 the property is listed in the name of R.E. Bozel, who is apparently one of the sons, Emmett, Eugene, or Ernest.[46]

James Hood Bradley

James Hood Bradley was born May 4, 1815[47] and he was a grocer,[48] an Old Line Whig, and a deacon in the Baptist Church.[49] He was also a city councilman[50] and a director of the Bank of Virginia.[51]

He married Lucilla Stanley,[52] and they had three children.[53]

1. William Edward Bradley, b. 27 Dec. 1841, d. 5 Oct. 1929, m. Margaret Swan.[54]
2. Mary L. Bradley, b. ca. 1850
3. Susan M. Bradley, b. ca. 1852

He operated a grocery store in Fredericksburg where he sold "sugars, coffees, teas, molasses, salt, iron, fish, bacon, lime, plaster, flour, and a quantity of other goods."[55]

His son, William Edward Bradley, enlisted in the Fredericksburg Artillery on March 7, 1862. He was wounded at Ream's Station on August 21, 1864. He was paroled at Appomattox

---

(1985) Page 83.

[43] 1860 & 1870 Fredericksburg, Virginia Censuses.

[44] 1875 Fredericksburg Tax Records.

[45] 1878 Fredericksburg Tax Records.

[46] 1879 Fredericksburg Tax Records.

[47] Confederate Cemetery Tombstone Inscription.

[48] 1860 Fredericksburg, Virginia Census.

[49] *The History of the City of Fredericksburg, Virginia* by S.J. Quinn, The Hermitage Press, Inc., Richmond, VA (1908) pages 77–79.

[50] *Fredericksburg News*, Jan. 29, 1861.

[51] Ibid. March 19, 1861.

[52] Confederate Cemetery Tombstone Inscription.

[53] 1860 Fredericksburg, Virginia Census.

[54] Confederate Cemetery Tombstone Inscription.

[55] *Weekly Advertiser*, 5 Aug 1854.

on April 9, 1865.[56]

James Bradley was one of the citizens of Fredericksburg who was arrested as a hostage and incarcerated in the Old Capitol Prison in Washington, D.C. in the summer of 1862.[57]

He was arrested again as a hostage by the Union troops in May 1864, but was released after he was taken to Washington, D.C.[58]

After the war, James Bradley served on the town council,[59] was on the membership committee of the Home Industry Organization,[60] and was a member of the Emigration Society, which encouraged Germans to immigrate to Fredericksburg and the surrounding countryside.[61]

He was also one of the many victims of robbery in Fredericksburg after the war. His store was broken into in December 1865 and again in December 1866. In the first robbery, he lost between $200 and $500 worth of goods.[62]

In 1868, he was appointed as a councilman.[63]

On May 19, 1869 James Hood Bradley died.[64] His wife, Lucilla Stanley Bradley died on September 19, 1908.[65]

William Francis Ferguson Broaddus, D.D.

William Francis Ferguson Broaddus was born April 30, 1801[66] in Caroline County Virginia[67] and he was the pastor of the

---

[56] *The Fredericksburg Artillery* by Robert K. Krick, H.E. Howard Inc. (1986) page 98.

The Appomattox Roster, Antiquarian Press, Ltd., New York (1962).

[57] *The War of the Rebellion: A Compilation of the Official Records of the Union and Confederate Armies*, Series II, Vol. IV, Washington: Government Printing Office (1899) Pages 861, 866.

[58] *History of the City of Fredericksburg, Virginia* by S. J. Quinn, Hermitage Press (1908) page 102.

[59] *Virginia Herald Dispatch*, 16 Apr 1868, 3x2.

[60] *Fredericksburg Ledger*, 22 Oct 1867.

[61] Ibid. 15 Dec 1868.

[62] Ibid. 12 Dec 1865, 4 Dec 1866.

[63] *Virginia Herald Dispatch*, 16 Apr 1868 3x2.

[64] Confederate Cemetery Tombstone Inscription.

[65] Ibid.

[66] *Fredericksburg News*, 13 Aug 1877, 3x5.

[67] *Ancestry World Tree Project*, www.ancestry.com/tree/.

Fredericksburg Baptist Church.[68] He was an Old Line Whig, and conducted a female school in addition to his pastoral work.[69]

He married Mary Ann Farrow October 28, 1819 and they had eight children.[70]

1. Edward Samuel Broaddus, b. ca. 1818
2. Amanda F. Broaddus, b. ca. 1820
3. Mary Louisa Broaddus, b. ca. 1824
4. Thomas E. Broaddus, b. ca. 1830
5. W. H. C. Broaddus, b. ca. 1831
6. Louisa Broaddus, b. ca. 1832
7. Lucy Broaddus, b. ca. 1833
8. John F. Broaddus, b. ca. 1834

In 1824, he was ordained as a minister.[71]

In 1840, he moved to Lexington Kentucky, but returned to Virginia in 1851, and came to Fredericksburg in 1853.[72]

He was married for the second time to Susan Burbridge on July 29, 1851 in Kentucky.[73]

In 1853, he married his third wife, Lucy Ann (Semple) Fleet, the widow of Dr. Charles B. Fleet. She was the daughter of Rev. Robert Baylor Semple, D.D., the founder of Columbian College (George Washington University), and the sister of Robert Baylor Semple, a popular mayor of Fredericksburg[74] who purchased Lewis and Elizabeth (Mills) Wrenn's farm in Spotsylvania County in February 1837.[75]

William and Lucy Broaddus had one child.[76]

1. Lucy Maria Broaddus, b. ca. 1854[77]

---

[68] "The Prison Diary of William F. Broaddus" edited by W. Harrison Daniel, *The Virginia Baptist Register*, No. 21 (1982), Baptist Historical Society, Richmond, Page 998.

[69] *The History of the City of Fredericksburg Virginia* by S.J. Quinn, Hermitage Press, Inc., Richmond, VA (1908) pages 77–79.

[70] *Ancestry World Tree Project*, www.ancestry.com/tree/.

[71] *Works Progress Administration of Virginia Historical Inventory: The M.G. Willis House, Spotsylvania* researched by N.M. Deaderick (May 21, 1937).

[72] Ibid.

[73] *Ancestry World Tree Project*, www.ancestry.com/tree/.

[74] *Star*, 17 Dec 1881, 3x3.

[75] Spotsylvania Deed Book CC, pages 484–485.

[76] Ancestry World Tree Project, www.ancestry.com/tree/.

Living in their household were two children from his wife's earlier marriage to Dr. Charles B. Fleet.[78]

1. Charles Browne Fleet, b. ca. 1843
2. Caroline V. Fleet, b. ca. 1845

William Broaddus became the minister of the Fredericksburg Baptist Church on September 18, 1853.[79]

He established a boarding school for girls in October 1853. The girls were taught "polite" English, literature, the French and Latin languages, etc. as well as the "Ornamental branches." Board, including washing, was $15 per month, and tuition was $30 for the whole term of 10 months. Music was at teacher's prices with no extra charges. Each pupil, however, was to furnish her own books and stationery.[80]

In 1854, while he was pastor of the Fredericksburg Baptist Church, the present church building was erected, and he conducted a successful school for young women in its basement until the war.[81]

On June 7, 1861, his son, John F. Broaddus, enlisted in the Fredericksburg Artillery and was promoted to corporal on April 1, 1862. While he was sick at home, he was captured by the Federal troops on November 9, 1862, but was paroled on the spot, and was eventually exchanged. He returned to duty February 12, 1863. He was paroled at Appomattox on April 9, 1865.[82]

His stepson, Charles Browne Fleet, enlisted in the Fredericksburg Artillery on June 1, 1861. He was promoted to corporal on Oct. 25, 1863, and to sergeant on April 15, 1864. He was paroled at Appomattox. Charles was described as being "absent minded and thoughtless." However, after the war he distinguished himself by inventing Chapstick and the Fleet enema, while he was the

---

[77] 1860 Fredericksburg, Virginia Census.

[78] Ibid.

[79] *Weekly Advertiser*, 17 Sep 1853.

[80] Ibid, 5 Nov 1853.

[81] *Historic Fredericksburg: The Story of an Old Town* by John T. Goolrick, Whittet & Shepperson Richmond VA.

[82] *The Fredericksburg Artillery* by Robert K. Krick, H.E. Howard Inc. (1986) page 98.

The Appomattox Roster, Antiquarian Press, Ltd., New York (1962).

American Civil War Soldiers, Ancestry.com.

proprietor of a drugstore in Lynchburg.[83]

On April 19, 1862, William Broaddus was a member of the committee of six prominent citizens appointed by the town council to confer with Federal authorities concerning the surrender of the town.[84]

William Broaddus was one of the citizens of Fredericksburg who was arrested as a hostage and incarcerated in the Old Capitol Prison in Washington, D.C. in the summer of 1862.[85]

His house survived the Battle of Fredericksburg in December 1862 despite published reports that it had burned.[86]

He left Fredericksburg and served as the pastor of the Charlottesville, (Virginia) Baptist Church from 1862 to 1865.[87]

Between 1860 and 1870, William F. Broaddus' real estate had decreased in value from $4,000 to $3,000, and his personal property had decreased in value from $15,000 to $2,300.[88]

After the war, he was active in an effort to educate the orphans of soldiers[89] and was a member of the International Order of Odd Fellows.[90] During his last several years, he was blind.[91]

William Francis Ferguson Broaddus died September 8, 1876.[92]

---

[83] *The Fredericksburg Artillery* by Robert K. Krick, H.E. Howard Inc. (1986) page 98.

The Appomattox Roster, Antiquarian Press, Ltd., New York (1962).

Green Mount After the War edited by Betsy Fleet, University Press of Virginia, page 16.

[84] "The Prison Diary of William F. Broaddus" edited by W. Harrison Daniel, *The Virginia Baptist Register*, No. 21 (1982), Baptist Historical Society, Richmond, Page 998.

[85] *The War of the Rebellion: A Compilation of the Official Records of the Union and Confederate Armies*, Series II, Vol. IV, Washington: Government Printing Office (1899) Pages 861, 866.

[86] "The Prison Diary of William F. Broaddus" edited by W. Harrison Daniel, *The Virginia Baptist Register*, No. 21 (1982), Baptist Historical Society, Richmond, Page 998.

[87] Ibid.

[88] 1860 & 1870 Virginia Censuses.

[89] *Fredericksburg Ledger*, 18 May 1868.

[90] *Virginia Herald Dispatch*, 4 Apr 1872, 2x6.

[91] *Works Progress Administration of Virginia Historical Inventory: The M.G. Willis House, Spotsylvania* researched by N.M. Deaderick (May 21, 1937).

[92] City Cemetery Tombstone Inscription.

The following year the Fredericksburg Baptist Church placed a marble tablet in his memory to the right of its pulpit. It said, "He was a good man and full of the Holy Ghost and of faith, and much people were added unto the Lord."[93]

On December 12, 1881, Lucy Ann Semple Fleet Broaddus died at the residence of her son, Charles Browne Fleet, in Lynchburg, Virginia.[94]

John Bryce

John Bryce was born in Scotland circa 1805,[95] but lived in Spotsylvania County for many years.[96] He was a farmer.[97]

John and Mary L. (Curtis) Bryce had two children.[98]

1. Helen Mary Bryce, b. ca. 1850
2. William F. Bryce, b. ca. 1851

He bought a farm on the Plank Road near Poplar Spring on Apr. 19, 1842.[99] In 1857 his kitchen, stable, and fodder stacks caught fire and burned. It was thought that the fire was the result of arson. Since he had no insurance, he suffered losses, which amounted to approximately $400.[100]

In 1871, John and his wife Mary were involved in a very messy divorce case. It was brought out in the hearing that he was abusive to his wife and children, squeezing them until they spit blood, and not providing adequate food or support for them. He was living in the home of Martha Ennis (Martha Stephens) at the time of the divorce. Lewis Wrenn was one of the witnesses who testified against him.[101]

John Bryce died in April 1874.[102]

Mary Bryce died at the residence of her son, William, in January

---

[93] *Fredericksburg News*, 13 Aug 1877, 3x5.
[94] *Star*, 17 Dec 1881, 3x3.
  City Cemetery Tombstone Inscription.
[95] 1860 Spotsylvania, Virginia Census.
[96] *Fredericksburg News*, 27 Apr 1874, 2x5.
[97] 1860 Fredericksburg, Virginia Census.
[98] Bryce vs. Bryce, 1871, Fredericksburg Courthouse Annex Basement.
[99] Fredericksburg Deed Book M, Page 260.
[100] *Weekly Advertiser*, Dec. 12, 1857.
[101] Bryce vs. Bryce, 1871, Fredericksburg Courthouse Annex Basement
[102] *Fredericksburg News*, 27 Apr 1874, 2x5.
  Virginia Herald Dispatch, 23 Apr 1874, 2x6.
  Fredericksburg Ledger, 28 Apr. 1874.

1888 after a lingering illness. She was seventy-five years old and was a member of the Methodist Church.[103]

Edwin M. Carter

Edwin M. Carter was a born in Connecticut circa 1807. He was a merchant,[104] and a wealthy shoemaker.[105] He and his wife, Elizabeth, had seven children.[106]

1. John P. Carter, b. ca. 1832
2. Ann J. Carter, b. ca. 1836
3. Edwin Carter, b. ca. 1837
4. Julia M. Carter, b. ca. 1841
5. Mary H. J. Carter, b. ca. 1844
6. William Chauncey Carter, b. ca. 1846
7. Elizabeth E. Carter, b. ca. 1850

On April 22, 1861, Edwin Carter's son, John P. Carter, enlisted in Co. B, 30th Virginia with the rank of sergeant, and was elected lieutenant on April 18, 1862. He was admitted to a Richmond hospital on January 11, 1865. No later military record has been found.[107] Perhaps he was one of the "walking wounded" who was able to escape from the Chimborazo Hospital before Richmond fell.

Another son, William Chauncey Carter enlisted as a musician in the regimental band of the 30th Virginia on August 22, 1863. He was paroled at Appomattox on April 9, 1865.[108]

Edwin Carter was named on the arrest warrant when hostages were taken from Fredericksburg by the Union in the summer of 1862, but he escaped arrest.[109]

After the war, he reopened his shop and advertised that he had for sale "boots, shoes, gaiters...hardware and carpenter's tools."[110]

---

[103] *Star*, 7 Jan. 1888, 3x1.

[104] 1860 Fredericksburg, Virginia Census.

[105] *30th Virginia Infantry* by Robert K. Krick, H.E. Howard, Inc., Publisher (1985) Page 88.

[106] 1850 & 1860 Fredericksburg, Virginia Censuses.

[107] *30th Virginia Infantry* by Robert K. Krick, H.E. Howard, Inc., Publisher (1985) page 88.

[108] Ibid.

[109] *The War of the Rebellion: A Compilation of the Official Records of the Union and Confederate Armies*, Series II, Vol. IV, Washington: Government Printing Office (1899) Page 366.

[110] *Fredericksburg Ledger*, 21 June 1865.

He was a member of the Bible Society,[111] an overseer of the poor,[112] and a member of the Emigration Society, which encouraged Germans to immigrate to Fredericksburg and the surrounding countryside.[113]

John Coakley

John Coakley was born February 14, 1805[114] and was a merchant.[115]

On November 23, 1836, John Coakley married Elizabeth Thom,[116] the daughter of Rauben Triplett and M. Eleanor (Reate) Thom.[117] They had two children.[118]

1. Mary Coakley, b. ca. 1838, d. 7 June 1867[119]
2. Virginia B. Coakley, b. ca. 1846

John Coakley was one of the citizens of Fredericksburg who was arrested as a hostage and incarcerated in the Old Capitol Prison in Washington, D.C. in the summer of 1862.[120]

Between 1860 and 1870, John Coakley's real estate decreased in value from $11,350 to $8,000, and his personal property had decreased from in value from $29,300 to $3,200.[121]

After the war he was a member of the Bible Society,[122] and a vestryman at St. George's Church.[123] He was elected a justice of the peace in July 1865.[124] The following week the Fredericksburg Ledger printed an article complaining that no steps had been taken to put the Gas Works in order, and that the people of Fredericksburg should

---

[111] *Fredericksburg News*, 22 Jan 1874.

[112] Ibid, 1 Jul 1875, 3x5.

[113] *Fredericksburg Ledger*, 15 Dec 1868.

[114] St. George's Cemetery Tombstone Inscription.

[115] 1860 Fredericksburg, Virginia Census.

[116] Virginia Marriage Register.

[117] *Ancestry World Tree Project*, www.ancestry.com/tree/.

[118] 1850 & 1860 Fredericksburg, Virginia Censuses.

[119] St. George's Cemetery Tombstone Inscription.

[120] *The War of the Rebellion: A Compilation of the Official Records of the Union and Confederate Armies*, Series II, Vol. IV, Washington: Government Printing Office (1899) Pages 366, 376, 861, 866.

[121] 1860 & 1870 Virginia Censuses.

[122] *Virginia Herald Dispatch*, 1 Jan 1872, 3x3.

[123] Ibid. 8 Apr 1872, 3x2.

[124] *Fredericksburg Ledger*, 20 Jul 1865.

harass the officials day and night until something was done. John Coakley was listed as one of the officials.[125]

In June 1874, the Virginia Herald Dispatch reported that John Coakley had been confined to his room with sickness for some months.[126]

John Coakley died on July 2, 1874[127] at the age of 69. His obituary said that he was "among our old and most respected citizens...He had long been confined to his room, and his suffering was great, but which he bore with Christian resignation."[128]

On March 11, 1890 Elizabeth Thom Coakley died at the age of 80.[129]

James H. Cooke

James H. Cooke was a druggist who was born circa 1796 in Dumfries, Virginia.[130] He opened the largest drug store, perhaps south of the Potomac River,[131] in Fredericksburg around 1824.[132]

He was an Old Line Whig and a prominent member of the Episcopal Church.[133]

He was also a member of the Phrenological Society,[134] and in 1857, he served as vice president of the American Pharma-cute-ical [sic] Association.[135] In his drug store, he sold "a general supply of carefully selected Drugs, Chemicals, Pharmaceutical Preparations, English, French, and American Surgical Instruments, Druggist's Glassware, English, French, German and American Perfumery, Fancy articles, Dyes and Dye-Stuffs, Paints, Oils, and Varnishes, Pine Oil

---

[125] Ibid. 27 Jul 1865.

[126] *Virginia Herald Dispatch*, 11 Jun 1874, 3x5.

[127] St. George's Cemetery Tombstone Inscription.

[128] *Fredericksburg Ledger*, 10 Jul 1874.

[129] St. George's Cemetery Tombstone Inscription.

[130] 1860 Fredericksburg, Virginia Census.
Fredericksburg, Virginia Death Record.

[131] *The History of the City of Fredericksburg Virginia* by S.J. Quinn, Hermitage Press, Inc., Richmond, VA (1908) page 79.

[132] *Fredericksburg Civil War Sites: April 1861–November 1862* by Noel G. Harrison, H.E. Howard, Inc. (1995) page 54.

[133] *The History of the City of Fredericksburg* Virginia by S.J. Quinn, Hermitage Press, Inc., Richmond, VA (1908) page 79.

[134] *Virginia Herald Dispatch*, 8 Jan 1834, 3x3.

[135] *Weekly Advertiser*, 19 Sep 1857.

and Burning Fluid Lamps, &c."[136]

On July 13, 1826, he married Emily M. Pearson,[137] the daughter of William Pearson.[138] They had two children.[139]

1. Robert R. Cooke, b. ca. 1827
2. Larkin S. Cooke, b. ca. 1832

Emily M. (Pearson) Cooke died at the age of 33 of pulmonary consumption on July 1, 1832.[140]

James Cooke was one of the Fredericksburg citizens arrested as a hostage and incarcerated in the Old Capitol Prison in Washington, D.C. in the summer of 1862.[141]

Between 1861 and 1863 Confederate troops purchased more than $10,000 worth of morphia, [sic.] pulverized ipecac, "blue mass," chloroform, and other supplies from Cooke's Drugstore.[142]

During the Battle of Fredericksburg in December 1862, Federal troops from the 118th Pennsylvania broke into Cooke's Drugstore, ransacked the store, and smashed glassware.[143]

In June 1865, he reopened his drug store in Fredericksburg.[144]

Between 1860 and 1870, James Cooke's real estate decreased in value from $4,500 to 0, and his personal property decreased in value from $3,250 to $1,000.[145]

After the war, he served as a vestryman at St. George's Church,[146] and was a mason.[147]

James H. Cooke died in Fredericksburg of lung disease on

---

[136] *Christian Banner*, 6 Sep 1850 4x2.

[137] Fredericksburg Marriage Register.

[138] *Virginia Herald Dispatch*, 4 Jul 1832, 3x2.

[139] 1850 & 1860 Fredericksburg, Virginia Censuses.

[140] *Virginia Herald Dispatch*, 4 Jul 1832, 3x2.
St. George's Cemetery Tombstone Inscription.

[141] *The War of the Rebellion: A Compilation of the Official Records of the Union and Confederate Armies*, Series II, Vol. IV, Washington: Government Printing Office (1899) Pages 366, 376, 861, 866.

[142] *Fredericksburg Civil War Sites: April 1861–November 1862* by Noel G. Harrison, H.E. Howard, Inc. (1995) page 54.

[143] *History of the Corn Exchange Regiment* by J.L. Smith, Philadelphia (1888).

[144] *Fredericksburg Ledger*, 10 June 1865.

[145] 1860 & 1870 Virginia Censuses.

[146] *Virginia Herald Dispatch*, 8 Apr 1872, 3x2.

[147] *Fredericksburg Ledger*, 15 Aug 1873.

August 10, 1873.[148] He was 78 years old. His obituary said, "He was a diligent and consistent member of the Episcopal Church and in all the relations of life was beloved and respected."[149]

Abraham Cox

Abraham Cox was born circa 1811 in Stafford County Virginia, and he was a tailor,[150] a Breckinridge Democrat,[151] and a Methodist.[152]

On April 27, 1836, he married Ariana Caldwell,[153] and they had four children.[154]

    1. Morgan M. Cox, born ca. 1840, d. 29 May 1865[155]

    2. Richard Cox, born ca. 1848

    3. Robert C. Cox, born ca. 1850

    4. Annie D. Cox, born ca. 1853

On January 26, 1858, Ariana Caldwell Cox died.[156]

Abraham Cox's son, Morgan M. Cox, enlisted in Co. C, 30th VA on May 23, 1861 with the rank of corporal. He was later promoted to sergeant. On April 1, 1865, during the Battle of Five Forks, he was captured and sent to Point Lookout. He died of chronic dysentery, and he was buried there on May 29, 1865. It was over a month and a half after Lee's surrender.[157]

Abraham Cox was one of the citizens of Fredericksburg who was arrested as a hostage and incarcerated in the Old Capitol Prison in

---

[148] Fredericksburg, Virginia Death Record.

[149] *Fredericksburg Ledger*, 12 Aug 1873.

[150] *Star*, 29 Dec 1897, 3x2.

[151] *The History of the City of Fredericksburg Virginia* by S.J. Quinn, The Hermitage Press, Inc., Richmond, VA (1908) Page 79.

[152] *Steward's Book* of the Fredericksburg Methodist Church.

[153] Fredericksburg, Virginia Marriage Register.

[154] 1860 Fredericksburg Virginia Census.

[155] *30th Virginia Infantry* by Robert K. Krick, H.E. Howard, Inc., Publisher (1985) Page 92.
Fredericksburg Ledger, 21 June 1865.

[156] *Fredericksburg News*, 4 Feb. 1858, 2x6.

[157] *30th Virginia Infantry* by Robert K. Krick, H.E. Howard, Inc., Publisher (1985) Page 92.
Fredericksburg Ledger, 21 June 1865.

Washington, D.C. in the summer of 1862.[158]

He was arrested again as a hostage by the Union troops in May 1864, and sent to Fort Delaware Prison.[159]

Between 1860 and 1870, his real estate decreased in value from $5,200 to $3,000, and his personal property decreased in value from $2,000 to $300.[160]

After the war, he did not resume his business as a tailor.[161]

In June of 1871, he was one of twenty-nine men from Fredericksburg who was taken to Richmond to serve on the jury in the Chahoon case.[162]

Abraham Cox died in on December 28, 1897. He was 86 years old. For some time before his death, he had been in feeble health. The newspaper said that he was the oldest white citizen in Fredericksburg, and had been a member of the Methodist Church for sixty years.[163] He was the last survivor of the hostages who were sent to the Old Capitol Prison in 1862.[164]

Milton Lowry Dudley

Milton Lowry Dudley was born on January 27, 1843 in Pulaski, Bedford County, Virginia. He was the son of Nathaniel M. and Mary Ann (Staten) Dudley, and a descendent of Governor Thomas Dudley of Massachusetts through his oldest son, Samuel.[165]

He enlisted in the 29th Virginia, Company H on April 2, 1862 as a sergeant. He deserted in April 1863, but he was returned.[166] He was

---

[158] *The War of the Rebellion: A Compilation of the Official Records of the Union and Confederate Armies*, Series II, Vol. IV, Washington: Government Printing Office (1899) Pages 366, 376, 861, 866.

[159] *History of the City of Fredericksburg, Virginia* by S. J. Quinn, Hermitage Press (1908) page 102.

[160] 1860 & 1870 Virginia Censuses.

[161] *Star*, 29 Dec 1897, 3x2.

[162] *Virginia Herald Dispatch*, 22 Jun 1871, 3x2.

[163] *Star*, 29 Dec 1897, 3x2.

[164] *History of the City of Fredericksburg, Virginia* by S. J. Quinn, Hermitage Press (1908) page 80.
Star, 29 Dec 1897, 3x2.

[165] *History of the Dudley Family* by Dean Dudley, Montrose, Mass. (1894) page 474.

[166] *29th Virginia Infantry* by John Perry Alderman, H.E. Howard, Inc. (1989) Page 102.

sent to the Chimborazo Hospital in Richmond with malaria on September 25, 1864, the same day that John Kobler Wrenn was sent there with malaria.[167] He was furloughed for 60 days on October 7, 1864, but was still absent sick in December.[168]

He was married on January 28, 1869 to Martha America Foster in Bedford County, Virginia.[169] They had five children.[170]

1. Mary E. Dudley, b. 17 Mar 1869[171]
2. Willie A. Dudley, b. ca. 1873
3. Ada Frances Dudley, b. 14 Sep 1876,[172] d. 14 Sep 1837,[173] m. Charles Adam Hamaker[174]
    i. William Edward Hamaker, b. 7 Dec 1897, d. Sep 1966,[175] m. Ruth Melchoir
    ii. Katurah Ann Hamaker, b. 7 Dec 1902,[176] d. ca. 1953, m. John Thomas Bass
    iii. Charles Lester Hamaker, b. 12 Oct. 1902, d. Dec 1967,[177] m. Louise Tappan
    iv. Grace Beatrice Hamaker, b. 16 Sep 1906,[178] d. after 1980, m. Frank Marion Sholes
    v. Samuel Russell Hamaker, b. 5 Dec 1908, d. Mar 1980,[179] m Elsie Stublen
    vi. Evelyn Mae Hamaker, b. 15 Aug 1817,[180] d. 9 Dec 1972,[181] m. 18 July 1933 Harry Underwood Mesic[182]

---

[167] Confederate Service Records for Milton L. Dudley and John K. Wrenn.
[168] *29th Virginia Infantry* by John Perry Alderman, H.E. Howard, Inc. (1989 Page 102.
[169] Bedford County Marriage Register.
[170] 1880 Bedford County, Virginia Census.
[171] Bedford County Virginia Birth Register.
[172] Franklin County, Virginia Birth Register.
[173] Virginia Death Certificate.
[174] Ibid.
[175] Social Security Death Index.
[176] Virginia Birth Certificate.
[177] Social Security Death Index.
[178] Virginia Birth Certificate.
[179] Social Security Death Index.
[180] Virginia Birth Certificate.
[181] Virginia Death Certificate.
[182] Virginia Marriage Certificate.

    1. Harry Randolph Mesic, b. 30 Dec 1935,[183] m. 18
Mar 1956 Harriet Lee Bey (author of this book)[184]
    2. Steven Dudley Mesic, b. 21 Nov 1947,[185] m. (1) 2
May 1968 Charlotte Butler (2) 11 July 1980
Minessa Lynn Phernetton
    4. Samuel E. Dudley, b. 15 Sep 1878,[186] d. Feb 1964[187]
    5. Nanie Dudley, b. 11 May 1883[188]

He applied for a Confederate disability pension on April 17,
1905 due to rheumatism.[189] He was granted the pension on December
7, 1905.[190]

He was still receiving the pension in 1912.[191]

He died sometime between the 1912 and the 1920 census.

Henry Ebert

Henry Ebert was born in Prussia circa 1833.[192] He immigrated to the
United States from Germany in 1854 after drawing the 'lucky ticket,'
which guaranteed his exemption him from the German Army.[193] For a
short time, he managed a farm for a fellow compatriot, and probably a
relative of his wife, named Lange. In 1858, he opened a grocery store
in his home. It was located on the southeast corner of the Sunken
Road and Mercer Street.[194]

---

[183] Virginia Birth Certificate.

[184] Virginia Marriage Certificate.

[185] Virginia Birth Certificate.

[186] Bedford County Birth Register.

[187] Social Security Death Index.

[188] Bedford County Birth Register.

[189] "Application of Soldier, Sailor, or Marine for Disability by Reason of
Disease or the Infirmities of Age".

[190] Botetourt County, Virginia Court Record.

[191] Roster of Confederate Pensioners of Virginia, January 1, 1912 and
October 1, 1912.

[192] 1860 Fredericksburg, Virginia Census.

[193] *Works Progress Administration of Virginia, Historical Inventory: Battle
House* by N.M. Deaderick (Jan 25, 1938).

[194] *Star*, 24 Nov 1896, 3x3.
*Works Progress Administration of Virginia, Historical Inventory: Battle
House* by N.M. Deaderick (Jan 25, 1938).
Fredericksburg Deed Book S, Page 385.

Henry and Sophia (Lange) Ebert had four daughters.[195]
1. Anna Ebert, b. ca. 1855, m. John Pfaff
2. Doretta Ebert, b. ca. 1857
3. Mary Ebert, b. ca. 1859, d. 1941
4. Louisa Ebert, b. 1868, m. C.L. Franklin

Henry Ebert was the one of the few people in Fredericksburg whose property actually increased in value between 1860 and 1870. His real estate increased in value from $800 to $1000, and his personal estate increased in value from $200 to $500.[196]

In April 1873, he applied for, and he was granted, a license to operate an ordinary (tavern).[197]

After an illness of five-week duration, Henry Ebert died in November 1896 at the age of 64.[198]

Henry Ebert's wife, Sophia, died in January 1913 after a lingering illness. She was 82 years old.[199]

On the death of Sophia Ebert, their property was left to Henry and Sophia's two unmarried daughters, Mary and Doretta.[200]

John A. English

John A. English was born September 4, 1819[201] in Fauquier County, and moved to Fredericksburg in 1840.[202] He was a member of the Methodist Church.[203]

On May 20, 1841, he married Judith B. Jones. She was the ward of Stiles P. Curtis,[204] who was listed in John English's household on the 1860 census.[205] John and Judith English never had any children.[206]

John English owned a hardware store and worked as a plumber

---

[195] *Fredericksburg Star*, 24 Nov 1896, 3x3.

[196] 1860 & 1870 Fredericksburg Virginia Censuses.

[197] *Virginia Herald Dispatch*, 17 Apr. 1873, 3x2.

[198] *Star*, 24 Nov 1896, 3x3.

[199] *Star*, 6 Jan 1913, 3x2.

[200] *Works Progress Administration of Virginia, Historical Inventory: Battle House* by N.M. Deaderick (Jan 25, 1938).

[201] Tombstone Inscription, City Cemetery.

[202] *Star*, 15 Oct 1892, 3x4.

[203] *Methodist Episcopal Church, Fredericksburg Records, 1834–1852.* Virginia State Library.

[204] Fredericksburg Virginia Marriage Register.

[205] 1860 Fredericksburg, Virginia Census.

[206] *Star*, 15 Oct 1892, 3x4.

and a tinner.[207] An advertisement for his store said that he sold "Nos. 1 and 2 common furniture, flooring, coach, body, leather, and brown Japan."[208] He also sold locks, hinges, table and pocket cutlery, coach findings of every description, viz. springs, axles, hubs, and spokes, and saddlery hardware, viz. stirrup irons, bridle bits, webbing, etc., and a good assortment of housekeeping articles.[209]

On December 10, 1849, John English sold Lewis Wrenn a hardware business, the stock in trade, and tools consisting of: tin, lead, iron, and other metallic wares and material, and tools for the sum of $655.00.[210] Lewis Wrenn operated a store at "English's Old Stand,"[211] but John English continued to run a hardware business at another location until the war.[212]

On November 18, 1852, John English gave a deposition corroborating Lewis Wrenn's testimony in the Parker vs. Wrenn lawsuit.[213]

During the war he was in the quartermaster's department of the Confederate army.[214]

After the war, John English became a real estate agent,[215] a member of the Odd Fellows,[216] and a member of Ruggles Grange.[217]

He ran unsuccessfully for town council and magistrate in 1872.[218]

To help the Presbyterian Church raise money for a library for their Sunday school, he served on a committee to arrange an excursion to Richmond in 1875.[219]

He was elected a magistrate in 1876,[220] and served on the

---

[207] Ibid.

[208] *Christian Banner*, 6 Sep 1850, 5x3.

[209] *Fredericksburg News*, 2 Jan 1852.

[210] Fredericksburg Deed Book P, Pages 380–382.

[211] *Fredericksburg News*, 2 Jan 1852, 4x5.

[212] *Star*, 15 Oct 1892, 3x4.

[213] Parker vs. Wrenn, Fredericksburg Courthouse Annex Basement.

[214] *Star*, 15 Oct 1892, 3x4.

[215] *Virginia Herald Dispatch*, 3 Jan 1870, 3x6.

[216] Ibid. 17 Feb. 1870, 2x5.

[217] Ibid. 13 Dec 1875, 3x1.

[218] Ibid. 27 May 1872, 3x1.

[219] Ibid. 26 Jul 1875, 2x6.

[220] Ibid. 29 May 1876, 3x1.

Railroad Committee in 1877.[221] He was elected an officer in the Odd Fellows in 1880.[222]

His wife, Judith B. Jones English, died July 17, 1885 at the age of 65.[223]

He died from a stroke[224] on October 13, 1892.[225] His obituary said he was "a prominent and well-to-do citizen."[226]

Beverly T. Gill

Beverly T. Gill was born in May 1807,[227] and was a master tailor,[228] an Old Line Whig, and a prominent member of the Presbyterian Church.[229] He and his wife, Emily E., had no children.[230]

He was one of the citizens of Fredericksburg arrested as a hostage and incarcerated in the Old Capitol Prison in Washington, D.C. in the summer of 1862.[231]

After the war, he served on the town council,[232] and reopened his tailoring shop. He advertised that he had "...an elegant assortment of Gentlemen's Clothing and Furnishing Goods, of the best quality, and made in the best style..."[233]

Somewhere around 1870, he moved to Baltimore, Maryland where he died at the age of 70 in August 1876. His obituary says "...he was appreciated for the high qualities that made him friends in every community where he was known."[234]

---

[221] *Fredericksburg News,* 23 Apr 1877, 3x4.

[222] *Star,* 7 Jan. 1880, 3x2.

[223] Ibid, 22 Jul 1885, 2x6.

[224] Ibid, 15 Oct 1892, 3x4.

[225] City Cemetery Tombstone Inscription.

[226] *Star,* 15 Oct 1892, 3x4.

[227] *Virginia Herald Dispatch,* 14 Aug 1876, 3x1.

[228] 1860 Fredericksburg, Virginia Census.

[229] *The History of the City of Fredericksburg Virginia* by S.J. Quinn, Hermitage Press, Inc., Richmond, VA (1908) pages 77–79.

[230] 1860 Fredericksburg, Virginia Census.

[231] *The War of the Rebellion: A Compilation of the Official Records of the Union and Confederate Armies,* Series II, Vol. IV, Washington: Government Printing Office (1899) Pages 861, 866.

[232] *Fredericksburg Ledger,* 20 Jul 1865.

[233] Ibid, 29 Sep 1865.

[234] *Virginia Herald Dispatch,* 14 Aug 1876, 3x1.

Isaac William Kerr Handy

Isaac William Kerr Handy was born 14 December 1815 in Washington D.C., which at that time was a part of Somerset County, Maryland.[235] He was a Presbyterian minister.

He was married at least three times.

He was arrested on 20 July 1863 in Sussex County, Delaware after saying at a dinner party the previous month in Delaware City, Delaware, that he no longer felt any loyalty to the American flag.[236]

He was taken to Fort Delaware Prison and was incarcerated there until October 13, 1864.[237]

After being released from prison, he went to Augusta County, Virginia to live, and was living there when he published his diary.[238]

He was married (1) to Mary Jane Rozelle Purnell on 29 October 1839. She was born December 20, 1821 in Queponco,[239] Worcester County, Maryland. They had at least three children.

    1. Frederick Alegernon Graham Handy, b. 22 March 1842.[240]

    2. M. Virginia P. Handy b. 18 August year unknown,[241] m. Unknown Young on 8 April 1864[242]

    3. Moses P. Handy[243] b. ca. 1847

Isaac Handy was married (2) to Sarah Selby Martin on 7 June 1850. She was born 19 April 1819 in Philadelphia, Pennsylvania[244]

---

[235] *Ancestry World Tree Project*, www.ancestry.com/tree/.233.

United States Bonds, or Duress by Federal Authority: A Journal of Current Events During an Imprisonment of Fifteen months, at Fort Delaware by Isaac W. K. Handy, D.D., Baltimore: Turnbull Brothers (1874). Pages 4–11.

[236] Ibid, Pages 602–604.

[237] Ibid, Title Page.

[238] *Ancestry World Tree Project*, www.ancestry.com/tree/.

[239] *United States Bonds, or Duress by Federal Authority: A Journal of Current Events During an Imprisonment of Fifteen months, at Fort Delaware* by Isaac W. K. Handy, D.D., Baltimore: Turnbull Brothers (1874). Pages 431, 573, 585, 593, 611.

[240] Ibid. Pages 71, 104, 212, 258.

[241] Ibid. Page 293.

[242] Ibid. Pages 4, 123, 239, 257, 312, 605.

[243] *Ancestry World Tree Project*, www.ancestry.com/tree/.

[244] *Ibid.*

United States Bonds, or Duress by Federal Authority: A Journal of Current Events During an Imprisonment of Fifteen months, at Fort

and apparently died before 1855.

They had at least one child.

> 4. James Henry Martin Handy, b. 4 August 1851 in Snow Hill, Maryland[245]

Isaac Handy was married (3) on 6 December 1855 to a daughter of John D. Dilworth.[246] They had at least six children

> 5. Gertrude E. Handy[247]
>
> 6. Lillie Handy[248]
>
> 7. Dilworth Handy, d. 20 October 1862.[249]
>
> 8. Egbert Handy[250]
>
> 9. Charley Handy[251]
>
> 10. Loulie Handy[252]

Isaac William K. Handy died 17 June 1878 in Somerset County, Maryland.[253]

James A. Jennings

James A. Jennings was born circa 1828,[254] and was a gunsmith, locksmith, and a bell hanger.[255]

On November 7, 1850, he married Lucretia Long[256] and they had four children.[257]

> 1. Mary A. Jennings, b. ca. 1854
>
> 2. John J. Jennings, b. ca. 1857
>
> 3. Desdemona Jennings, b. ca. 1858
>
> 4. Eliza Jennings, b. ca. 1860

His house burned during the Battle of Fredericksburg in

Delaware by Isaac W. K. Handy, D.D., Baltimore: Turnbull Brothers (1874) Pages 4, 605.

[245] Ibid, Page 234.

[246] Ibid, Page 8.

[247] Ibid, Pages 123, 191, 193, 230, 244, 453, 605.

[248] Ibid, Page 265, 605.

[249] Ibid, Pages 72, 182.

[250] Ibid, Page 605.

[251] Ibid, Pages 72, 605.

[252] Ibid, Pages 10, 605.

[253] *Ancestry World Tree Project*, www.ancestry.com/tree/.

[254] 1860 Fredericksburg, VA Census.

[255] *Weekly Advertiser*, 10 Jan 1857.

[256] Virginia Marriage Register.

[257] 1860 Fredericksburg, Virginia Census.

December 1862.[258]

He sold his property in 1863 to Dorothea Heinichen, who bought a number of pieces of property in Fredericksburg between April 1863 and August 1868, as did other members of the Heinichen family.[259]

In December 1869, he built a new frame home on Main Street.[260]

When he died in June 1876, he was the last of the Mexican War volunteers in Fredericksburg, who went out in 1846 in Col. Hamtramck's Regiment.[261]

Thomas Fitzhugh Knox, Jr.

Thomas Fitzhugh Knox was born circa 1808 at Windsor Lodge, in Culpeper County, Virginia.[262] He was a miller,[263] who won awards for the quality of his flour,[264] a large wheat speculator, flour manufacturer, an Old Line Whig, and a prominent member of the Episcopal Church.[265] He moved to Fredericksburg in 1821.[266]

In May 1832, he married Virginia A. Soutter[267] and they had ten children.[268]

    1. Virginia Soutter Knox, b. 11 Jul 1835, d. 27 Dec 1910[269]

    2. Robert Taylor Knox, b. 1837, d. 1915[270]

    3. Thomas S. Knox, b. ca. 1839

    4. James Soutter Knox, b. 2 Feb 1842, d. 30 May 1909[271]

---

[258] 1865 Fredericksburg Tax Records.

[259] Fredericksburg Deed Book T, Page 380.

[260] *Fredericksburg Ledger*, 31 Dec 1869.

[261] *Virginia Herald Dispatch*, 5 Jun 1876, 3x2.

[262] *Star*, 25 June 1880, 3x1.

[263] 1860 Fredericksburg, Virginia Census.

[264] *Weekly Advertiser*, 26 Nov 1853.

[265] *The History of the City of Fredericksburg Virginia* by S.J. Quinn, Hermitage Press, Inc., Richmond, VA (1908) pages 77–79.

[266] *Star*, 25 June 1880, 3x1.

[267] *Virginia Herald Dispatch*, 30 May 1832, 3x3.

[268] 1860 Fredericksburg, Virginia Census.
  Fredericksburg News, 4 Apr 1851, 3x1.
  Ibid. 12 Feb 1857, 2x5.

[269] Confederate Cemetery Tombstone Inscription.

[270] Ibid.

[271] Ibid.

   5. Samuel Gordon Knox, b. ca. 1844
   6. Alexander Bell Knox, b. ca. 1845, d. Aug 1870[272]
   7. Douglas H. Knox, b. July 1847, d. Feb 1914, m. Loula
      Brockenbrough[273]
   8. Charles Faulconer Knox, b. ca. 1851, d. Apr 1851[274]
   9. Mary Campbell Knox, b. 19 Jan 1852, d. 10 Mar 1923, m.
      William Eustace Moncure[275]
   10. Edward Maxwell Knox, d. Feb 1857[276]

Before the war, Thomas Knox served on the city council.[277]

Five of his sons served in the Confederate Army.

On April 22, 1861, his son, Robert Taylor Knox, enlisted in Company B, 30th Virginia with the rank of Sergeant. On February 14, 1862, he reenlisted in Company C, 30th Virginia as a Private. He was elected Lieutenant on April 15, 1862, and a full sergeant major on July 15, 1862. From January 16, 1865 until April 4, 1865, he commanded Company C.[278]

On April 22, 1861, his son, James Soutter Knox, enlisted in Company B, 30th Virginia with the rank of Sergeant. He was elected Lieutenant on April 15, 1862, and made commander of Company B from September 1862 until the end of the war, although his commission as captain did not reach him until March 14, 1865.[279]

Both James Soutter Knox and Robert Taylor Knox were taken as prisoners of war at Sayler's Creek on April 6, 1865. Robert Taylor Knox was released from Johnson's Island Prison on June 1, 1865 and James Soutter Knox was released from Johnson's Island Prison on June 18, 1865.[280]

A third son, Thomas S. Knox enlisted in Company B, 30th Virginia as a private on May 8, 1861. On June 13, 1861, he was

---

[272] *Virginia Herald Dispatch,* 29 Aug 1870, 2x6.

[273] Confederate Cemetery Tombstone Inscription.

[274] *Fredericksburg News,* 4 Apr 1851, 3x1.

[275] Confederate Cemetery Tombstone Inscription.

[276] *Fredericksburg News,* 12 Feb 1857, 2x5.

[277] *Weekly Advertiser,* 26 Mar 1853.

[278] *30th Virginia Infantry* by Robert K. Krick, H.E. Howard, Inc., Publisher (1985) Page 109.

American Civil War Soldiers, Ancestry.com.

[279] *30th Virginia Infantry* by Robert K. Krick, H.E. Howard, Inc., Publisher (1985) Page 108.

[280] Ibid, Pages 108–109.

appointed sergeant major of the regiment, and then on July 15, 1861 he was elected lieutenant of Company A. On October 10, 1861, he was appointed captain and commissary for the 30th Virginia. In April 1862, he was permanently replaced and his connection with the 30th Virginia was never renewed. He served as post commissary in Danville where he was accused of irregularities in his impressments of flour, but a court martial cleared and reinstated him. He was soon relieved of duty and sent to Petersburg. On September 10, 1864, he left from Fredericksburg, and on the 12th, he crossed the Potomac River. He was accused of defalcation and embezzlement of a large amount of money.[281]

A fourth son, Samuel Gordon Knox, enlisted as a private in Company B, 30th Virginia on March 1, 1864. He was hospitalized with malaria in October 1864, and was furloughed from the hospital on January 28, 1865. There are no further military records of him.[282]

A fifth son, Alexander Bell Knox, enlisted as a private in Company C, 30th Virginia on March 16, 1864. He was wounded in the left leg at Dinwiddie Court House on March 31, 1865. On April 11, 1865, he was paroled at Farmville, VA, but was still being treated in military hospitals until the next month.[283]

Thomas Fitzhugh Knox was one of the citizens of Fredericksburg who was arrested as a hostage and incarcerated in the Old Capitol Prison in Washington, D.C. in the summer of 1862.[284]

He was arrested again as a hostage by the Union troops in May 1864, but was released after he was taken to Washington, D.C.[285]

After the war, he served on the town council,[286] was a vestryman at St. George's Church,[287] and was a member of Ruggles

[281] Ibid, Page 109.

[282] Ibid.

[283] Ibid. Page 108.

[284] The War of the Rebellion: A Compilation of the Official Records of the Union and Confederate Armies, Series II, Vol. IV, Washington: Government Printing Office (1899) Pages 861, 866.

[285] *History of the City of Fredericksburg, Virginia* by S. J. Quinn, Hermitage Press (1908) page 102.

[286] *Fredericksburg Ledger,* 20 Jul 1865.
Virginia Herald Dispatch, 16 Apr 1868, 3x2.
Star, 24 May 1879, 3x1..

[287] *Virginia Herald Dispatch,* 8 Apr 1872, 3x2.

Grange.[288]

Between 1860 and 1870, Thomas Knox's real estate had decreased in value from $50,000 to $8,000 and his personal property decreased in value from $22,500 to $500.[289]

Thomas Fitzhugh Knox died in June 1880 at the age of 83.[290]

John Kobler

John Kobler was born in Culpeper County, Virginia on August 29, 1768. He joined the Methodist Episcopal Church on December 6, 1786, and began his work as a Methodist minister on October 3, 1789. He was described as being rather tall and slender, and having a serene look, and a baldhead.

On February 22, 1809 he married Mary Newman, a widow from Madison County, Virginia. They had no children.

John Kobler bought land in Spotsylvania County on February 13, 1817, and his wife bought property in Fredericksburg in 1822.

After moving to Fredericksburg, where he was affectionately known as Father Kobler, he became active in the Fredericksburg Branch of the American Colonization Society. Although his wife owned slaves, he was opposed to slavery, and educated her slaves in preparation for their being freed and sent to Liberia. They were freed upon her death.[291]

Eliza Pilcher was a witness to his will in 1841.[292]

On July 26, 1843, John Kobler died "with glory on his lips." He was buried under the pulpit of the Fredericksburg Methodist Church on Hanover Street.[293]

John Lawrence Marye

John Lawrence Marye was born February 9, 1798 in

---

[288] Ibid. 13 Dec 1875, 3x1.

[289] 1860 & 1870 Fredericksburg Virginia Censuses.

[290] *Star,* 25 June 1880, 3x1.

[291] *John Kobler's Dream: A History of the Fredericksburg United Methodist Church 1802−1975* by John Janney Johnson, Whittet & Shepperson, Richmond, Virginia (1976) pages 14−25.

[292] Will of John Kobler, Virginia Archives, Richmond, Virginia.

[293] *John Kobler's Dream: A History of the Fredericksburg United Methodist Church 1802−*1975 by John Janney Johnson, Whittet & Shepperson, Richmond, Virginia (1976) Page 14.

Fredericksburg, Virginia. He was a lawyer,[294] and served in the war of 1812.[295] He married Anne Marie Burton in Albemarle County on October 16, 1816. They had fourteen children.[296]

1. James Braxton Marye, b. 4 Mar 1818, m. 25 Nov 1840 Jane Christian Jett
2. Robert Burton Marye, b. 1819, d. 25 May 1881, m. Jane Waller
3. Lawrence Slaughter Marye, b. 1821, d. May 1831[297]
4. John Lawrence Marye, Jr., b. Nov 1823, m. 29 Oct 1846 Mildred Stone Browne
5. Susan Evelyn Marye, b. 12 Jan 1825, d. 9 Sep 1826
6. Susan F. Marye, b. 17 Mar 1827, d. 29 Apr 1835
7. Alfred James Marye, b. 14 Jan 1830, d. 7 Jul 1830
8. Morton Wayne Marye, b. 7 Sep 1831, m. Homoisel Voss
9. Lawrence Slaughter Marye, b. Oct 1834, m. Maria Willia Wilson
10. Edward Avonmore Marye, b. 20 Feb 1835, d. 5 Oct 1864
11. Anne Marie Marye, b. ca. 1838, m. Robert Dabney
12. Charles Bonnycastle Marye, b. Mar 1840, d. 31 Dec 1912
13. Alexander Stuart Marye, b. 31 Jan 1841, d. 18 Dec 1915, m. Margueretta Tilghman
14. Evelyn Marye, b. Mar 1844

John Lawrence Marye was a successful lawyer in his early life and a farmer and flour merchant in his later life. He was also active in public service.

Sometime after 1821, he built Brompton. Originally, it had a rectangular shape, but later wings and a porch were added giving it a graceful appearance.[298]

In February 1829, he was elected vice-president of the Fredericksburg Colonization Society,[299] an organization that worked to have all slaves freed. They were taught a trade so they could support their families and themselves, and then sent to Liberia where

---

[294] 1850 & 1860 Fredericksburg, Virginia Censuses.
[295] *Star*, 19 Jan 1884, 3x2.
[296] *Ancestry World Tree Project*, www.ancestry.com/tree/.
[297] Virginia Herald Dispatch, 11 May 1831, 3x2.
[298] "Brompton: Front Door of the Battle" by Donald C. Pfanz, www.fredericksburg.com/CivilWar/Battle/0721CW.
[299] *Virginia Herald Dispatch*, 25 Feb 1829, 3x3.

they could start a new life.

In 1831, tragedy struck his family when two of his children died within a week of each other, 10-year-old Lawrence Slaughter Marye,[300] and 4-year-old Susan Evelyn Marye.[301]

His wife, Anne Marie Marye died in November 1858.[302]

Before the war, he opened a flourmill, from which he was able to supply the people of Fredericksburg with flour during and after the war, helping them to survive.[303]

John Marye was a delegate to the state convention and helped to defeat a resolution to present Virginia voters with an ordinance of secession in March 1861. In April 1861, he joined the majority of delegates in approving an identical resolution, after President Lincoln called for 75,000 militiamen to force the seceded state back into the Union.[304]

He hoped that the North and South would settle their differences peacefully, but, after all peace efforts were exhausted, he joined a majority of other delegates in reluctantly voting the state out of the Union.[305]

At the outbreak of the war, he controlled 780 acres of land: 300 acres improved, and 480 acres unimproved. He owned at least 14 slaves[306] and hired three slaves, including a 13-year-old, mulatto female belonging to Lewis Wrenn.[307]

His son, Edward Avonmore 'Ned' Marye enlisted in the Fredericksburg Artillery on May 13, 1861 with the rank of lieutenant. Two days after the Battle of Sharpsburg (Antietam), his bay mare valued at $350 was killed at Shepherdstown. Charles B. Fleet (Rev.

---

[300] Ibid, 11 May 1831, 3x2.

[301] Ibid, 4 May 1831, 3x.

[302] *Fredericksburg News*, 30 Nov 1858, 3x1.
   Virginia Herald Dispatch, 15 Dec 1858, 3x1.

[303] Ibid, 27 Jul 1868, 3x1.

[304] "Rebellion on the Rappahannock: Secession in Spotsylvania County, Virginia," (M.A. thesis, Louisiana State University by A Wilson Greene, 1977, pages 20–29, cited in *Fredericksburg Civil War Sites: April 1861 –November 1862*, by Noel G. Harrison, H.E. Howard, Inc. Publisher, page 15.

[305] *Virginia Herald Dispatch*, 27 Jul 1868, 3x1.

[306] *Fredericksburg Civil War Sites: December 1862 –April 1865*, by Noel G. Harrison, H.E. Howard, Inc. Publisher Page 141.

[307] 1860 Fredericksburg, Virginia Slave Census.

William F. Broaddus' stepson) said that Ned was "neither a good officer nor much of a gentleman." On October 5, 1864 Edward Avonmore Marye, died of disease.[308]

On June 1, 1861, his son, Alexander Stuart Marye, also enlisted in the Fredericksburg Artillery. On May 2, 1865, he was paroled at Greensboro, NC. Willie Pegram, the famous Confederate artillerist, called Alexander Stuart Marye "a literary eccentricity" with "no common sense whatever."[309]

John Marye married a distant cousin, Jane Hamilton on July 7, 1862.[310] They had no children.

Before the Battle of Fredericksburg, on November 25, 1862, John and Jane Marye evacuated from Brompton to her ancestral home, Forest Hill. They took their furniture from Brompton with them and planned to ship the furniture to Richmond.[311]

On December 4, 1862 John Marye and his wife, Jane, went to Fredericksburg for Election Day. His son, Jack Marye, was elected without opposition as a Delegate to the Legislature to replace Douglas Gordon, who had resigned.[312]

After the Battle of Fredericksburg, on December 17, 1862, Jane's sister, Matilda Hamilton, wrote in her diary, "We went to Brompton, now made famous by the battle, for Marye's Heights was the prize the Yankees aimed at. Another scene of desolation presented itself there. It was such a beautiful place. The Yankees were burying their dead today under Flag of Truce. I saw them cold and naked lying ready for the trenches they were to be buried in. Yankee surgeons were there attending their wounded, our prisoners, under Flag of Truce."[313]

A Confederate staff officer who visited Brompton shortly after the battle observed, "Not an inch of the surface of the bricks on the front of the house was free from the mark of a Minie ball. Bushels of flattened ones were to be seen on the ground, while the woodwork

---

[308] *The Fredericksburg Artillery* by Robert K. Krick, H.E. Howard, Inc. (1986) page 106.

[309] Ibid.

[310] *Ancestry World Tree Project*, www.ancestry.com/tree/.

[311] "An Eye Witness Account of The Battle of Fredericksburg: From the diary of a daughter of George and Maria Hamilton of Forest Hill," Virginia Historical Society, Richmond Virginia.

[312] Ibid.

[313] Ibid.

was torn to pieces by them."[314]

During the Battle of Chancellorsville, on May 3, 1863, Union forces stormed Marye's Heights and seized Brompton. The Confederate troops retook Brompton shortly thereafter.

The following year Brompton was used as a hospital by the Union Ninth Corps' Second Division for the wounded from the Battles of the Wilderness and Spotsylvania Courthouse. The house was packed from cellar to garret with hundreds of injured men.

After the war, John Marye returned to Brompton and began repairing the house.[315]

During a rash of robberies after the war, John Marye's meat house was robbed of its entire content of edible foods in August 1867.[316]

On July 25, 1868,[317] after eating a hearty meal, and taking a stroll in garden, John Marye took a nap. About five o' clock, he awoke and made plans to accompany family members on a visit to some neighbors. Before leaving, he went into the library to get a glass of water. When his family heard the sound of the water pitcher falling against the tumbler, they rushed into the library, and found him sitting in a chair, unconscious. They laid him on the floor with his head in his wife's lap, where he died a few minutes later.[318]

John Marye's widow, Jane Hamilton Marye, was given a monthly pension of $8.00 in January 1884, for her husband's service in the war of 1812.[319] She died in 1913 at the age of ninety, and she was buried in her family's plot at Forest Hill, near Hamilton's Crossing in Spotsylvania County.[320]

Wiley Roy Mason

Wiley Roy Mason was born in 1804 at 'Cleveland' in King George County, Virginia, the son of Enoch and Lucy Wiley (Roy) Mason.[321] He was an attorney.[322]

---

[314] "Brompton: Front Door on the Battle" by Donald C. Pfanz, http://www.fredericksburg.com/CivilWar/Battle/0721CW.

[315] Ibid.

[316] *Fredericksburg Ledger*, 20 Aug 1867.

[317] *Ancestry World Tree Project*, www.ancestry.com/tree/.

[318] *Virginia Herald Dispatch*, 27 July 1868, 3x1 and 2x6.

[319] *Star*, 19 Jan 1884, 3x2.

[320] *Star*, 1 Dec 1913, 3x2.

[321] *Ancestry World Tree Project*, www.ancestry.com/tree/.

On November 8, 1828, he married Susan Taylor Smith. They had eleven children.[323]

1. Monimia Fairfax Mason
2. Anna Augusta Mason, b. 4 Sep 1829
3. Margaret Boyd Mason, b. 19 Aug 1831
4. Wiley Roy Mason, b. 31 Mar 1833, m. Susan Thornton, daughter of William G. and Charlotte (Hamilton) Thornton
5. Susan Augusta Mason, b. 8 Jan 1840
6. Julien Jaquelin Mason, b. 22 Dec 1841
7. Octavia Mason, b. 25 Oct 1843
8. Enoch Wellford Mason, b. 1844
9. Eugene Mason, b. 13 Apr 1847
10. Henry A. Mason, b. 31 Jul 1851
11. Ellen Mason, b. 2 Sep 1852

His son, Wiley Roy Mason, Jr., was a Major in the Confederate Army. He served on the staff of Gen. C.W. Field, and "served with distinction and gallantry...and was wounded three times."[324]

Wiley Roy Mason, Sr. was named on the arrest warrant when hostages were taken from Fredericksburg by the Union in the summer of 1862, but he escaped arrest.[325]

He may have been the "Mr. Mason" mentioned as being a refugee from the Battle of Fredericksburg, who was at the Hamilton Family's 'Forest Hill' with John Marye, and Montgomery Slaughter on November 25, 1862.[326] (His son, Maj. Wiley Roy Mason, married the daughter of Charlotte (Hamilton) Thornton).

Wiley Roy Mason, Sr. died on July 27, 1865.[327]

James McGuire

James McGuire was born circa 1814, and he was a merchant.[328]

---

[322] 1860 Fredericksburg Virginia Census.
Daily Star, 25 Oct 1909.
[323] *Ancestry World Tree Project*, www.ancestry.com/tree/.
[324] *Daily Star*, 25 Oct 1909.
[325] *The War of the Rebellion: A Compilation of the Official Records of the Union and Confederate Armies*, Series II, Vol. IV, Washington: Government Printing Office (1899) Pages 366, 376.
[326] "An Eye Witness Account of The Battle of Fredericksburg: From the diary of a daughter of George and Maria Hamilton of Forest Hill," Virginia Historical Society, Richmond Virginia.
[327] Ancestry World Tree Project, www.ancestry.com/tree/.

In his store, he sold "Dry Goods, Groceries, Hats, Shoes, Boots, Hardware (sic.) and Cutlery, some extra cheap."[329] He also sold Chappell's Fertilizer and Super Phosphate of Lime.[330] He was an Old Line Whig, and a prominent member of the Presbyterian Church.[331]

On November 11, 1840, James McGuire married Jane Elizabeth Ellis.[332] They had three children.[333]

1. Emma L. McGuire, b. ca. 1843
2. Robert Wilson McGuire, b. ca. 1844
3. Irene McGuire, b. ca. 1846

Before the war, he served on the city council.[334]

His son, Robert Wilson McGuire, enlisted in the Fredericksburg Artillery on March 24, 1862. He suffered a gunshot wound in the leg at the Battle of Fredericksburg on December 13, 1862, but was able to return to duty on May 15, 1863. He was promoted to corporal on December 1, 1864, and was paroled at Appomattox on April 9, 1865.[335]

James McGuire was one of the citizens of Fredericksburg who was arrested as a hostage and incarcerated in the Old Capitol Prison in Washington, D.C. in the summer of 1862.[336]

He was arrested again as a hostage by the Union troops in May 1864, but was released after he was taken to Washington, D.C.[337]

After the war, he served on the town council,[338] and was one of

---

[328] 1860 Fredericksburg, Virginia Census.

[329] *Christian Banner*, 6 Sep 1850 4x3.

[330] *Weekly Advertiser,* 12 Nov 1853.

[331] *The History of the City of Fredericksburg* Virginia by S.J. Quinn, Hermitage Press, Inc., Richmond, VA (1908) pages 77–79.

[332] Virginia Marriage Register.

[333] 1850 & 1860 Fredericksburg, Virginia Censuses.

[334] *Weekly Advertiser*, 26 Mar 1853.

[335] *The Fredericksburg* Artillery by Robert K. Krick, H.E. Howard, Inc. (1986) page 108.
The Appomattox Roster, Antiquarian Press, Ltd., New York (1962) Page 105.

[336] *The War of the Rebellion: A Compilation of the Official Records of the Union and Confederate Armies, Series* II, Vol. IV, Washington: Government Printing Office (1899) Pages 861, 866.

[337] *History of the City of Fredericksburg, Virginia* by S. J. Quinn, Hermitage Press (1908) page 102.

[338] *Fredericksburg Ledger*, 20 Jul 1865.

the many victims in Fredericksburg of theft. He was robbed in September 1867 and in March 1869.[339]

Between 1860 and 1870, his real estate had increased in value from $2,000 to $2,500, but his personal estate decreased in value from $8,000 to $2,500.[340]

He became the collector of taxes for the town in July 1873.[341]

James McGuire died sometime before November 1879.[342] He is buried in the City Cemetery, but there are no dates on his tombstone.

Elizabeth (Mullen) Mills

Elizabeth (Mullen) Mills was the wife of James T. Mills, who was a first cousin of Elizabeth (Mills) Wrenn. James T. Mills was the son of James H. and Nancy (McMullan) Mills.

Elizabeth (Mullen) and James T. Mills had three children.[343]
1. Benjamin F. Mills
2. Charles Henry Mills
3. Margaret Mills, m. William Proctor

During the Battle of Fredericksburg in December 1862, their house burned.[344] The house was listed in the name of Elizabeth Mills and others, so James T. Mills may have been deceased.

Harriet Olivia (Shelton) (King) (Cessle) Mills

Harriet Olivia (Shelton) (King) (Cessle) Mills was the fourth wife of James H. Mills. He was her third husband. He was the son of Henry Achilles and Elizabeth Mills and the uncle of Elizabeth Mills Wrenn. James H. and Harriet Olivia Mills had one child.[345]
1. Sarah Jane (Jennie) L. Mills

During the Battle of Fredericksburg in December 1862, their house burned.[346] The house was listed in the name of Harriet O. Mills, so James H. Mills may have been deceased.

Virginia Herald Dispatch, 16 Apr 1868, 3x2.

Fredericksburg Ledger, 16 Mar 1869.

[339] Ibid. 17 Sep 1867.

[340] 1860 & 1870 Fredericksburg, Virginia Censuses.

[341] *Virginia Herald Dispatch*, 14 Jul 1873, 3x1.

[342] *Star*, 30 Nov 1879, 3x1.

[343] Jillyne Keene, Mills' Family Historian.

[344] 1865 Fredericksburg Tax Record.

[345] Jillyne Keene, Mills' Family Historian.

[346] 1865 Fredericksburg Tax Record.

Littleton Morgan Mills

Littleton Morgan Mills, was born circa 1843 in Virginia, and worked as a clerk.[347] He was the son of Walter M. and Pamela Amelia (Young) Mills.[348]

He was a first cousin once removed of Elizabeth (Mills) Wrenn.

On May 23, 1861, he enlisted in Company C, 30th Virginia. He was discharged because he was a mail carrier on October 24, 1863, but was back in the service and reported as AWOL January–February 1864. He was paroled at Ashland, VA on April 25, 1865, but there is no explanation of why he was in Ashland.[349]

After the war, he married Lauretta E. Peyton and they had three children.[350]

1. Morgan Raegan Mills, m. Willie Mae Brauer
2. Nannie E. Mills, m. William C. Cheatwood
3. Nettie L. Mills

Robert Henry Mills

Robert Henry Mills was born in September 1836 in Virginia, and was a laborer. His parents were Willis and Sarah M. (Perry) Mills.[351]

He was the first cousin of Elizabeth (Mills) Wrenn.

He enlisted in the 30th Virginia, Company A on April 24, 1861. He was court-martialed in September 1861 for being AWOL. At the Battle of Sharpsburg [Antietam] on September 17, 1862, he received a slight wound s in the knee. He deserted and took the oath on August 4, 1863.[352]

He had one child from a spouseless relationship.

1. John Henry Mills

He married (1) Sophia Watson and they had no children.

He married (2) Marianna A. Heslop and they had two children.

---

[347] *30th Virginia Infantry* by Robert K. Krick, H.E. Howard, Inc., Publisher (1985), page 114.

[348] Jillyne Keene, Mills' Family Historian.

[349] *30th Virginia Infantry* by Robert K. Krick, H.E. Howard, Inc., Publisher (1985), page 114.

[350] 1870 Fredericksburg, Virginia Census.

[351] Jillyne Keene, Mills' Family Historian.

[352] *30th Virginia Infantry* by Robert K. Krick, H.E. Howard, Inc., Publisher (1985), page 114.

1. John Henry Mills, m. Mary Elizabeth Unknown
2. Mary Mills, m. David Heslop

Robert Henry Mills died after 1900.[353]

Walter M. Mills

Walter M. Mills was born in March 1815 in Virginia, and was the son of James H. Mills and Nancy McMullan.[354] He was a master tailor.[355] He was a first cousin of Elizabeth (Mills) Wrenn, and the father of Littleton Morgan Mills.

He married Pamela Amelia Young and they had six children.[356]

1. Frances Ellen Mills, b. 23 Mar 1846, d. 12 Dec 1923, m. Samuel R. Keene
2. George A. Mills
3. Henrietta Wina Mills, m. Rufus Bainbridge Merchant
4. Littleton Morgan Mills, b. ca 1843, m. Lauretta E. Peyton
5. Walter Roy Mills

He was charged (along with his father, James H. Mills) with assaulting William Jennings (brother of James H. Jennings) on December 24, 1843 with the intent to kill him.[357]

He was arrested as a hostage by the Union troops in May 1864, and sent to Fort Delaware Prison.[358]

Walter M. Mills died March 24 1876.[359]

William H. Norton

William H. Norton was born circa 1820, and he was a carpenter.[360] He owned a housewright shop.[361] According to the Spotsylvania Industrial Census, between June 1, 1859 and June 1, 1860 he had 12 employees, and processed lumber for four houses

---

[353] Jillyne Keene, Mills' Family Historian.

[354] Ibid.

[355] 1860 Fredericksburg, Virginia Census.

[356] Ibid.
   Jillyne Keene, Mills' Family Historian.

[357] Corporation of Fredericksburg vs. James T. Mills and Walter M. Mills, 1844.

[358] *History of the City of Fredericksburg, Virginia* by S. J. Quinn, Hermitage Press (1908) page 102.

[359] Jillyne Keene, Mills' Family Historian.

[360] 1860 Fredericksburg, Virginia census.

[361] *Weekly Advertiser*, 8 Aug 1857.

valued at $16,000 and did other work valued at $4,000.[362]

He was an Old Line Whig and a member of the Baptist Church.[363]

He and his wife, Eliza Jane, had seven children.[364]

1. Mary Norton, b. ca. 1840
2. Mary E. (Bettie) Norton, b. ca. 1843,
3. William Andrew Norton, b. ca. 1846
4. Virginia F. Norton, b. ca. 1848, m. Dec 1877 J.C. Aylier[365]
5. Brazilia C. Norton, b. ca. 1852
6. Broaddus Norton, b. ca. 1854
7. Charles H. Norton, b. ca. 1856

He was one of the citizens of Fredericksburg who was arrested as a hostage and incarcerated in the Old Capitol Prison in Washington, D.C. in the summer of 1862.[366]

After the war, he worked as a carpenter,[367] house builder,[368] ship joiner, and millwright[369] in Fredericksburg.

William H. Norton died in Baltimore in February 1887 at the age of 69,[370] and he is buried in the Confederate Cemetery in Fredericksburg.

His wife, Eliza Jane, died in October 1891.[371]

Phillis

Phillis was a slave owned by Eliza C. Pilcher Wrenn. She is included in a list of household articles that were placed in trust by Eliza the day before she married Lewis Wrenn.[372]

---

[362] Cited by Noel G. Harrison in Fredericksburg Civil War Sites: April 1861 –November 1862, page 61.

[363] *The History of the City of Fredericksburg Virginia* by S.J. Quinn, Hermitage Press, Inc., Richmond, VA (1908) page 79.

[364] 1850 & 1860 Fredericksburg, Virginia Censuses.

[365] *Fredericksburg News*, 12 Dec 1877, 3x6.

[366] *The War of the Rebellion: A Compilation of the Official Records of the Union and Confederate Armies*, Series II, Vol. IV, Washington: Government Printing Office (1899) Pages 366, 376, 861, 866.

[367] *Fredericksburg News*, 19 Jan 1874, 3x1.

[368] *Fredericksburg Ledger*, 30 May 1873, 3x1.

[369] *Fredericksburg News*, 19 Jan 1874, 3x1.

[370] *Star*, 5 Feb 1887, 3x1.

[371] Ibid. 17 Oct 1891, 3x2.

[372] Fredericksburg Deed Book M, Page 333.

Phillis was born ca. 1825.[373]

No further records of Phillis have been found.

Thomas Francis Proctor

Thomas Francis Proctor was born on March 4, 1838 in Spotsylvania County. He was a shoemaker living in the household with Allen Stratton on the 1860 Census.[374] On August 14, 1860, he married Elizabeth F. Jones in Stafford, Virginia.[375]

He joined Company A, 30th Virginia as a corporal on April 22, 1861. He was dropped from the rolls July 12, 1861 when he claimed that he had never been mustered in.

On March 4, 1862, he reenlisted in the 30th Virginia. He was detailed as a courier for a court martial in Petersburg, Virginia during November and December 1863.

At the Battle of Drewry's bluff on May 16, 1864, he was wounded in the shoulder. The wound must not have been too bad, because two weeks later he was still with the 30th Virginia, when he was captured at Totopotomoy Creek during the Battle of Cold Harbor. He was sent to Elmira Prison and stayed there until June 19, 1865. From there he was sent to Point Lookout where he was paroled. His parole described him as being five feet seven inches and having dark hair and blue eyes.[376]

After the war, he worked in the National Cemetery located on the southern end of Marye's Heights,[377] and was a leader in veterans' organizations.[378]

Thomas Francis Proctor died in Louisa County, Virginia on October 9, 1933 at the age of 95. He is buried in the Fredericksburg City Cemetery.[379]

---

[373] 1860 Fredericksburg, Virginia Slave Schedule.

[374] 1860 Fredericksburg, VA Census.

[375] Stafford, Virginia Marriage Register.

[376] *30th Virginia Infantry* by Robert K. Krick, H.E. Howard, Inc., Publisher (1985) Page 120.

[377] "On the Parallels" by Banjamin [sic] Borton, Monitor Register Print, Woodstown, NJ (1903) quoted in *Works Progress Administration of Virginia Historical Inventory: "Battlehouse* by N.M. Deaderick, Fredericksburg, Virginia (Jan. 25, 1938).

[378] *30th Virginia Infantry* by Robert K. Krick, H.E. Howard, Inc., Publisher (1985) Page 120.

[379] Ibid.

John H. Roberts

John H. Roberts was born circa 1807. He was a merchant,[380] a member of the Masons,[381] and an old Line Whig.[382]

Early in his adult life, he was a lieutenant in the U.S. Navy.[383]

He married Ellen R. Badger in Philadelphia on March 31, 1835.[384] They had six children.[385]

1. William C. Roberts, b. ca. 1836, d. Jan 1868 [386]
2. Samuel M. Roberts, b. ca. 1838
3. Isabella B. Roberts, b. ca. 1839
4. Ellen Roberts, b. ca. 1842
5. Gabriella B. Roberts, b. ca. 1846
6. Susan M. Roberts, b. ca. 1848

On May 23, 1861, his son, William C. Roberts, enlisted in Company C, 30th Virginia as a private. He was paroled in Richmond on April 18, 1865.[387] There is no explanation of why he was in Richmond.

John Roberts was one of the citizens of Fredericksburg arrested as a hostage and incarcerated in the Old Capitol Prison in Washington, D.C. in the summer of 1862.[388]

Between 1860 and 1870, John Roberts' real estate had decreased in value from $3,100 to $0.00, and he did not have a personal estate.[389]

In December 1872, John H. Roberts died at the age of 67. He had been an invalid for two or three years.[390] His obituary said, "He

---

[380] 1860 Fredericksburg, Virginia Census.

[381] *Virginia Herald Dispatch*, 2 Dec 1872, 3x1.

[382] *The History of the City of Fredericksburg Virginia* by S.J. Quinn, Hermitage Press, Inc., Richmond, VA (1908) page 79.

[383] *Virginia Herald Dispatch*, 2 Dec 1872, 3x1.

[384] Ibid. 8 Apr 1835, 3x2.

[385] 1860 Fredericksburg, Virginia Census.

[386] *Virginia Herald Dispatch*, 16 Jan 1868, 2x6.

[387] *30th Virginia Infantry* by Robert K. Krick, H.E. Howard, Inc., Publisher (1985) page 122.

[388] *The War of the Rebellion: A Compilation of the Official Records of the Union and Confederate Armies*, Series II, Vol. IV, Washington: Government Printing Office (1899) Pages 366, 376, 861, 866.

[389] 1860 & 1870 Fredericksburg, Virginia Censuses.

[390] *Fredericksburg Ledger*, 3 Dec 1872.

was a gentleman of marked integrity of character, and held the respect of the community in which he was born, lived and in which he died."[391]

His wife, Ellen, died on January 29, 1880 at the age of 62.[392]

George Rowe

George Rowe was born January 21, 1793 in Stafford County, Virginia.[393]

He married Lucy L. Leitch in Stafford County on February 10, 1817, and they had eleven children.[394]

1. Absalom Peyton Rowe, b. 17 Nov 1817
2. Albert B. Rowe, b. 17 Dec 1819, d. 8 May 1848
3. Sarah Rowe, b. 11 Jul 1822
4. Mary Ann Rowe, b. 28 Oct 1824
5. John Gallatin Rowe, b. 27 Feb 1827
6. George Henry Clay Rowe, b. 12 Jan 1830, d. 9 March 1878, m. 20 Oct 1853 Virginia G. Sledd
7. Robert Semple Rowe, b. 9 Aug 1832
8. Lucy Frances Rowe, b. 27 Dec 1834
9. James Montague Rowe, b. 7 Nov 1837, d. 26 Jun 1838
10. Edgar Cephas Rowe, b. 29 Oct 1839
11. R. Ella Rowe, b. 31 Jan 1847

His wife, Lucy Rowe, was described as being an unusually tiny woman, but he weighed nearly 300 pounds. It was said that his carriage could be identified a long ways off, with its spring seat bending low to the ground on one side, but the other side elevated into the Spotsylvania ozone.[395]

After marrying, they moved to Fredericksburg, and though George Rowe lacked educational advantages, through hard work he became a successful cattle dealer.[396]

He retired from business in 1841 and became an ordained

---

[391] *Virginia Herald Dispatch*, 2 Dec 1872, 3x1.

[392] *Star*, 7 Feb 1880, 2x5.

[393] *Minor Sketches of Major Folk* by Dora C. Jett, Richmond Old Dominion Press (1928) pages 96–97.

[394] Ancestry World Tree Project, www.ancestry.com/tree/.

[395] *Minor Sketches of Major Folk* by Dora C. Jett, Richmond Old Dominion Press (1928) pages 96–97.

[396] *Fredericksburg Ledger*, 26 Jan. 1866.

minister in the Baptist Church. He was the pastor of the Salem Baptist Church in Spotsylvania County for several years.[397]

In 1857, he had become the pastor of the African Baptist Church, which had 700 members, and he served in that position until the church was disbanded in 1862, because of the war.[398]

His wife, Lucy, died on March 27, 1863.[399]

George Rowe died January 18, 1866 and he is buried in the Masonic Cemetery in Fredericksburg.[400]

George Henry Clay Rowe

George Henry 'Clay' Rowe was born January 12, 1830 in Virginia. He was a lawyer and the son of George and Lucy L. (Leitch) Rowe.[401] He was a talented jurist, a Democrat, a Douglas elector during the 1860 presidential election, and a member of the Baptist Church.[402]

On October 20, 1853, he married Virginia G. Sledd in Henrico County, VA. They had four children.[403]

1. Nannie M. Rowe, b. 1854
2. William Winston Rowe, b. 30 Apr 1856, d. 26 Sep 1865[404]
3. Eustace Conway Rowe, b. 30 Nov 1857
4. Virginia J. Rowe, b. Apr 1860

In the middle of the night, a fire destroyed his home, along with the furniture, a valuable library, paintings, jewelry, watches, money, clothing, etc. in February 1858. The family barely had time to escape with their lives, and without a change of clothing. Clay Rowe's hair was singed by the fire while rescuing one of his children.[405]

He was one of the citizens of Fredericksburg arrested as a

---

[397] Ibid, 26 Jan. 1866.

[398] Ibid.

Fredericksburg News, 1 Dec 1857, 2x2.

[399] Ancestry. com

[400] *Minor Sketches of Major Folk* by Dora C. Jett, Richmond Old Dominion Press (1928) pages 96–97.

[401] Ancestry World Tree Project, www.ancestry.com/tree/.

[402] *The History of the City of Fredericksburg* Virginia by S.J. Quinn, The Hermitage Press, Inc., Richmond, VA (1908) page 78.

[403] *Ancestry World Tree Project*, www.ancestry.com/tree.

[404] *Fredericksburg Ledger*, 29 Sep 1865.

[405] *Fredericksburg News*, 16 Feb 1858, 2x1.

Virginia Herald Dispatch, 17 Feb 1858, 2x2.

hostage and incarcerated in the Old Capitol Prison in Washington, D.C. in the summer of 1862.[406]

The 1870 Fredericksburg, Virginia Census listed his wife, Virginia, as the head of the household. George H.C. Rowe was listed as a former lawyer and insane. He was 39 years old.[407]

On March 9, 1878, he died suddenly of heart disease at Williamsburg, VA. He was 48 years old.[408]

Father Abram J. Ryan

Father Abram J. Ryan is known as the poet priest of the Confederacy. He was born on February 5, 1838 in Hagerstown, MD to Irish immigrant parents.

His poetry almost exclusively focuses on Roman Catholicism and his love of the South.

On November 1, 1856, he was ordained as a priest, and taught theology, first at Niagara University in New York, then at the diocesan seminary in Cape Girardeau, MO. He became a chaplain in the Confederate Army on September 1, 1862 and served until the end of the war.

During their defeat and Reconstruction, his poems spoke to the spirit of the Southern people. He remained loyal to the South for the rest of his life and served at parishes throughout the South. He became the editor of *The Star*, a Catholic weekly in New Orleans, and *The Banner of the South*, a religious and political weekly in Augusta.

Father Ryan died on April 22, 1886, a priest, a Confederate, and a poet.[409]

John Francis Scott

John Francis Scott was born November 7, 1803,[410] and he owned a foundry.[411] He carried on an extensive business up with the Confederate government, until the time the Union troops took

---

[406] *The War of the Rebellion: A Compilation of the Official Records of the Union and Confederate Armies*, Series II, Vol. IV, Washington: Government Printing Office (1899) Pages 366, 376, 861, 866.

[407] Ancestry World Tree Project, www.ancestry.com/tree/.

[408] *Fredericksburg News*, 14 Mar 1878.

[409] *South Carolina League of the South*, www.sclos.org/research/fatherryan.html.

[410] City Cemetery Tombstone Inscription.

[411] 1860 Fredericksburg, Virginia Census.

possession of Fredericksburg. He was an Old Line Whig and a prominent member of the Episcopal Church.[412]

John and Mary Scott had seven children.[413]

1. Bettie L. Scott, b. ca. 1838
2. William Lane Scott, b. ca. 1839
3. Fannie S. Scott, b. ca. 1843
4. John Scott, b. 22 Feb 1845, d. 27 June 1862[414]
5. Susan G. Scott, b. ca. 1848, m. Sep 1871 J.J. Clemens[415]
6. Arabella Scott, b. ca. 1851, d. 24 June 1855[416]
7. Annie B. H. Scott, b. 21 Mar 1851, d. 3 Jan 1862[417]

Before the war, he manufactured everything from screws to portable steam sawmills in his foundry.[418] During the occupation of Fredericksburg, the Union troops seized his foundry and used it to produce goods for the Union.[419]

His oldest son, William Lane Scott, enlisted in the Fredericksburg Artillery on March 21, 1862, and he was paroled at Appomattox.[420]

His youngest son, John Scott, enlisted in the Fredericksburg Artillery on April 20, 1862, and he was wounded in action at Mechanicsville on June 26, 1862.[421] He died the next day.[422] He was 17 years old.

John Scott was one of the citizens of Fredericksburg arrested as a hostage and incarcerated in the Old Capitol Prison in Washington,

---

[412] *The History of the City of Fredericksburg Virginia* by S.J. Quinn, Hermitage Press, Inc., Richmond, VA (1908) page 79.

[413] 1860 Fredericksburg, Virginia Census.

[414] City Cemetery Tombstone Inscription.

[415] *Virginia Herald Dispatch*, 14 Sep 1871, 2x6.

[416] City Cemetery Tombstone Inscription.

[417] Ibid.

[418] *Weekly Advertiser*, 5 Nov 1853.
Ibid, 10 Jan 1857.

[419] *Christian Banner*, 14 Jul 1862, 1x4.

[420] *The Fredericksburg Artillery* by Robert K. Krick, H.E. Howard, Inc. (1986) page 108.
The Appomattox Roster, Antiquarian Press, Ltd., New York (1962).

[421] *The Fredericksburg Artillery* by Robert K. Krick, H.E. Howard, Inc. (1986) page 108.

[422] City Cemetery Tombstone Inscription.

D.C. in the summer of 1862.[423]

After the war, he opened an icehouse and offered home delivery. He sold tickets for the ice at his foundry.[424]

He was elected treasurer of the Temperance Society,[425] and was a member of the Home Industry Organization.[426]

Between 1860 and 1870, his real estate increased in value from $16,000 to $18,000, but his personal estate decreased in value from $30,000 to $1,000.[427]

John Francis Scott died on February 6, 1871.[428] His obituary said that he "lived universally respected and died universally regretted."[429] As an enduring memorial to him, a tribute was included in the records of St. George's Church stating "our high appreciation and recognition of his earnest piety, his unflinching integrity, his christian [sic.] purpose to 'do unto all men as he would have them do unto him,' his untiring energy and diligence in the performance of every duty, the nobleness, generosity and unselfishness of his nature, the warmth of his friendship, his liberality and kindness of heart enduring him to all, his active benevolence and charity to the poor and needy, by whom he will be sadly mourned and his memory cherished."[430]

David Sisson

David Sisson was born in 1815 in North Farnham, Richmond County, Virginia.[431] He was a retail grocer.[432] He was a distant cousin of Lewis Wrenn through the Strother family.

He married Catherine E. Yarrington on December 26, 1843 in Richmond County, Virginia. They had three children.[433]

---

[423] *The War of the Rebellion: A Compilation of the Official Records of the Union and Confederate Armies*, Series II, Vol. IV, Washington: Government Printing Office (1899) Pages 366, 376, 861, 866.

[424] *Virginia Herald Dispatch*, 15 Apr 1867, 2x6.

[425] Ibid, 1 Aug 1867, 3x1.

[426] *Fredericksburg Ledger*, 22 Oct 1867.

[427] 1860 & 1870 Fredericksburg, Virginia Censuses.

[428] City Cemetery Tombstone Inscription.

[429] *Fredericksburg Ledger*, 7 Feb 1871, 3x1.

[430] Ibid. 14 Feb 1871, 3x1.

[431] Ancestry World Tree Project, www.ancestry.com/tree/.

[432] 1860 Fredericksburg, Virginia Census.

[433] Ancestry World Tree Project, www.ancestry.com/tree/.

1. Landon Sidney Sisson, b. Jan 1849, d. 6 Nov 1912, m (1) Marie J. Shears (2) Clementine R. Jennings
2. Mary Emma Nora Sisson, b. 25 June 1850, d. 14 June 1851
3. Infant Sisson, b. 7 Apr 1855, d. 7 Apr 1855

The Sisson family moved to Fredericksburg sometime before July 9, 1851, the date their daughter, Mary Emma Nora Sisson, died.[434]

He purchased the property on the Turnpike where he lived and operated a grocery store on June 15, 1854.[435]

On April 7, 1855 David Sisson's wife, Catherine, died in childbirth.

David Sisson married (2) Sarah Abbott on December 4, 1856 in Fredericksburg.[436]

During the Battle of Fredericksburg, Sarah Abbott Sisson remained in their home. John W. Ames, Brevet Brigadier-General of the Union Army describes advancing with his troops and coming to "a low brick house, with an open door in its gable end, from which shone a light, and into which we peered when passing. Inside sat a woman, gaunt and hard-featured, with crazy hair and a Meg Merrilies face, still sitting by a smoking candle, though it was nearly two hours past midnight...alone in a house between two hostile armies, two corpses lying across her door-steps, and within, almost at her feet, four more! So, with wild eyes and face lighted by her smoky candle, she stared across the dead barrier into the darkness outside with the look of one who heard and saw not, and to whom all sounds were a terror." Gen. Ames spent the next day lying on the ground between the Sisson house and the stone wall. He wrote, "It was almost startling to see, on looking at the brick house, the Meg Merrilies of the night before standing at her threshold. With the same lost look of helpless horror that her face had worn by candle-light, she gazed up and down our prostrate lines, and the disenchantment of day and sunshine failed to make her situation seem in any way prosaic and commonplace. The desolate part she had to play suited well her gaunt and witch-like features. Shading her eyes with her hand at last, as if to banish a vision and call her senses back to earth, she searched our lines once more; then, with a hopeless shake of the head, she moved slowly back

---

[434] *Fredericksburg News*, 22 July 1851, 3x1.

[435] Fredericksburg Deed Book R, Page 100.

[436] Ancestry World Tree Project, www.ancestry.com/tree/.

into the dismal little tomb she was forced to occupy."[437]

Thomas Galway in *The Valiant Hours* describes, "At the angle of the road, forming a 'flat iron,' stood a small brick grocery store. The blunt end of the house which was presented to us, was wide enough for a door which we found barred at our approach. A few blows from the butt of a musket opened it and we carried our bleeding comrades in, laying them first on the counter and then, as their numbers increased, on the floor, wherever in fact there was room. Strangest of all we found here a woman who, either by accident or a foolhardy desire to save her property had, after barring the door, descended into the cellar.

This house was right in the vortex of the whirlpool of destruction. Bullets whistled through it in every direction. Shells exploded, shattering, with their terrible detonation, every glass in the windows. The wounded began to beg for water, and their comrades, after looking everywhere in vain for a well, dragged the poor woman out of her cellar. Opening the back door, which looked out on the enemy's terrible batteries on the heights, they forced her out into the pelting shower of missiles to show them the well. Poor woman! She must have gone mad with fear, if she finally escaped with her life."[438]

After the war, many of the townspeople became victims of robberies. In August 1869, thieves carried off all of David Sisson's beehives, except one, which was too large to be easily carried off. The beehives were abandoned when the thieves could not figure out how to get the honey out of them.[439]

Between 1860 and 1870, David Sisson's real estate decreased in value from $800 to $500, and his personal estate decreased in value fro $150 to $0.[440]

In December 1884, David Sisson died. His obituary said that he "was a good citizen and many years a member of the Baptist church."[441]

---

[437] "In Front of the Stone Wall at Fredericksburg" by John W. Ames, Brevet Brigadier-General, *Battles and Leaders*, Vol. III, New York, The Century Co. Pages 122–124.

[438] *The Valiant Hours* by Thomas F. Galway, Harrisburg PA (1961) Page 61.

[439] *Fredericksburg Ledger*, 6 Aug 1869, 3x1.

[440] 1860 & 1870 Fredericksburg, Virginia Censuses.

[441] *Star*, 3 Jan 1885, 3x5.

Montgomery Slaughter

Montgomery Slaughter was born in January 21, 1818 at the homestead called 'Hermitage' in Culpeper County Virginia,[442] the son of William and Harriet (Ficklen) Slaughter.[443]

He was a miller, a merchant,[444] and the wartime mayor of Fredericksburg.[445] He was a large wheat speculator and flour manufacturer, an Old Line Whig, and a member of the Episcopal Church.[446]

He married Eliza Lane Slaughter on May 6, 1845.[447] They had eight children.[448]

1. William Lane Slaughter, b. 1847, d. 1905[449]
2. Ellen A. Slaughter, b. ca. 1848, d. Aug 1850[450]
2. Mary Montgomery Slaughter, b. ca. 1851, d. Mar 1886[451]
   m. Edward Lewis
3. Fanny Scott Slaughter, b. ca. 1853
4. Montgomery Slaughter, , Jr., b. ca. 1856
5. Phillip M. Slaughter, b. ca. 1858
6. Charles Slaughter, b. ca. 1869
7. Bessie Slaughter m. Unknown Crone
8. Alice Slaughter, d. Nov 1856[452]

In his store he sold coffee, molasses, sugar, tea, rice, candles, soap, sperm oil, tanners oil, sole leather, nails, hammered and rolled iron, blistered steel, boxes, hollow ware castings, herring, mackerel, salt, alum, plaster, lime, cotton yarn, bagging, sheeting, shirting, twine, rope, paper, drab wool, glazed hats, buckets, brushes, white wash, window glass, bacon, cotton grain bags, flour, candlewick, carpet warp, knitting cotton, sail twine, cotton and woolen plaids,

---

[442] *Free Lance*, 9 Dec 1897.
[443] Ancestry World Tree Project, www.ancestry.com/tree/.
[444] 1860 Fredericksburg, Virginia Census.
[445] *Fredericksburg News*, 19 Mar, 1861, 3x1.
   Ibid, 17 May 1861, 2x5.
[446] *The History of the City of Fredericksburg Virginia* by S.J. Quinn, Hermitage Press, Inc., Richmond, VA (1908) page 78.
[447] Virginia Marriage Register.
[448] 1860 Fredericksburg, Virginia Census.
[449] City Cemetery Tombstone Inscription.
[450] *Fredericksburg News*, 13 Aug 1850, 3x1.
[451] *Free Lance*, 2 Mar 1886.
[452] *Fredericksburg News*, 13 Nov 1856, 3x1.

heavy drab and black kerseys for Negro clothing, blankets, axes, sad irons, nail rods, hoop/band/and sheet iron, tobacco, indigo, salt, pepper, allspice, saltpetre [sic], Epsom salts, segars [sic], blacking and brushes, brooms, starch, wheat, flour, corn, and flaxseed, and goods for country merchants.[453]

He was one of the citizens of Fredericksburg arrested as a hostage and incarcerated in the Old Capitol Prison in Washington, D.C. in the summer of 1862.[454]

On December 11, 1862, Montgomery Slaughter evacuated to Forest Hill,[455] the home of the Hamilton family.

On December 17, 1862 Matilda Hamilton wrote, "I saw dead Yankees everywhere. In Montgomery Slaughter's lot twenty lay in the most revolting state–[they] seemed to have been torn to pieces."[456]

Between 1860 and 1870, his real estate had decreased in value from $16,000 to $15,000, and his personal estate had decreased in value from $44,000 to $10,000.[457]

He was the victim of vandalism in November 1873, when a prankster carried his gate to another part of town.[458]

On December 2, 1873 his wife, Eliza Lane Slaughter, died. She was 47 years old.[459]

After having served as a magistrate, councilman, and the mayor of Fredericksburg from 1860 until he was removed from office by the military authorities controlling Virginia, Montgomery Slaughter was elected as a judge in January 1882.[460]

Montgomery Slaughter died in December 7, 1897. He had suffered two strokes and was very feeble at the time of his death. His obituary said he was "a man of extraordinary good sense and great

---

[453] *Christian Banner*, 6 Sep 1850, 3x4.

[454] *The War of the Rebellion: A Compilation of the Official Records of the Union and Confederate Armies*, Series II, Vol. IV, Washington: Government Printing Office (1899) Pages 366, 376, 861, 866.

[455] "An Eye Witness Account of The Battle of Fredericksburg: From the diary of a daughter of George and Maria Hamilton of Forest Hill," Virginia Historical Society, Richmond Virginia.

[456] Ibid.

[457] 1860 & 1870 Fredericksburg, Virginia Censuses.

[458] *Fredericksburg Ledger*, 21 Nov 1873.

[459] *Fredericksburg News*, 4 Dec 1873, 3x6.

[460] *Free Lance*, 9 Dec 1897.

Fredericksburg Star, 18 Jan 1882, 3x1.

strength of character and a merchant of more than ordinary judgment and discrimination. He was always affable, approachable, and agreeable."[461]

Jefferson William Smith

Jefferson William Smith was born circa 1839. He lived in the household with Allen Stratton, and he was a wheelwright.[462]

On April 22, 1861, he enlisted in Company A, 30th Virginia Regiment with the rank of corporal. In April 1862, he was promoted to sergeant.

At South Mountain, on September 14, 1862, he was taken as a prisoner of war, but was exchanged on November 20, 1862. On February 19, 1863 he was admitted to Chimborazo Hospital with ulcer of leg, and returned to active duty on April 6, 1863.

At Dinwiddie Court House, on March 31, 1865, he was wounded in the right knee and thigh, and was sent to a hospital in Petersburg. He was captured in the hospital on April 3, 1865.

Records show that he was still under treatment in the hospital where he was captured on May 25, 1865.

He was released from Camp Hamilton VA on May 31, 1865.[463]

Jefferson Smith married Mary Shelton on January 15, 1868.[464]

He died April 24, 1904 at the age of 65, and he is buried in the Confederate Cemetery in Fredericksburg.[465]

Martha Stephens (Stevens, Ennis, Innis, Farrow)

Martha Stephens was one of the most colorful and controversial figures who lived in Fredericksburg. She was born circa 1824 somewhere west of Fredericksburg, perhaps in Culpeper County. Her maiden name was Farrow. The people of Fredericksburg found her to be offensive, because she was a very outspoken, coarse person, not at all religious, and she smoked a pipe.

---

[461] *Free Lance,* 9 Dec 1897.

[462] 1860 Fredericksburg, Virginia Census.

[463] *30th Virginia Infantry* by Robert K. Krick, H.E. Howard, Inc., Publisher (1985) Page 127.

[464] Stafford, Virginia Marriage Register.
Virginia Herald Dispatch, 20 Jan 1868, 2x7.

[465] *30th Virginia Infantry* by Robert K. Krick, H.E. Howard, Inc., Publisher (1985), Page 127.

Somewhere between 1837 and 1843, she became the common law wife to Elijah Ennis (or Innis).[466] They had two children.

1. John Bell Ennis, b. Aug 1842, d. Dec 1881, m. 2 March 1865 Ellen J. Hessburg[467]
2. Virginia Ennis, b. ca. 1842, d. 1861

By 1850, she was living on the Sunken Road, and was running a grocery store and "speak easy" out of her house. There were three young women living with her, and it has been suggested that she may have been running a brothel.

Since married women in Virginia did not have property rights before 1877, Martha protected herself by putting her property in trust with Peter Goolrick as her trustee. E.N. Stephens witnessed the document. Although it was unusual for women during her time, she bought and sold several pieces of property during her lifetime.[468]

In December 1854, Martha Stephens was charged with selling whiskey and other ardent spirits without a license, but the case was dropped.[469]

On the 1860 census, she was living with a cabinetmaker named Edward N. Stephens. They had two children together.[470]

1. Mary S. Stephens, b. ca. 1850, d. before 1871
2. Agnes Sybil Stephens, b. 15 Dec 1855, d. Apr 1897, m. (1) 1874 J.R. Mazeen (2) after 1887 J.A. Taylor

Her son, John Ennis, enlisted in the 30th Virginia, Company B on May 25, 1861. He was seriously wounded in the neck at Sharpsburg on September 17, 1862. In June of 1863, he was able to return to his unit.[471]

After the Battle of Fredericksburg, Martha Stephens claimed that she never left her house during the battle, but stayed there aiding

---

[466] "Martha Stephens: Heroine or Hoax?" by Donald C. Pfanz, www.fredericksburg.com/CivilWar/Battle/0728CW.

[467] Virginia Marriage Register.

[468] "Martha Stephens: Heroine or Hoax?" by Donald C. Pfanz, . www.fredericksburg.com/CivilWar/Battle/0728CW.
Fredericksburg Deed Book T, pages 91, 376, 244, 379.

[469] Commonwealth vs. Farrow, Fredericksburg Courthouse.

[470] "Martha Stephens: Heroine or Hoax?" by Donald C. Pfanz, www.fredericksburg.com/CivilWar/Battle/0728CW.
1850 Spotsylvania, Virginia Census.

[471] *30th Virginia Infantry* by Robert K. Krick, H.E. Howard, Inc. (1985) Page 96.

and comforting wounded soldiers. Although there were thousands of soldiers in the vicinity, not one mentioned Martha Stephens being there, not even Gen. Joseph Kershaw who occupied the Stephens' house as his headquarters during the battle.[472]

In her defense, during her lifetime when she was making those claims, no one came forward and said that she could not have been in her home, because she was seen at the Salem Church, in a refugee house, or elsewhere. It is possible that she was hiding in her cellar, like Sarah Sisson.

Her house was 'in the center of a leaden storm' for eight hours. "Hundreds of bullets crashed through [her] small wooden [house], and nearly 10,000 men were killed or wounded within sight of her porch. Among the casualties was Gen. [Thomas R.R.] Cobb, who was struck by a Union artillery shell just outside [her] house."[473] The shell that stuck Gen. Cobb had traveled through the Stephens' house. It seems impossible that Martha could have been in her house and not be wounded, unless she was hiding in the cellar.

After the battle, she refused to repair her house, and it became a tourist attraction, with many of the tourists giving her contributions. It was said that her house became a "cash cow."[474]

Martha Stephens was again charged with selling liquor without a license in 1863, but the charges were dropped after she bought a license.[475]

During the depression of 1865, she bought a 92 $^1/_2$ acre farm in Spotsylvania County.[476]

After the war, Martha Stephens became famous when the 'story' of her ministering to soldiers from both sides during the Battle of Fredericksburg was printed in some history books.

Martha Stephens died in her house in December 1888 at the age of 68. Her obituary said she was "a very kind hearted and generous soul." Before her death, she made a profession of faith in Christ and

[472] "Martha Stephens: Heroine or Hoax?" by Donald C. Pfanz, www.fredericksburg.com/CivilWar/Battle/0728CW.

[473] Ibid.

[474] Ibid.

[475] Commonwealth vs. Innis, 1863, Fredericksburg Courthouse.

[476] "Martha Stevens: The Woman Behind the Legend" by Teri A. Jeske, The Journal of Fredericksburg History, Volume 2, Historic Fredericksburg Foundation, Inc. (1997.

became associated with the Presbyterian Church.[477]

Monroe Stevens

Monroe Stevens was born circa 1823–1825, the son of Edmund Stevens.[478] He worked as a drayman before the war,[479] but became a farmer when he purchased farmland after the war.[480]

He married Elizabeth Robinson on May 26, 1847[481]. They had two children.[482]

> 1. Ashton Joseph Stevens, b. ca. 1847, m. 1 Feb 1892 Virginia Newton
> 2. Marcellus M. Stevens, b. ca. 1850

On January 1, 1852, Monroe Stevens bought his property on the Turnpike from Samuel Alsop.[483] He sold the property on March 1, 1879 to E.D. Cole.[484]

Between 1860 and 1870, his real estate value remained the same ($2000) and his personal estate decreased from $250 to $210.[485]

Monroe Steven was already living in Stafford County in 1865 and a tenant was living in his property on the turnpike.[486] In October 1913, Monroe Stevens died at Stafford, Virginia at the age of 87.[487] In his will, he left his grandson, Joseph A. Stevens, 50 acres of his Hickory Hill Farm in Stafford County and his house at Hickory Hill.

He left his son, Ashton Joseph Stevens, the remaining 114 1/2 acres of Hickory Hill Farm.

He bequeathed his son, Marcellus Stevens, all of his property in Spotsylvania County, Virginia, both personal and real.

His grandson, John C. Stevens, was left the farm known as

---

[477] *Star*, 22 Dec 1888.

[478] Harris Adm. etc vs. Stevens and Others, Fredericksburg Court House Records.

[479] 1860 Fredericksburg, Virginia Census.

[480] 1870 Stafford Virginia Census.
Stafford County Wills.

[481] Virginia Marriage Register.

[482] 1860 Fredericksburg, Virginia Census.

[483] Fredericksburg Deed Book Q, Page 258.

[484] Fredericksburg Deed Book Z, Page 44.

[485] 1860 Fredericksburg, Virginia Census.
1870 Falmouth, Virginia Census.

[486] 1865 Fredericksburg Land Tax Records.

[487] *Daily Star*, 20 Oct 1913, 3x4.

Merry Oaks, with all the personal, kitchen, and household furniture.

$200 in cash was to be put into the bank for his grandson, Elisha Stevens, until he reached the age of twenty-five.

His grandson, Donnie C. Stevens, was appointed executor, but no provision was made for him in the will, or for the other eight grandchildren.[488]

Allen Stratton

Allen Stratton was born circa 1815. He and his wife, Mary, who was born circa 1819, had six children.[489]

1. Sarah Stratton, b. ca. 1843
2. Allen Stratton, Jr., b. ca. 1845
3. N. W. Stratton, b. ca. 1850
4. William H. Stratton, b. ca. 1853
5. Mary E. Stratton, b. ca. 1856
6. Anna L. Stratton, b. ca. 1859

He hired two slaves: a 25-year-old black male, owned by a Miss Bullard, and a 16-year-old mulatto female owned by Mrs. Hall. At least one "slave house" was located on his property.[490]

He bought the property for his house and wheelwright shop from Abs. McGee on December 7, 1855.[491] The property extended across Wellford's Field from the Turnpike to Mercer Square.

His home and shops received extensive damage during the Battle of Fredericksburg, so he moved into a rental home on the Turnpike owned by George Rowe. He rented his house and property to a tenant.[492]

Apparently, the Stratton family took shelter in the cellar at Brompton during the 1862 Battle of Fredericksburg. Allen Stratton's wife, Mary, was reported to have died from shock and exposure during the battle.[493]

By 1866, Allen Stratton had moved to Washington, D.C.[494]

---

[488] Stafford County Wills.

[489] 1860 Fredericksburg, Virginia Census.

[490] 1860 Fredericksburg, Virginia Slave Schedule.

[491] Fredericksburg Deed Book R, Page 473.

[492] 1865 Fredericksburg Land Tax Record.

[493] Fredericksburg Civil War Sites: December 1862–April 1865 by Noel G. Harrison, H.E. Howard, Inc., Lynchburg, Virginia (1995) Pages 180–181.

[494] Ibid.
  1866 Fredericksburg Land Tax Record.

On January 17, 1874, he sold his property in Fredericksburg to James H. Roy.[495]

Benjamin Temple

Benjamin Temple was born January 12, 1801,[496] and was a wealthy farmer, and an Old Line Whig.[497]

He married Lucy Lilly Robinson and they had 12 children.[498]

1. Elizabeth Lilly Temple, b. 1827
2. Virginia Nelson Temple, b. 1829
3. Robert Henry Temple, b. 1831
4. Charles Wellford Temple, b. 10 Jan 1834, d. 25 Apr 1889
5. Molly Brooke Temple, b. 1835
6. Judith Willantina Temple, b. 1837
7. Benjamin Brooke Temple, b. 1839
8. John Taylor Temple, b. 11 Dec 1840, d. 30 Nov 1870
9. William Skyren Temple, b. 1842
10. Bernard Moore Temple, b. 1843
11. Ludwell Robinson Temple, b. 6 Oct 1846, d. 6 Oct 1876
12. Lucy Lilly Temple, b. 1849

In 1839, he bought the estate known as Berclair.[499]

He was one of the citizens of Fredericksburg arrested as a hostage and incarcerated in the Old Capitol Prison in Washington, D.C. in the summer of 1862.[500]

During the Civil War, six of his sons were already serving in the Confederate Army when his youngest (15-year-old) son, Ludwell

---

[495] Fredericksburg Deed Book W, Page 464.

[496] Weldon G. Cannon, "Temple folder," Virginiana Room, Rappahannock Regional Library.
1860 Fredericksburg, Virginia Census.

[497] *The History of the City of Fredericksburg Virginia* by S.J. Quinn, Hermitage Press, Inc., Richmond, VA (1908) page 79.

[498] 1860 Fredericksburg, Virginia Census.
City Cemetery Tombstone Inscriptions.
Weldon G. Cannon, Temple Texas, "Temple Folder," Virginiana Room, Rappahannock Regional Library, Fredericksburg, Virginia.

[499] W.P.A. Historical Inventory Project, sponsored by the Virginia Conservation Commission.

[500] *The War of the Rebellion: A Compilation of the Official Records of the Union and Confederate Armies*, Series II, Vol. IV, Washington: Government Printing Office (1899) Pages 366, 376, 861, 866.

Robinson Temple, ran away and enlisted. His wife, Lucy, wrote to General Lee saying that she already had six sons in the army and Ludwell was still a child. She urged General Lee to send him home. General Lee wrote her a note commending her on her large contribution to the army and stated that he had ordered the boy to return home. Ludwell was unhappy that he was sent home, and later rejoined the army.[501]

Benjamin Temple's son, William 'Skyren' Temple, enlisted in the Fredericksburg Artillery in January 1861 and mustered into Confederate service on April 23, 1861. He was promoted to sergeant on October 19, 1861, but almost immediately furnished J.L. Wellford as a substitute and was discharged. Later he served in the Purcell Artillery [Capt. Cayce's Co. Virginia Light Artillery,[502]] and the 9th Virginia Cavalry.[503] While serving with his brother, Brooke, in Stringfellow's Scouts, 9th Virginia Cavalry[504] he wore his boots completely out, until there was nothing left but the tops, and his feet were literally on the cold ground.[505]

His son, John Taylor Temple, enlisted in the 30th Virginia, Company B on April 22, 1861. He was promoted to corporal, then sergeant, before being elected as a lieutenant in April 1862. He was hospitalized for malaria in Richmond on October 12, 1864. He returned to duty on November 2, 1864, but there are no later records for him after November 27, 1864. He died on November 30, 1870 from service-induced illness.[506]

His son, Benjamin 'Brooke' Temple, was in Europe taking a postgraduate course in medicine when the war broke out. He hurried back to the States and served in the Confederate unit of Stringfellow's Scouts, 9th Virginia Cavalry,[507] for the duration of the war. His was wounded in the arm, and the minie ball remained in his arm for the

---

[501] "Berclair" *The Blue Hen's Brood* by William Ludwell Harrison, "Temple folder," Virginiana Room, Rappahannock Regional Library.

[502] *Civil War Compiled Military Service Records,* National Archives.

[503] *The Fredericksburg Artillery* by Robert K. Krick, H.E. Howard Inc. (1986) page 109.

[504] *Civil War Compiled Military Service Records,* National Archives.

[505] "Berclair" *The Blue Hen's Brood* by William Ludwell Harrison, "Temple folder," Virginiana Room, Rappahannock Regional Library.

[506] *30th Virginia Infantry* by Robert K. Krick, H.E. Howard, Inc., Publisher (1985) page 130.

[507] *Civil War Compiled Military Service Records,* National Archives.

rest of his life.[508]

His son, Bernard Moore Temple served in the 55th Virginia Infantry, Capt. Cayce's Co., Virginia Light Artillery,[509] and was wounded in battle and spent some time in the Chimborazo hospital in Richmond. While in the hospital his clothes consisted of a pair of pants, an army blanket fastened with a safety pin for a coat, worn out shoes, and no socks. When a nurse invited the group he was with to a dance, the men went down to the river and took a bath, then scrubbed their clothes, and hung them in the sun to dry. That night at the dance, the girls were kinder to the men who were shabbily dressed than to those who were elegantly uniformed.[510]

His son, Robert Henry Temple, served in the engineering corps of the Confederate Army.[511]

His son, Charles Wellford Temple, served in the 9th Virginia Cavalry.[512]

Between 1860 and 1870, Benjamin Temple's real estate decreased in value from $25,000 to $10,000 and his personal estate decreased in value from $65,000 to $1,500.[513]

Benjamin Temple died on July 12, 1872. He was 71 years old.[514] His obituary said, "Mr. Temple was possessed of many estimable qualities. No more honorable man lived. He was a good neighbor, a warm friend, and was highly esteemed by all who knew him."[515]

His wife, Lucy Lilly Robinson Temple died June 17, 1884.[516] She was 77 years old.[517]

Charles Carter Wellford

Charles Carter Wellford was born December 19, 1802 in

---

[508] "Berclair" *The Blue Hen's Brood* by William Ludwell Harrison, "Temple folder, Virginiana Room, Rappahannock Regional Library.

[509] *Civil War Compiled Military Service Records,* National Archives.

[510] "Berclair" *The Blue Hen's Brood* by William Ludwell Harrison, "Temple folder," Virginiana Room, Rappahannock Regional Library.

[511] Ibid.

[512] *Civil War Compiled Military Service Records,* National Archives.

[513] 1860 & 1970 Fredericksburg, Virginia Censuses.

[514] Tombstone Inscription, Fredericksburg City Cemetery.

[515] *Fredericksburg Ledger,* 16 July 1872.

[516] Tombstone Inscription, Fredericksburg City Cemetery.

[517] *Star,* 2 June 1884.

Fredericksburg, Virginia.[518] He was a dry grocery merchant,[519] and owned a machine works,[520] and Catherine Furnace.[521] He was an Old Line Whig and an elder in the Presbyterian Church.[522]

He married Mary Catherine Stiff in March 1824.[523] They had six children.[524]

1. Betty Wellford, b. ca. 1827
2. Charles Beverly Wellford, b. ca. 1829
3. Lucy G. Wellford, b. ca. 1832
4. John L. Wellford, b. ca. 1837
5. Thomas Wellford, b. ca. 1838
6. Mary (Mollie) C. Wellford, b. ca. 1841

When the Hope Fire Company was organized in Fredericksburg on April 6, 1857, Charles Wellford was unanimously elected as the commander.[525]

His son, Charles Beverly Wellford, enlisted in the Confederate army as a private. On April 4, 1862, he requested release from duty to help run a vital war industry at Catherine Furnace.[526]

Charles Carter Wellford was one of the citizens of Fredericksburg arrested as a hostage and incarcerated in the Old Capitol Prison in Washington, D.C. in the summer of 1862.[527]

Union troops shelled his house in December 1862.[528]

After the war, soldiers of the occupying army assaulted and beat him, while he was standing in front of his home. They attacked and hit him three or four times about the head. When his son, Thomas,

---

[518] Ancestry World Tree Project, www.ancestry.com/tree/.
[519] 1860 Fredericksburg, Virginia Census.
[520] *Virginia Herald Dispatch*, 11 Mar 1862, 1x2.
[521] *The Fredericksburg Artillery* by Robert K. Krick, H.E. Howard Inc. (1986) page 97.
[522] *The History of the City of Fredericksburg Virginia* by S.J. Quinn, The Hermitage Press, Inc., Richmond, VA (1908) pages 77–79.
[523] *Virginia Herald Dispatch*, 27 Mar 1824, 3x5.
[524] 1850 & 1860 Fredericksburg, Virginia Censuses.
[525] *Fredericksburg News*, 13 Apr 1857, 2x5.
[526] American Civil War Soldiers, Ancestry.com.
[527] *The War of the Rebellion: A Compilation of the Official Records of the Union and Confederate Armies*, Series II, Vol. IV, Washington: Government Printing Office (1899) Pages 861, 866.
[528] 1865 Fredericksburg, Virginia Land Tax Record.

came to his aid, they attacked and severely beat him, too.[529]

Charles Carter Wellford was elected to the city council in July 1865.[530]

Charles Carter Wellford died December 19, 1870.[531] He was 68 years old. His obituary said he was "one of our oldest and most respected and beloved citizens."[532]

His wife, Mary Catherine Stiff Wellford, died on October 9, 1878. She was 73 years old.[533]

Achilles A. Wrenn

Achilles A. Wrenn was born circa 1821, the son of William Thomas Wrenn (Lewis Wrenn's brother) and Malinda Mills (Elizabeth [Mills] Wrenn's sister), and he was a boss tinner.[534]

He married (1) Mary Ann Poartch in October or November 1838.[535] They had two children.

    1. Unknown Female Wrenn, m. Unknown Warner[536]
    2. Hellen M.A. Wrenn, b. April 1840[537] d. June 1918[538] m. 10 June 1860 Charles H. Wheeler[539]

He married (2) Catherine Rose on April 30, 1851.[540] They had two children.[541]

    1. Orianda Wrenn, b. ca. 1852
    2. Malinda Wrenn, b. ca. 1855

Col. Beverly Wellford Wrenn

Beverly Wellford Wrenn was born on July 4, 1847.[542] He was

---

[529] *Fredericksburg Ledger*, 7 Jun 1865.
[530] Ibid, 20 Jul 1865.
[531] *Ancestry World Tree Project*, www.ancestry.com/tree/.
[532] *Fredericksburg Ledger*, 30 Dec 1870, 3x3.
[533] *Star*, 12 Oct 1878, 2x5.
[534] 1860 Fredericksburg, Virginia Census.
[535] *Political Arena*, 2 Nov 1838, 3x1.
[536] Letter dated 8 Apr 1896 from C.E. Godfrey to Phillip Marshall Wrenn.
[537] Ibid.
1900 Fredericksburg, Virginia census.
[538] *Star*, 13 June 1918, 3x4.
[539] *Weekly Advertiser*, 16 June 1860, 3x2.
[540] Fredericksburg, Virginia Marriage Index, 1752–1957.
[541] 1860 Fredericksburg, Virginia Census.
[542] Confederate Cemetery Tombstone Inscription.

the son of Albert Walker and Catherine E. (Benson) Wrenn.

Although no service records have been found for him, the Confederate Veteran Magazine said that at the time of his death he was a member of a New York Confederate Veterans Organization, and had been in 'Special Service' in the Confederacy.[543]

Family tradition says that he was detailed to work for one of General Robert E. Lee's staff members, and he carried the message from Lee to Grant, concerning the surrender of the Confederate Army.[544]

He married Georgia Roberds Williams on October 28, 1868 in Augusta, Georgia.[545] They had three sons.[546]

1. Beverly Wellford Wrenn, Jr.
2. Allen Robert Wrenn
3. Henry (Harry) Bradley Plante Wrenn

After the war Beverly Wellford Wrenn was a property appraiser and architect for the firm of Henry Bradley Plante.[547] In 1889–1890, he was living in Atlanta, Georgia and was working for the East Tennessee, Virginia, & Georgia Railroad.[548] Later he moved to New York and worked for the railroad.[549]

Beverly Wellford Wrenn died on February 6, 1912 in New York.[550] He died of tetanus from a gunshot to his leg.[551]

Eliza C. (Pilcher) Wrenn

Eliza C. Pilcher was the second wife of Lewis Wrenn. She was born circa 1810.[552]

There is a lot of confusion over the identity of Eliza Pilcher. Court records show that her surname was Carter earlier in her life.[553] She may have been the Eliza Carter, daughter of Joseph Carter, who

---

[543] *Confederate Veteran Magazine*, May 1912.

[544] Thomas Wellford Wrenn, Beverly Wellford Wrenn's family historian.

[545] *Virginia Herald*, 9 Nov 1868, 2x6.

[546] Thomas Wellford Wrenn, Beverly Wellford Wrenn's family historian.

[547] Ibid.

[548] Atlanta, Georgia Directories 1889–1890.

[549] Thomas Wellford Wrenn, Beverly Wellford Wrenn's family historian.

[550] *Confederate Veteran Magazine*, May 1912.

[551] Thomas Wellford Wrenn, Beverly Wellford Wrenn's family historian.

[552] 1860 Fredericksburg, Virginia Census.

[553] Carter vs. Clark, 1844 Chancery Court Records in the Fredericksburg Courthouse Annex Basement.

married James B. Carter in Caroline County on December 14, 1821. If so, she was eleven years old at the time of the marriage,[554] according the ages recorded on the 1850 and 1870 Fredericksburg, Virginia Censuses (or twenty-one according the age recorded on the 1860 Fredericksburg, Virginia Census).

In October 1829, Eliza Carter sued the estate of John Carter of Caroline County. The case went through the courts of Caroline County and Fredericksburg for 17 years, until it was settled in 1846.

According to the court records, in 1822, while she was living in Orange County, John Carter gave Eliza Carter an I.O.U. John Carter died circa 1829 still owing her money.

In March 1830, the case was continued in court in Fredericksburg. At that time, she was identified as Elizabeth Carter. There were further hearings in Fredericksburg in 1832 and 1833, where she was identified as Eliza Carter. In a hearing in 1835, she was identified as Mrs. Elizabeth Carter. In an 1836 hearing, she was identified as Eliza Carter.

In 1837, when she joined a Sunday school class in the Methodist church, her name had changed to Eliza Pilcher.[555]

On September 20, 1842, Eliza C. Pilcher married Lewis Wrenn.[556] The day before the wedding, Eliza put all of her personal property into a trust, with George Rowe acting as the trustee.[557]Since married women in Virginia could not own property at that time, she was able to protect her personal property by having it put in a trust.

At the next hearing of her lawsuit in May 1844, her name was Eliza, wife of Lewis Wrenn, late Eliza Carter. At that time, the court ordered the sale of the land of the late John Carter in order to repay the I.O.U.

It was not until 1846, that she received her money.[558]

On November 7, 1848, Martin Spicer and Richard W. Bozel assaulted Eliza Wrenn. The testimony at the trial was not recorded, but the men were found guilty of "striking, bruising, wounding, ill treating, and other wrongs," and doing "great damage" to Eliza C.

---

[554] Caroline County Marriage Record.

[555] *Stewards Book*, Fredericksburg Methodist Church.

[556] Fredericksburg, Virginia Marriage Register.

[557] Fredericksburg Deed Book M, page 333.

[558] Carter vs. Clark, 1844 Chancery Court Records in the Fredericksburg Courthouse Annex Basement.

Wrenn.[559] The word 'rape' is not mentioned, but it is not likely that Eliza Wrenn would testify in open court that she had been raped, considering the stigma and shame directed against the victims of rape at that time. The use of the word 'damage' is interesting, in that it suggests harm that cannot be undone.

When Lewis Wrenn died in Goldsboro, NC in 1877, Eliza was there with him.[560] No further records of Eliza (Carter) (Pilcher) Wrenn have been found.

The parentage of Eliza and the identity of her husband(s), other than Lewis Wrenn, are unproven, and the date and place of her death are unknown.

Elizabeth Wrenn

The first clue to the possible existence of Elizabeth Wrenn was found in the Virginia Historical Society, in Richmond, Virginia, in the King Papers. In the Wrenn folder is a genealogy contributed by Richard Thurtle (deceased), who married a descendent of William Cobb Wrenn, the ninth son of John Kobler Wrenn. The genealogy contained some inaccuracies, and listed no sources, but it could not be easily dismissed, as some of the information seemed to be taken from a family Bible. For one thing he listed the day of the month that each of John Kobler Wrenn's children was born. The month and the year can easily be found in census records, but nowhere else had the days of the month been found, even after many years of research.

That some of his information came from a family Bible seemed to be confirmed when a descendent of John Lee Wrenn (the fourth son of John Kobler Wrenn) was located, and he had in his possession John Lee Wrenn's family Bible. In it the month, day, and year of the birth of each of John Kobler Wrenn's children was recorded, and they matched Richard Thurtle's information. This Bible did not list information on the next generation back.

Richard Thurtle's genealogy information went back further. It had the names of all of Lewis Wrenn's sons. The only other source, that was found afterward, for the names of his sons is in letters written by a lawyer named C.E. Godfrey to Phillip Marshall Wrenn. The

---

[559] Commonwealth vs. Martin Spicer and Richard Bozel, 1849, Cr-HU-R, 470-283.

[560] Letter dated 28 Aug 1877 from F. H. Ivey, Pastor Baptist Church (in Goldsboro, NC) to Robinson Boswell Wrenn.

names in these letters match Richard Thurtle's names. The letters, which concern a lawsuit by the heirs of the Mills family, are in the possession of a descendent of Phillip Marshall Wrenn.

Richard Thurtle's genealogy contained something not mentioned in the Godfrey letters, the names of two daughters of Lewis Wrenn. His information concerning a daughter named Elizabeth Wrenn proved to be erroneous, but that does not necessarily mean that she did not exist. It may simply mean that the information that Richard Thurtle had about her was wrong.

The 1840 Virginia Census may support his claim. It shows a female aged 5 to 10 in the household of Lewis Wrenn. (However, this child may possibly be Hellen Wrenn, daughter of Achilles A. and Mary Ann (Poartch) Wrenn, who is listed in the household of Lewis Wrenn on the 1850 Fredericksburg, Virginia Census. Apparently, Mary Ann (Poartch) Wrenn died before 1850.)

What may be additional evidence of the existence of Elizabeth Wrenn is in the Virginia Baptist Historical Society's Records of the Fredericksburg Baptist Church in Richmond, Virginia. They have a record of Elizabeth Wrenn dying in 1844. If Lewis Wrenn did have a daughter, Elizabeth, who was born in 1831 and died in 1844, she would have been nine years old (aged 5 to 10) on the 1840 census, and 13 years old when she died. This raises the question, however, of why would Lewis Wrenn bury his daughter at the Baptist Church when he was a Methodist?

Another possible explanation of the record at the Virginia Baptist Historical in Richmond, Virginia could be that it was Lewis Wrenn's first wife, Elizabeth (Mills) Wrenn who died in 1844. If that is true, then she was still alive when he married Eliza C. Pilcher in 1842.

Elizabeth (Mills) Wrenn

Elizabeth Mills was born circa 1800 in Virginia,[561] the daughter of Achilles and Clarissa (Stevens) Mills.[562] Her parents owned land near the Old Salem Church in Spotsylvania County, Virginia. She married Lewis Wrenn circa 1820, and they had five sons. It has not been proven that she had any daughters. She died circa 1841, and it is

---

[561] *Wren's of Virginia: 1652–1832* by John Howard Wren, Private Publication, page 99.

[562] Letter dated 19 May 1897 from C.E. Godfrey to Phillip Marshall Wrenn.

not known where she was buried.

George Henry Wrenn

George Henry Wrenn was born April 12,[563] 1826 (the year is estimated]). He was the third son of Lewis and Elizabeth (Mills) Wrenn.

He married (1) Nancy Pursley, the daughter of Henry and Castina Pursley, on April 3, 1848.[564]

On May 4, 1850 he married (2) Ann Eliza Montgomery, the daughter of Samuel Montgomery.[565] They had ten children, before moving to Augusta County, Virginia,[566] where their last two children were born.

1. William H. Wrenn, b. ca. 1851
2. Nancy J. Wrenn, b. ca. 1853, m. (1) Unknown Taylor, (2) W.J. Spilman
3. Rebecca Jane Wrenn, b. ca. 1855
4. Lewis M. Wrenn, b. ca. 1858
5. Robert L. Wrenn, b. ca. 1859
6. Samuel J. Wrenn, b. ca. 1859
7. Mildred A. Wrenn, b. ca. 1861
8. George Lee Wrenn, b. ca. 1863
9. Harriet A. Wrenn, b. ca. 1865
10. Theophilis Wrenn, b. ca. 1869
11. John Wesley Wrenn, b. Mar 1870[567]
12. George Wrenn, b. 6 Aug 1874[568]

It is not known when he died, but on June 6, 1897, C.E. Godfrey wrote in a letter to Phillip Marshall Wrenn that he had just received a letter from George Henry Wrenn.

John Kobler Wrenn

John Kobler Wrenn was born on July 24, 1841[569] in

---

[563] Letter dated 5 Apr 1896 to Phillip Marshall Wrenn from C.E. Godfrey.
[564] Botetourt County, Virginia Marriage Register.
[565] Ibid.
  Civil War Soldiers, Ancestry.com..
[566] 1870 Augusta County, Virginia Census.
[567] Augusta County, Virginia Birth Register.
[568] Ibid.
[569] John Lee Wrenn Family Bible.

Fredericksburg, Virginia and he was a tinner. He was the fifth son of Lewis and Elizabeth (Mills) Wrenn.

He enlisted in the 30th Virginia, Company C on May 23, 1861. He was wounded 'slightly in the head' at Sharpsburg (Antietam) on September 17, 1862, and was hospitalized for debility May–August 1864, and for malaria in October–December 1864. He was captured in Richmond on April 3, 1865, and paroled there on April 17, 1865.[570] There is no explanation of why he was in Richmond. Perhaps he was one of the 'walking wounded' who was able to escape from Chimborazo Hospital just before Richmond fell.

He married Martha Elizabeth Phillips, the daughter of Capt. Steven D. and Sarah (Branch) Phillips on January 4, 1866 in Goldsboro, North Carolina.[571] They had 13 children.

1. Walter Phillips Wrenn, b. 23 Nov. 1866, d. 25 Dec 1913,[572] m. Rosie Cobb[573]
2. Charles Montgomery Wrenn, b. 15 Feb 1868, d. 23 Jun 1924,[574] m. Nannie Susan Lockamy[575]
3. Stephen Louis Wrenn, b. 15 Jun 1870, d. 30 Jan 1943,[576] m. 22 Aug 1893 Viola Randolph Kapp in Baltimore MD[577]
4. John Lee Wrenn, b. 3 Oct 1872, d. 20 May 1923,[578] m. 28 Dec 1892 Nora Ida Ellis[579]
5. Paul Theodore Wrenn, b. 6 Jul 1874, d. 7 May 1880[580]
6. Franklin Bugnell Wrenn, b. 24 Jun 1876, d. 5 Aug 1929,[581] m. Jessie[582] Unknown

---

[570] Virginia Infantry by Robert K. Krick, H.E. Howard, Inc., Publisher (1985) page 136.

[571] North Carolina Marriage Certificate.

[572] John Lee Wrenn Family Bible.

[573] *Wayne County, North Carolina Cemeteries*, Page 429.

[574] John Lee Wrenn Family Bible.

[575] Susan Elizabeth (Wrenn) Dotson, Charles Montgomery Wrenn's family historian.

[576] John Lee Wrenn Family Bible.

[577] Maryland Marriage Certificate.

[578] John Lee Wrenn Family Bible.

[579] Richard K. Neumann, John Lee Wrenn's family historian.

[580] John Lee Wrenn Family Bible.

[581] Ibid.

[582] Marion Elizabeth (Wrenn) Humphreys, granddaughter of John Kobler Wrenn.

7. Harry Leonard Wrenn, b. 11 Aug 1878,[583] d. 10 Jul 1947,[584] m. 2 Mar 1901 Elizabeth Lee Wiggins[585]

   a. Frances Adelle Wrenn, b. 9 Jun 1902,[586] d. 16 Oct 1991,[587] m. 3 Aug 1924 Ollie Lyon Dupon[588]

   b. Marion Elizabeth Wrenn, b. 8 May 1904,[589] d. 27 Oct 1999,[590] m. 22 Dec 1926 Uriah J. Humphreys[591]

   c. Harry Leonard Wrenn, Jr., b. 30 Oct 1906,[592] d. 21 Jan 2001,[593] m. 1 Dec 1936 Bleeka Mae Walker[594]

   d. John Wilmot Wrenn, b. 1 Feb 1908,[595] d. 29 Nov 2002,[596] m. 12 Mar 1936 Genevieve Rosar[597]

   e. Bessie Lee Wrenn, b. 10 Nov 1915,[598] d. 10 Jun 1975,[599] m. 16 Jun 1935 Daniel Douglas Bey, Jr.[600]

      i. Sandra Elizabeth Bey, b. 9 May 1936,[601] m. (1) 13 Sep 1955 Kennard Smith Vandergrift, Jr.[602] (2) 29 Dec 1978 Joseph Jaconetta[603]

      ii. Harriet Lee Bey (the author of this book), b. 4 Aug 1937,[604] m. 18 Mar 1937 Harry Randolph Mesic[605]

---

[583] North Carolina Death Certificate.

[584] Ibid.

[585] North Carolina Marriage Register.

[586] Washington, D.C. Birth Certificate.

[587] North Carolina Death Certificate.

[588] North Carolina Marriage Certificate.

[589] Georgia Birth Certificate.

[590] North Carolina Death Certificate.

[591] Florida Marriage Certificate.

[592] Georgia Birth Certificate.

[593] Virginia Death Certificate.

[594] North Carolina Marriage Certificate.

[595] Georgia Birth Certificate.

[596] Florida Death Certificate.

[597] Georgia Marriage Certificate.

[598] Georgia Birth Certificate.

[599] Florida Death Certificate.

[600] Virginia Marriage Certificate.

[601] Virginia Birth Certificate.

[602] North Carolina Marriage Certificate.

[603] Florida Marriage Certificate.

[604] Virginia Birth Certificate.

[605] Virginia Marriage Certificate.

     f. Ralph Wiggins Wrenn, b. 29 Aug 1917,[606] m. 28 Mar 1941[607] Margaret Phodia Ridge

  8. Leon Olando Wrenn, b. 12 Jul 1880, d. 9 Sep 1953[608]

  9. William Cobb Wrenn, b. 26 Oct 1882, d. ca. 1920,[609] m. Katherine Cecilia Hodnutt[610]

10. Ada Virginia Wrenn, b. 28 Dec 1884, d. 10 Aug 1965,[611] m. 29 Aug 1904 Charles D. Farmer[612]

11. Mary Elizabeth Wrenn, b. 5 Feb 1887, d. 7 Jun 1975, m. Uriah Melvin Gillikin[613]

12. Lester Alonzo Wrenn, b. 6 Feb 1889,[614] d. before 1900

13. James Hubert Wrenn, b. 24 May 1891[615]

John Kobler Wrenn died on September 11, 1815 in Goldsboro, North Carolina of carcinoma of the stomach.[616]

Martha Elizabeth (Phillips) Wrenn died January 3, 1933.

Lewis Wrenn

Lewis Wrenn was a sixth generation American.[617] He was born September 19, 1800,[618] the youngest child of John Wren by his second wife, Rebecca Spelman (Munford).[619] Through his paternal grandmother, Mary Strother, he was descended from King Edward III of England and was related to every royal house in Europe.[620]

---

[606] Georgia Birth Certificate.

[607] North Carolina Marriage Certificate.

[608] John Lee Wrenn Family Bible.

[609] Ibid.

[610] Marion Elizabeth (Wrenn) Humphreys, granddaughter of John Kobler Wrenn.

[611] John Lee Wrenn Family Bible.

[612] *News & Observer*, Raleigh, North Carolina, 11 Aug 1865.

[613] John Lee Wrenn Family Bible.

[614] Ibid.

[615] Ibid.

[616] North Carolina Death Certificate.

[617] *Wren's of Virginia: 1652–1832: A History of One Early American Family* by John Howard Wren, Private Publication, page 79.

[618] 1860 Fredericksburg Virginia Census.

John Barnhart, Strother's Family Historian.

[619] *Wren's of Virginia 1652–1832: A History of One Early American Family* by John Howard Wren, private publication (1993).

[620] *The Royal Descents of 500 Immigrants to the American Colonies or the*

He married first to Elizabeth Mills, daughter of Achilles and Clarissa (Stevens) Mills circa 1820.[621] They had five sons:

1. Lewis W. Wrenn, b. ca. 1822,[622] m. 4 Sep 1850, Martha J. Jennings[623]
2. Robinson Boswell Wrenn, b. 21 Jan 1824[624] d. 12 Oct 1899,[625] m. (1) 22 Apr 1852 his first cousin, Susan C. Wrenn,[626] the daughter of William 'Thomas' Wrenn and Malinda Mills (2) 19 Dec 1856 Martha Oella Hudson[627]
3. George Henry Wrenn, b. 12 Apr 1826,[628] m. (1) 3 April 1848 Nancy Pursley[629] (2) 4 May 1850 Ann Eliza Montgomery[630]
4. Phillip Marshall Wrenn, b. 20 June 1828[631] d. 3 Feb 1908[632] m. ca. 12 Sep 1850 Sarah Elizabeth Brimmer[633]
5. John Kobler Wrenn, b. 24 July 1841,[634] d. 11 Sep 1915[635] m. 4 Jan 1866 Martha Elizabeth Phillips[636]

In May of 1826, Lewis Wrenn sued Thomas and Samuel Hicks for "trespass assault and battery" damage for $500.[637]

Seven months later, in December 1826, he purchased a 111 acre farm in Spotsylvania County from John and Esther J. Moncure for $222.00.[638] He sold the farm to Robert Baylor Semple, a popular

---

United States by Gary Boyd Roberts, Genealogical Publishing Co. Inc. (1993) Page 184.

[621] Letter dated 17 Jun 1896 from C.E. Godfrey to Phillip Marshall Wrenn. Spotsylvania Deed Book CC, Pages 484–485.

[622] 1870 Lynchburg, Virginia census.

[623] Virginia Marriage Certificate.

[624] Jack Lynch, Robinson Boswell Wrenn's family historian.

[625] Washington DC Death Certificate.

[626] Culpeper, VA Marriage Register.

[627] Alexandria, VA Marriage Certificate.

[628] Letter dated 5 Apr 1896 from C.E. Godfrey to Phillip Marshall Wrenn.

[629] Botetourt County, Virginia Marriage Register.

[630] Ibid.

[631] Gene Pool Database, Ancestry.com.

[632] *Culpeper Exponent* 7 Feb 1908, 5x2.

[633] Culpeper, VA Marriage Register.

[634] John Lee Wrenn Family Bible.

[635] *Wayne County, NC Cemeteries*, page 443.

[636] Wayne County, North Carolina Marriage Certificate.

[637] Wren vs. Hicks, 1826, Fredericksburg Courthouse Annex Basement.

[638] Spotsylvania County, VA Deed Book BB, Pages 35–37.

mayor of Fredericksburg,[639] on February 8, 1837.[640]

He moved his family to Fredericksburg, and bought a house in August of 1838 for $350 in Thornton Town (a suburb of Fredericksburg) on the corner of William and Barton Streets from Elizabeth (Mills) Wrenn's first cousin, George T. Jennings and his wife Susan E. (Portch) Jennings.[641]

His wife, Elizabeth (Mills) Wrenn died circa 1841.[642]

On September 20, 1842, Lewis was married for the second time to Eliza (Carter) Pilcher.[643]

In October 1843, Lewis paid $5.00 for a retail license to sell segars [sic]. In November of the same year, he paid $10.00 for a retail license to sell dry goods.[644] The property in Thornton Town was put into the trust for Eliza (Pilcher) Wrenn on November 15, 1843.[645]

The court certified that Lewis Wrenn was a man of good character in February 1844,[646] so he could buy a license to sell ardent spirits in his home. On June 3, 1844, Lewis' name was included on a list of "merchants, grocers, ordinary keepers, and keepers of private entertainment" that had not bought a license, but had a shop and the appearance of selling groceries or spirits. He was again certified by the court as being a man of good character in July 1844, June 1845, and May 1846. Lewis paid $150 in May of 1846 and June of 1847 for a license to operate an ordinary and $20 tax on the ordinary.[647]

Lewis and Eliza Wrenn bought a piece of property in Liberty Town (a suburb of Fredericksburg adjoining Thornton Town) known as 'The Wagon Yard' on August 30, 1845 from Joseph B. Ficklin for $1500.[648]

They sold the house in Thornton Town on March 26, 1846 to

---

[639] *Star*, 17 Dec 1881, 3x3.

[640] Spotsylvania Deed Book CC, pages 484–485.

[641] Fredericksburg Deed Book L, Page 60.

[642] Family tradition says that Elizabeth Mills Wrenn died in childbirth, when John Kobler Wrenn was born.

[643] Fredericksburg, Virginia Marriage Register.

[644] Records in the Rappahannock Regional Heritage Center, Fredericksburg, Virginia.

[645] Fredericksburg Deed Book N, page 123–124.

[646] Spotsylvania Court Proceedings, February 1844.

[647] Records in the Rappahannock Regional Heritage Center, Fredericksburg, Virginia.

[648] Fredericksburg Deed Book N, Page s 496–499.

Frederick Schrickel for the same price they paid for it, $350.[649]

The 'Wagon Yard' was sold on November 17, 1847 to Augustine G. Hudson (the father-in-law of Lewis' son, Robinson Boswell Wrenn) for $1300, a loss of $200.[650]

At the time of the sale, Lewis and Eliza were living in a house (later known as Williamsville)[651] at the intersection of the Sunken Road and the Swift Run Gap Turnpike.[652] They bought that piece of property from John L. and Anne Marye on December 27, 1847 for $800.[653]

On December 10, 1849, John English sold Lewis Wrenn a hardware business, the stock in trade and tools consisting of: tin, lead, iron, and other metallic wares and material, and tools for the sum of $655.00.[654] Lewis Wrenn operated a store at "English's Old Stand," where he sold grates, stoves, refrigerators, shower baths, pumps, etc.[655]

After being sued for debts,[656] Lewis' home, household goods, and tools of trade were sold in a court-ordered public auction on October 19, 1853. His wife, Eliza, bought his property at the auction and had it put into a trust with George Rowe as her trustee.[657]

The next month Lewis and Eliza won a lawsuit against the city for a permanent injury Eliza sustained from a fall on a public sidewalk two years previously. They were awarded $100.[658] That same week, Eliza opened a coopering business with Lewis acting as her agent.[659]

During the Federal occupation of the summer of 1862, Lewis was arrested for taking down a fence that did not belong to him.[660] Most likely, he planned to use it for firewood, as the townspeople

---

[649] Fredericksburg Deed Book O, Pages 137–139.

[650] Fredericksburg Deed Book O, Page 500–501.

[651] Fredericksburg News, 19 March 1852, 4x5.

[652] Swift Run Gap Turnpike is now Hanover Street.

[653] Fredericksburg Deed Book P, pages 6–7.

[654] Fredericksburg Deed Book P, Pages 380–382.

[655] *Fredericksburg News*, 2 Jan 1852, 4x5.

[656] Parker vs. Wrenn, Fredericksburg Courthouse Annex basement.

[657] Fredericksburg Deed Book Q, page 491.

[658] *Weekly Advertiser*, 12 Nov 1853, 2x1.

[659] Ibid. 12 Nov 1853, 2x5.

[660] Fredericksburg Court Record, May 19, 1862, Fredericksburg Courthouse Annex basement.

were not allowed to leave town to gather wood.

Lewis was one of the citizens of Fredericksburg who was arrested as a hostage and incarcerated in the Old Capitol Prison in Washington, D.C. in the summer of 1862.[661]

He was arrested again as a hostage by the Union troops in May 1864, and sent to Fort Delaware Prison.[662]

On December 27, 1865, Lewis transferred his membership from Salem Baptist Church to the Fredericksburg Baptist Church.[663]

Between 1860 and 1870, his real estate had decreased in value from $1,500 to $1,000 and his personal property had decreased in value for $1,200 to $0.00.[664]

Lewis served as a delegate to the Baptist Convention in June 1874, along with Rev. William F.F. Broaddus.[665]

Lewis sold Williamsville to William E. and Esther E. Pusey on April 1, 1876 for $575 at a loss of $225. He was living in Fauquier County at the time of the sale.[666]

Lewis Wrenn died on August 19, 1877 in Goldsboro, North Carolina at the home of his son, John Kobler Wrenn. A letter from the pastor of the Baptist Church in Goldsboro to Robinson Boswell Wrenn said that Lewis "had been sick four or five months, and bore his affliction with Christian patience and resignation. He was willing and even anxious to depart, and his death was peaceful, and even triumphant. He retained his faculties to the last, his mind was clear, his faith firm, and his hope strong."[667] The newspaper said he was 78 years old, and he was "A good man, full of faith and the Holy Ghost."[668]

It is not known when or where his wife, Eliza C. (Pilcher)

[661] *The War of the Rebellion: A Compilation of the Official Records of the Union and Confederate Armies*, Series II, Vol. IV, Washington: Government Printing Office (1899) Pages 366, 376, 861, 866.

[662] *History of the City of Fredericksburg, Virginia* by S. J. Quinn, Hermitage Press (1908) page 102.

[663] *Fredericksburg Baptist Church Records*, Baptist Historical Society, Richmond, Virginia.

[664] 1860 & 1870 Fredericksburg, Virginia Censuses.

[665] *Fredericksburg Ledger*, 2 Jun 1874.

[666] Fredericksburg Deed Book X, page 413.

[667] Letter dated Aug. 28, 1877 from F. H. Ivey, Pastor Baptist Church to Mr. R.B. Wrenn.

[668] *Goldsboro Messenger*, 30 Aug 1877, page 3.

Wrenn, died.

Lewis W. Wrenn

Lewis W. Wrenn was born circa 1822 in Virginia, and was a saddler.[669] He was the oldest son of Lewis and Elizabeth (Mills) Wrenn.

He was a veteran of the Mexican War,[670] and during the Civil War he was a private in the 3rd Virginia Reserves, Company G. He appears on a list of Prisoners of War who were surrendered by General Robert E. Lee in April 1865.[671]

He married Martha J. Jennings, daughter of Mary Jennings on September 4, 1850,[672] and they lived in Lynchburg, Virginia. They had six children.[673]

    1. Rozella Wrenn, b. ca. 1852
    2. William M. Wrenn, b. ca. 1854
    3. Lydia Wrenn, b. ca. 1856
    4. Lewis O. Wrenn, b. ca. 1860
    5. Annie B. Wrenn, b. ca. 1865
    6. John A. Wrenn, b. ca. 1866

It is unknown when Lewis W. Wrenn died. The last census on which he appeared as a head of a household was the 1860 Lynchburg, Virginia census. However, he was reported to be alive on June 17, 1896.[674]

Nancy Wrenn

The first clue to the existence of Nancy Wrenn was found in the Virginia Historical Society, in Richmond, Virginia, in the King Papers. In the Wrenn folder is a genealogy contributed by Richard Thurtle (deceased), who married a descendent of William Cobb Wrenn, the ninth son of John Kobler Wrenn. The genealogy contained some inaccuracies, and listed no sources, but it could not be easily

---

[669] 1860 Lynchburg, Virginia Census.

[670] Index to Mexican War Pension Applications transcribed by Barbara Schull Wolfe.

[671] Confederate Service Records for L.W. Wrenn.

[672] Lynchburg, Virginia Marriage Register.

[673] 1870 Lynchburg, Virginia census.

[674] Letter from C.E. Godfrey to Phillip Marshall Wrenn, dated June 17, 1896.

dismissed, as some of the information seemed to be taken from a family Bible. For one thing he listed the day of the month that each of John Kobler Wrenn's children was born. The month and the year can easily be found in census records, but nowhere else had the days of the month been found, even after many years of research.

That some of his information came from a family Bible seemed to be confirmed when a descendent of John Lee Wrenn (the fourth son of John Kobler Wrenn) was located, and he had in his possession John Lee Wrenn's family Bible. In it the month, day, and year of the birth of each of John Kobler Wrenn's children were recorded, and they matched Richard Thurtle's information. This Bible did not list information on the next generation back.

Richard Thurtle's genealogy information went back further. It had the names of all of Lewis Wrenn's sons. The only other source, that was found afterward, for the names of his sons is in letters written by a lawyer named C.E. Godfrey to Phillip Marshall Wrenn. The names in these letters match Richard Thurtle's names. The letters, which concern a lawsuit by the heirs of the Mills family, are in the possession of a descendent of Phillip Marshall Wrenn.

Richard Thurtle's genealogy contained something not mentioned in the Godfrey letters, the names of two daughters of Lewis Wrenn. The information concerning a daughter named Elizabeth Wrenn proved to be erroneous. That does not necessarily mean that she did not exist. It means that the information that Richard Thurtle had about her was wrong.

The other daughter listed was Nancy Wrenn, who according to Richard Thurtle married Robert Stevens.

Years of searching has uncovered only a few possible clues concerning Nancy Wrenn, but nothing that is indisputable.

The first clue was found in the 1860 Slave Schedule for Fredericksburg, Virginia. On it there is listed a thirteen-year-old female, mulatto slave owned by Lewis Wrenn, who was working for John Marye.

The second clue was a line in the diary of Matilda Hamilton. On Tuesday, December 30, 1862 she wrote, "We went to Fredericksburg, to Brompton, now kept by Mrs. Nancy Stevens and black Charles."[675]

---

[675] *An Eye Witness Account of The Battle of Fredericksburg: From the diary of a daughter of George and Maria Hamilton of Forest Hill*, Virginia Historical Society, Richmond Virginia.

This clue is perplexing. The statement seems to confirm the existence of Nancy (Wrenn) Stevens, but if Matilda Hamilton thought Nancy Stevens were a slave, she would have called her 'Nancy Stevens,' not 'Mrs. Nancy Stevens.' This implies that Nancy Stevens may have been a slave who looked white, or conversely, a white who was being passed off as a slave.

The next clue came from an incident shortly after the war, where a woman at Brompton was talking in a "familiar way" with a black man named Charles. (Remember that Matilda Hamilton had mentioned a black man named Charles with Mrs. Nancy Stevens.) After witnessing the scene, a bystander remarked, "That woman has got a nigger husband."[676] The remark suggests that the woman was either white, or appeared to be white. Cohabitation, or marriages between blacks and whites, was illegal at that time, so the woman had to be legally a black to be married to a black.

The last clue was found in the Fredericksburg court records.[677] On November 7, 1848, Eliza Wrenn was assaulted by Martin Spicer and Richard W. Bozel. The testimony at the trial was not recorded, but the men were found guilty of "striking, bruising, wounding, ill treating, and other wrongs," and doing "great damage" to Eliza C. Wrenn. The word 'rape' is not mentioned, but it is not likely that Eliza Wrenn would testify in open court that she had been raped, considering the stigma and shame directed against the victims of rape at that time. The use of the word 'damage' is interesting, in that it suggests harm that cannot be undone. If a rape did, indeed, occur and a child resulted from the assault, it would be white, as both of the perpetrators and the victim were white.

If Nancy Wrenn were the product of a rape, as Eliza's child born during Eliza's marriage to Lewis Wrenn, she would become the legal child and an heir of Lewis Wrenn. If he were not in agreement to becoming her legal father, the only other choice would have been to conceal the pregnancy of Eliza, and the birth of Nancy. It is possible that she is the female, mulatto slave working for John Marye identified on the 1860 Fredericksburg Slave Schedule.

These clues are open to other interpretations, but the scenario

---

[676] The South: A Tour of Its Battlefields and Ruined Cities by J. T. Trowbridge, L. Stebbins, Hartford, Ct (1867) page 111.

[677] Commonwealth vs. Martin Spicer and Richard Bozel, 1849, Cr-HU-R, 470-283.

outlined is plausible.

Phillip Marshall Wrenn

Phillip Marshall Wrenn was born on 20 June 1828,[678] and he was a tinner.[679] He was the fourth son of Lewis and Elizabeth (Mills) Wrenn.

He married Sarah Elizabeth Brimmer on September 12, 1850.[680] They had nine children.[681]

1. Charles Alphas Wrenn, b. 17 Jun 1851, d. 19 Aug 1923,[682] m. 5 Jan 1878 Martha Anne Washington Jones
2. Ida Elizabeth Wrenn, b. 1853, d. 1854
3. Elias B. Wrenn, b. 20 May 1855, m. 12 Aug 1879 Margaret E. Pace
4. Ella Isadora Fustina Wrenn, b. 6 Sep 1857, m. 31 Oct 1877 James T. Jennings
5. St. George Washington Wrenn, b. 1859
6. Phillip Jackson Wrenn, b. 1862, m. Florence Taylor
7. French Eugene Wrenn, b. 1865, d. 1887
8. Lewis Isaac Wrenn, b. 1869, m. 3 Sep 1890 Lillie M. Graves
9. William Hampton 'Omega' Wrenn, b. 26 Feb 1871, d. 29 Aug 1929, m. Agnes Lee O'Donnell

During the Civil war Phillip Marshall Wrenn enlisted in the 13th Virginia Infantry, Company E on April 17, 1861 at Brandy Station. The company disbanded on November 8, 1861.[683] He enlisted in the 4th Virginia Cavalry, Company D as a private in April 1863 at Oak Shade, Virginia. He was wounded in April 1863, and was out of service for the rest of the war.[684] However, his name appears on a receipt roll for clothing in the third quarter of 1864.[685] His name was also included on a 1909 roster of the 6th Virginia Cavalry, Company

---

[678] Jane Via Dickey, Phillip Marshall Wrenn's family historian.

[679] 1850 Culpeper County Virginia census.

[680] Culpeper, Virginia Marriage Register.

[681] 1850, 1860, and 1870 Censuses.

Jane Via Dickey, Phillip Marshall Wrenn's family historian.

[682] Culpeper Exponent, 6 Sep 1923, 9x3.

[683] *13th Virginia Infantry* by David F. Riggs, H.E. Howard, Inc (1988).

[684] *4th Virginia Cavalry* by Kenneth Stiles.

Confederate Service Records, Card Nos. 50779805, 50780008.

[685] Confederate Service Record for P.M. Wrenn.

I.[686]

Phillip Marshall Wrenn died on February 3, 1908 at Kelly's Ford, Virginia.[687]

Robinson (Robertson, Roberson, Robert, Robin) Boswell Wrenn

Robinson Boswell Wrenn was born January 21, 1824[688] in Virginia and was a house carpenter.[689] He was the second son of Lewis and Elizabeth (Mills) Wrenn.

He was a veteran of the Mexican War,[690] and he died on October 12, 1899 in Washington, D.C.[691]

He married his first cousin, Susan C. Wrenn, the daughter of William 'Thomas' and Malinda T. (Mills) Wrenn [Thomas was Lewis Wrenn's brother, and Malinda was Elizabeth (Mills) Wrenn's sister] on April 22, 1852.[692] She died in November 1852 at the age of sixteen.[693]

He next married Martha Oella Hudson on December 19, 1856 and they lived in Alexandria, Virginia, then Washington, D.C. They had twelve children.[694]

1. Norman Welford Wrenn, b. 22 Oct 1857, d. 15 Sep 1943, m. 11 June 1888 Ella Frances Sharkey[695]
2. Ada May Wrenn, b. Sep 15 1859, d. 13 Feb 1943, m. 17 Aug 1887 Benjamin Franklin Thomas Bell
3. Georgie Hudson Wrenn, b. 18 Oct 1861, d. 14 Sept 1954, m 12 Dec 1888 John Bottomley
4. Thomas Jackson Wrenn, b. 29 Nov 1862, d. 16 Apr 1920, m. (1) 13 Jul 1885 Clara Rose Wise Annie[696] (2) 7 Sept

---

[686] *6th Virginia Cavalry* by P. Musick.

[687] *Daily Star,* 10 Feb 1908, 2x5.

[688] Jack Lynch, Robinson Boswell Wrenn's family historian.

[689] 1850, 1860 & 1870 Alexandria, Virginia Censuses.

[690] Index to Mexican War Pension Applications transcribed by Barbara Schull Wolfe.

[691] Washington, D.C. Death Certificate.

[692] Culpeper, Virginia Marriage Register.

[693] *Fredericksburg News*, 29 Nov 1852, 3x1.

[694] Jack Lynch, Robinson Boswell Wrenn's family historian. (All of the following data came from Jack Lynch unless otherwise noted)

[695] Marriage Record in Maryland Archives

[696] Washington D.C. Marriage License

1897 Blanche Estelle Hawkins[697] (3) 10 Nov 1903 Annie Elizabeth Mooney[698]

5. Robert E. Lee Wrenn, b. 7 Feb 1865, d. 25 Apr 1915,[699] m. 9 Oct 1894 Rosa Howard Anderson

6. Arthur Herbert Wrenn, b. 15 Jun 1867, d. 26 Jan 1910

7. Augustus Cantor Wrenn, b. 31 Jan 1871, d. 11 May 1837, m. (1) 3 Jul 1894 Ida Virginia Kemp (2) 1928 Katherine I. Easton[700]

8. William Maynard Wrenn, b. 31 Jan 1871, m. 16 Dec 1900 Sina (Dina) Marie Plenge[701]

9. Mary Oella Wrenn, b. 23 May 1873, d. 27 Feb 1907, m. (1) 26 Dec 1891 Francis Vincent Johnson (2) 27 May 1901 Henry C. Donaldson[702]

10. Frank Gayle Wrenn, b. 12 Sep 1875, d. 29 July 1931, m. ca. 1905 Julia Isabelle Cooney

11. Lucie Ernestine Wrenn, b. 11 Feb 1878, d. 19 Sep 1950, m. 10 Jun 1903 James Hubert Haley

12. Katherine Leslie Wrenn, b. 11 Feb. 1878, d. May 1946, m. 3 May 1946 Frederick August Kummel[703]

---

[697] Washington D.C. Marriage License

[698] Washington D.C. Marriage License

[699] Hospital Death Record

[700] MD Death Certificate

[701] NY Marriage License

[702] Washington D.C. Marriage License

[703] Washington D.C. Marriage License

GENEALOGY OF LEWIS WRENN

1. Edward III, King of England = Philippa of Hainault

2. John of Gaunt, Duke of Lancaster = Catherine Roet

3. Joan Beaufort = Ralph Neville, 1st Earl of Westmoreland

4. George Neville, 1st Baron Latymer = Elizabeth Beauchamp

5. Sir Henry Neville = Joan Bourchier

6. Richard Neville, 2nd Baron Latymer = Anne Stafford

7. Dorothy Neville = Sir John Dawney

8. Anne Dawney = Sir George Conyers

9. Sir John Conyers = Agnes Bowes

10. Eleanor Conyers = Lancelot Strother

11. William Strother = Elizabeth

12. Mary Strother = William Wren

13. John Wren = Rebecca Spelman (Munford)

14. Lewis Wrenn

Lewis Wrenn's house on Hanover Street (Swift Run Gap Turnpike) in 1865 showing damages from the battles.
Photograph by Theo Miller and owned by Jerry Brent. Used by permission.

Site of Lewis Wrenn's house on Hanover Street (Swift Run Gap Turnpike) today. The stone foundation, chimney an the left, and, perhaps, other parts of the house are from the original house.

Photograph by Harry R. Mesic

The Wagon Yard in 1927, the location of Lewis Wrenn's home on Liberty Street in Liberty Town. A tavern is in the back of the warehouse on the right, and may be the same location as Lewis Wrenn's Liberty Town Tavern. Picture was taken in 1927.

Francis Benjamin Johnston Collection, Library of Congress

The Wagon Yard in 2003. A restaurant is located where the tavern used to be. *Photograph by Harry R. Mesic*

Monroe Stevens' home on Hanover Street (Swift Run Gap Turnpike).
Photograph by Harry R. Mesic

Hickory Hill in Stafford County. Home of Monroe Stevens after the Battle of Fredericksburg. *Photograph by Harry R. Mesic*

Site of David Sisson's home and store. Hanover Street is on the right.
Photograph by Harry R. Mesic

George Rowe's home on Hanover Street.
Photograph by Harry R. Mesic

Brompton, home of John Marye. View from the Sunken Road in 2003.
Photograph by Harry R. Mesic

Brompton, with rifle pits in the front yard in 1864.
Photograph by James Gardner, Library of Congress

Allen Stratton's home on Littlepage Street. Picture was taken in 2003.

Photograph by Harry R. Mesic

Store and Home of Henry Ebert. Picture was taken in 1927.

Francis Benjamin Johnston Collection, Library of Congress

The foundation of Martha Stephens' home on the Sunken Road is within the fenced area.   *Photograph by Harry R. Mesic*

THE GRAVE OF
MARTHA STEVENS

LIVING ON CHEERFULLY AT THE SCENE
OF HER CIVIL WAR FAME, MRS. MARTHA
STEVENS, A MIDWIFE AND PRACTICAL
NURSE, BECAME THE IDOL OF A POSTWAR
GENERATION. BATTLEFIELD VISITORS
WERE ENTRANCED BY THE STOUT AND JOLLY
WHITE-HAIRED "GRANNY" STEVENS, ALWAYS
MODEST IN HER OLD-FASHIONED
SUNBONNET.
SHE DIED ON DECEMBER 19, 1888 AT THE
AGE OF 64 AND LIES BURIED IN THIS
PRIVATE GRAVEYARD.

Martha Stephens is buried to the left of the foundation of her house in the picture at the top of page. She was able to convince enough people that she was a true heroine of the Battle of Fredericksburg that she was immortalized in history books and on this marker at her homesite.
                              Photograph by Harry R. Mesic

Home of Edwin Carter on Caroline Street. He lived above his store.
Photograph by Harry R. Mesic

Home of Charles Carter Wellford on Caroline Street.
Photograph by Harry R. Mesic

Home of John Coakley on Hanover Street.

Photograph by Harry R. Mesic

James Cooke's drugstore on Caroline Street. His home was above the drugstore.

Photograph by Harry R. Mesic

Home of George Henry Clay Rowe on Caroline Street.
Photograph by Harry R. Mesic

Home of Thomas Knox on Princess Anne Street.
Photograph by Harry R. Mesic

Site of William Norton's housewright shop on Caroline Street. His home was on Wellford's Field. *Photograph by Harry R. Mesic*

Home of John Scott on Hanover Street.

Photograph by Harry R. Mesic

The Sentry Box, home of Col. Wiley Roy Mason, Jr. on Sophia Street.
Photograph by Harry R. Mesic

Second home of Montgomery Slaughter on Hanover Street.
Photograph by Harry R. Mesic

Home of Benjamin Temple on Caroline Street in Fredericksburg.

Photograph by Harry R. Mesic

Berclair, home of Benjamin Temple in Spotsylvania County. This is where Lewis and Eliza Wrenn found refuge during the Battle of Fredericksburg.

Photograph by Harry R. Mesic

Home of John Hurkamp on Hanover Street. Union General John Sedgwick used this house as his headquarters.

Photograph by Harry R. Mesic

Home of John Kobler, minister of the Fredericksburg Methodist Church, on Hanover Street. John Kobler Wrenn was named for him.

Photograph by Harry R. Mesic

Home of Rev. William Broaddus on Princess Ann Street.

Photography by Harry R. Mesic

Farmers' Bank (National Bank of Fredericksburg, postwar) on Princess Anne Street where Lewis Wrenn and eleven other citizens of Fredericksburg were held after being arrested on August 13, 1862.

Photograph by Harry R. Mesic

Chatham in Stafford County, headquarters of General Burnside, as seen from Fredericksburg. The hostages were marched across a pontoon bridge to this house. *Photograph by Harry R. Mesic*

Fredericksburg from Chatham.

Photograph by Harry R. Mesic

Chatham in December 1862. Lewis Wrenn and the other hostages were taken here before being sent to the Old Capitol Prison in Washington D.C. in 1862 and the Fort Delaware Prison in 1864.

Francis T. Miller Collection, Library of Congress

Old Capitol Prison, Washington D.C. This was once the Capitol Building for the United States. *Civil War Photographs, Library of Congress*

Fort Delaware on Pea Patch Island.
Photo by Eric Crossan, Courtesy of the Fort Delaware Society

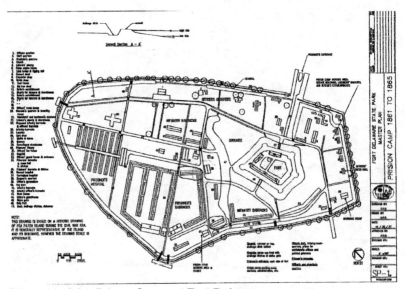

Diagram of the Prison Camp at Fort Delaware.
Artist Rendition by David Richman,
Delaware Division of Parks and Recreation,
Courtesy of the Fort Delaware Society.

272

Hazel Run. In this wooded area behind Marye's Heights and Willis Hill, women and children sought refuge from the Battle of Fredericksburg, camping in the snow. Picture was taken from the bridge over Hazel Run in 2003.

Photograph by Harry R. Mesic

Graves of Confederate soldiers in the Confederate Cemetery, Fredericksburg, Virginia. *Photograph by Harry R. Mesic*

Salem Church in Spotsylvania County. Refugees from the Battle of
Fredericksburg camped on the grounds of this church.

Photographs by Harry R. Mesic

Fredericksburg Methodist Church on Hanover Street. The current structure was erected on the foundation of the building that was destroyed during the bombardment of Fredericksburg in December 1862. The Methodist Church rescinded Lewis Wrenn's membership when he was charged with fraud in 1852, before he had his day in court. *Photograph by Harry R. Mesic*

Stained glass window in the Fredericksburg Methodist Church.
Photograph by Harry R. Mesic

St. George's Episcopal Church on Princess Anne Street. The spire of the church could be seen through the smoke and flames as Fredericksburg was being bombarded.

Photograph by Harry R. Mesic

Fredericksburg Baptist Church on Princess Anne Street. The congregation welcomed Lewis Wrenn into their fellowship after the Methodists rejected him. He joined the church in 1865 and became one of its leaders. 277   *Photograph by Harry R. Mesic*

Fredericksburg Court House on Princess Anne Street.

Photograph by Harry R. Mesic

View of the battlefield from Marye's Heights. Most of the battlefield has been lost to development. *Photographer Unknown, Library of Congress*

The Sunken Road *Photographer Unknown, Library of Congress*

Swift Run Gap Turnpike (Hanover Street) in 1864. Lewis Wrenn's house is barely visible above the chimney of the building in the foreground. David Sisson's store is to the left of the chimney, and George Rowe's house is to the right of the chimney.

Francis T. Miller Collection, Library of Congress

Confederate dead behind the stone wall. May 1863.
Andrew Jackson Russell, Library of Congress

Black fugitives crossing the Rappahannock, May 12, 1864.
Timothy H. O'Sullivan, Library of Congress

Burying the dead in Fredericksburg.

Timothy H. O'Sullivan, Library of Congress

Burying the dead from the Battle of the Wilderness, May 12, 1864.

Francis T. Miller Collection, Library of Congress

Wounded from the Battle of the Wilderness.
Francis T. Miller Collection, Library of Congress

Wounded Union soldiers at Fredericksburg in May 1864.
Francis T. Miller Collection, Library of Congress

Ruins near Marye's Heights

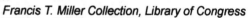

Ruins of the Phillips' house in February 1863. Burnside used this house for his headquarters.

John Kobler and Martha Elizabeth (Phillips) Wrenn with 10 of their 13 children.
Front row: Walter, Mary, John, Martha, Ada, Hubert
Back Row: Charles, Stephen, John, Frank, Harry, Leon
Picture owned by Susan Wrenn Dotson. Used by permission.

General George Edward Pickett, Division Commander in the Army of Northern Virginia. John Kobler Wrenn served under him from December 1862 until the end of the war.
Francis T. Miller, Library of Congress

General Robert E. Lee
Photographer Unknown,
Library of Congress

General Ambrose Everett
Burnside, Commander of
The Army of The Potomac
during the Fredericksburg
Campaign, November 1862
to January 1863.
Francis T. Miller,
Library of Congress

General Thomas R.R. Cobb was wounded while standing beside Martha Stephens's house on December 13, 1862 and died later that day. He was within sight of his grandparents' home, where he played as a child.

Francis T. Miller, Library of Congress

General Maxcy Gregg of South Carolina was killed at Fredericksburg, December 13, 1862.　　　　*Francis T. Miller, Library of Congress*

INDEX

287

ABOUT THE AUTHOR

Harriet Bey Mesic learned to love history while growing up in Virginia, where she was surrounded by historical buildings and sacred battlefields. After moving to South Carolina, she worked for nineteen years as the editor and head writer for the *L. E. Beacon* newsletter. While doing genealogy research on her great-grandfather, Lewis Wrenn, she became both fascinated and appalled by the plight of the inhabitants of Fredericksburg, Virginia, during the Civil War. She expanded her research to include the neighbors and fellow inmates of Lewis, and wanted to tell their story, not as a recitation of cold facts, but in a way that would give the reader some empathy for the cruelty and devastation they experienced.

301- 219-8445

301- 906-8288